Wound Repair and Regeneration

Wound Repair and Regeneration: Mechanisms, Signaling

Special Issue Editor

Sadanori Akita

MDPI • Basel • Beijing • Wuhan • Barcelona • Belgrade • Manchester • Tokyo • Cluj • Tianjin

Special Issue Editor
Sadanori Akita
Fukuoka University
Japan

Editorial Office
MDPI
St. Alban-Anlage 66
4052 Basel, Switzerland

This is a reprint of articles from the Special Issue published online in the open access journal *International Journal of Molecular Sciences* (ISSN 1422-0067) (available at: https://www.mdpi.com/journal/ijms/special_issues/wound_healing_regeneration).

For citation purposes, cite each article independently as indicated on the article page online and as indicated below:

LastName, A.A.; LastName, B.B.; LastName, C.C. Article Title. *Journal Name* **Year**, *Article Number*, Page Range.

ISBN 978-3-03936-471-8 (Hbk)
ISBN 978-3-03936-472-5 (PDF)

Contents

About the Special Issue Editor

Sadanori Akita has been a Professor and Chief of the Department of Plastic Surgery, Wound Repair and Regeneration of Fukuoka University School of Medicine, since 2016. He did his residency in plastic surgery at Nagasaki University Hospital. He received his Ph.D. from the Graduate School of Nagasaki University, where he specialized in plastic and reconstructive surgery. Under the supervision of Shlomo Melmed M.D., Dr. Akita later did a research fellowship at Cedars-Sinai Medical Center, University of California, Los Angeles (UCLA), on cytokine expression and its regulation in vivo by using a transgenic animal model. He served as a general secretary of the World Union of Wound Healing Societies, which was held in Yokohama, Japan, 2–6 September 2012 (http://wuwhs2012.com/), and as president of the World Union of Wound Healing Societies for the years 2012–2016. He was the president of the World Union of Wound Healing Societies (WUWHS) from September 2012 to September 2016 and is currently the president of the Asian Wound Care Association (AWCA). His research interests include cytokines and stem cells in wound healing, difficult wound healing (radiation injury), regenerative tissue enhancement in HIV-drug related-wasting patients, reconstructive surgery, burns, craniofacial surgery and hemangioma/avascular malformations.

 International Journal of
Molecular Sciences

Editorial

Wound Repair and Regeneration: Mechanisms, Signaling

Sadanori Akita

Department of Plastic Surgery, Wound Repair and Regeneration, Fukuoka University, School of Medicine,
7-45-1 Nanakuma, Jonan-ku, Fukuoka 8140180, Japan; akitas@hf.rim.or.jp

Received: 2 December 2019; Accepted: 13 December 2019; Published: 15 December 2019

Wound healing plays an integral part of cellular and molecular events. This process may be implicated in tissue regeneration. Regeneration can be contributed to complete tissue restoration and improvement of tissue disfigurement towards the original condition. Also, such cellular and molecular events are orchestrated both spatially and temporally.

Tissue regeneration, scar-less wound healing, and fibrosis are all dependent upon the phylogenetic event of the organism, as well as the inflammatory responses, which are influenced by age, sex, and interaction with the environment [1]. Under these conditions, the lack of a true blastema allows for only scarring wound repair in the inbred MRL/MpJ strain of mice and the outbred CD-1 and Swiss Webster laboratory mouse stocks [2].

In cytokines, IL-1 and TNF-α are always present during wound repair, but their pleiotropic and synergistic effects are not well understood. Rather than improving wound repair in young males, IL-1 signaling blockade increased epithelial thickness and IL-1β and TNF-α expression, and diminished epidermal apoptosis. TNF-α impaired wound repair in middle-aged females, which exhibited acanthosis and overexpression of IL-1, but no change in apoptosis. These findings suggest that this mechanism of epidermal thickening differs from that observed in IL1-ra-treated animals [3].

In this issue, Aoki et al. report a sphingosine-1-phosphate (S1P), which is a lipid mediator that promotes angiogenesis, cell proliferation, and attracts immune cells. They clarify the roles of S1P in skin wound healing by altering the expression of its biogenic enzyme, sphingosine kinase-1 (SphK1). The SphK1 overexpression also leads to less scarring, and the interaction between transforming growth factor (TGF)-β1 and S1P receptor-2 (S1PR2) signaling is likely to play a key role [4].

Kanno et al. find an interferon (IFN)-γ, known for its inhibitory effects on collagen synthesis by fibroblasts in vitro; however, information is limited regarding its role in wound healing in vivo. IFN-γ might be involved in the proliferation and maturation stages of wound healing through the regulation of neutrophilic inflammatory responses in IFN-γ-deficient (KO) mice [5].

Wound impairment is accelerated and completed with the local administration of recombinant human (rh)-growth hormone (GH) accelerating PU healing in non-obese diabetic/severe combined immunodeficient mice engrafted with a full-thickness human skin graft model in 60 days [6].

Other than skin, matrisome properties of scaffolds directing fibroblasts in idiopathic pulmonary fibrosis [7] and liver regeneration are enhanced by hepatocyte-derived angiogenesis via B-cell CLL/lymphoma/nuclear factor-Kappa B signaling [8], while wound repair and regeneration mechanisms of autologous adipose-derived stem cells in some patients with human immunodeficiency virus (HIV), treated by highly active antiretroviral therapy, are elucidated and analyzed in detail [9].

In novel aspects, the cloning and identification of Periplaneta americana, the American cockroach, thymosin (Pa-THYs) are obtained by bioinformatics and it is found that Pa-THYs also stimulate the expression of several key growth factors to promote wound healing. The data suggest that Pa-THYs could be a potential drug for promoting wound repair [10].

Lastly, maresins (MaRs) and macrophages are reviewed, focusing on the potent action of MaRs to enhance M2 macrophage phenotypic profiles to possibly alleviate inflammatory pain [11].

References

1. Eming, S.A.; Martin, P.; Tomic-Canic, M. Wound repair and regeneration: Mechanisms, signaling, and translation. *Sci. Transl. Med.* **2014**, *6*, 265sr6. [CrossRef] [PubMed]
2. Gawriluk, T.R.; Simkin, J.; Thompson, K.L.; Biswas, S.K.; Clare-Salzler, Z.; Kimani, J.M.; Kiama, S.G.; Smith, J.J.; Ezenwa, V.O.; Seifert, A.W. Comparative analysis of ear-hole closure identifies epimorphic regeneration as a discrete trait in mammals. *Nat. Commun.* **2016**, *7*, 11164. [CrossRef] [PubMed]
3. Abarca-Buis, R.F.; Martínez-Jiménez, A.; Vera-Gómez, E.; Contreras-Figueroa, M.E.; Garciadiego-Cázares, D.; Paus, R.; Robles-Tenorio, A.; Krötzsch, E. Mechanisms of epithelial thickening due to IL-1 signalling blockade and TNFα administration differ during wound repair and regeneration. *Differentiation* **2018**, *99*, 10–20. [CrossRef] [PubMed]
4. Aoki, M.; Aoki, H.; Mukhopadhyay, P.; Tsuge, T.; Yamamoto, H.; Matsumoto, N.M.; Toyohara, E.; Okubo, Y.; Ogawa, R.; Takabe, K. Sphingosine-1-Phosphate Facilitates Skin Wound Healing by Increasing Angiogenesis and Inflammatory Cell Recruitment with Less Scar Formation. *Int. J. Mol. Sci.* **2019**, *20*, 3381. [CrossRef] [PubMed]
5. Kanno, E.; Tanno, H.; Masaki, A.; Sasaki, A.; Sato, N.; Goto, M.; Shisai, M.; Yamaguchi, K.; Takagi, N.; Shoji, M.; et al. Defect of Interferon γ Leads to Impaired Wound Healing through Prolonged Neutrophilic Inflammatory Response and Enhanced MMP-2 Activation. *Int. J. Mol. Sci.* **2019**, *20*, 5657. [CrossRef] [PubMed]
6. Cristóbal, L.; de los Reyes, N.; Ortega, M.A.; Álvarez-Mon, M.; García-Honduvilla, N.; Buján, J.; Maldonado, A.A. Local Growth Hormone Therapy for Pressure Ulcer Healing on a Human Skin Mouse Model. *Int. J. Mol. Sci.* **2019**, *20*, 4157. [CrossRef] [PubMed]
7. Rendin, L.E.; Löfdahl, A.; Åhrman, E.; Müller, C.; Notermans, T.; Michaliková, B.; Rosmark, O.; Zhou, X.-H.; Dellgren, G.; Silverborn, M.; et al. Matrisome Properties of Scaffolds Direct Fibroblasts in Idiopathic Pulmonary Fibrosis. *Int. J. Mol. Sci.* **2019**, *20*, 4013. [CrossRef] [PubMed]
8. Chou, C.-H.; Ho, C.-M.; Lai, S.-L.; Chen, C.-N.; Wu, Y.-M.; Shun, C.-T.; Wen, W.-F.; Lai, H.-S. B-Cell Activating Factor Enhances Hepatocyte-Driven Angiogenesis via B-Cell CLL/Lymphoma 10/Nuclear Factor-KappaB Signaling during Liver Regeneration. *Int. J. Mol. Sci.* **2019**, *20*, 5022. [CrossRef] [PubMed]
9. Suzuki, K.; Akita, S.; Yoshimoto, H.; Ohtsuru, A.; Hirano, A.; Yamashita, S. Biological Features Implies Potential Use of Autologous Adipose-Derived Stem/Progenitor Cells in Wound Repair and Regenerations for the Patients with Lipodystrophy. *Int. J. Mol. Sci.* **2019**, *20*, 5505. [CrossRef] [PubMed]
10. Jing, J.; Sun, X.; Zhou, C.; Zhang, Y.; Shen, Y.; Zeng, X.; Yue, B.; Zhang, X. Cloning, Expression and Effects of *P. americana* Thymosin on Wound Healing. *Int. J. Mol. Sci.* **2019**, *20*, 4932. [CrossRef] [PubMed]
11. Hwang, S.-M.; Chung, G.; Kim, Y.H.; Park, C.-K. The Role of Maresins in Inflammatory Pain: Function of Macrophages in Wound Regeneration. *Int. J. Mol. Sci.* **2019**, *20*, 5849. [CrossRef] [PubMed]

International Journal of
Molecular Sciences

Article

Sphingosine-1-Phosphate Facilitates Skin Wound Healing by Increasing Angiogenesis and Inflammatory Cell Recruitment with Less Scar Formation

Masayo Aoki [1,2], Hiroaki Aoki [2,3], Partha Mukhopadhyay [2], Takuya Tsuge [1], Hirofumi Yamamoto [4], Noriko M. Matsumoto [1], Eri Toyohara [1], Yuri Okubo [1], Rei Ogawa [1] and Kazuaki Takabe [2,5,6,*]

1   Department of Plastic, Reconstructive and Aesthetic Surgery, Nippon Medical School, Tokyo 113-8603, Japan
2   Division of Surgical Oncology, Department of Surgery, Virginia Commonwealth University School of Medicine and Massey Cancer Center, Richmond, VA 23298-0011, USA
3   Department of Surgery, The Jikei University School of Medicine, Tokyo 105-8461, Japan
4   Department of Molecular Pathology, Osaka University, Suita 565-0871, Japan
5   Division of Breast Surgery, Department of Surgical Oncology, Roswell Park Comprehensive Cancer Center, Buffalo, NY 14263, USA
6   Department of Surgery, University at Buffalo Jacob School of Medicine and Biomedical Sciences, the State University of New York, Buffalo, NY 14203, USA
*   Correspondence: kazuaki.takabe@roswellpark.org; Tel.: +1-716-845-5540

Received: 11 June 2019; Accepted: 8 July 2019; Published: 10 July 2019

Abstract: Wound healing starts with the recruitment of inflammatory cells that secrete wound-related factors. This step is followed by fibroblast activation and tissue construction. Sphingosine-1-phosphate (S1P) is a lipid mediator that promotes angiogenesis, cell proliferation, and attracts immune cells. We investigated the roles of S1P in skin wound healing by altering the expression of its biogenic enzyme, sphingosine kinase-1 (SphK1). The murine excisional wound splinting model was used. Sphingosine kinase-1 (SphK1) was highly expressed in murine wounds and that SphK1$^{-/-}$ mice exhibit delayed wound closure along with less angiogenesis and inflammatory cell recruitment. Nanoparticle-mediated topical SphK1 overexpression accelerated wound closure, which associated with increased angiogenesis, inflammatory cell recruitment, and various wound-related factors. The SphK1 overexpression also led to less scarring, and the interaction between transforming growth factor (TGF)-β1 and S1P receptor-2 (S1PR2) signaling is likely to play a key role. In summary, SphK1 play important roles to strengthen immunity, and contributes early wound healing with suppressed scarring. S1P can be a novel therapeutic molecule with anti-scarring effect in surgical, trauma, and chronic wound management.

Keywords: sphingosine-1-phosphate; sphingosine kinase-1; sphingosine1-phosphate receptor-2; skin wound healing

1. Introduction

Wound healing is a dynamic and complex process that consists of sequential, albeit somewhat overlapping, inflammatory, proliferative, and remodeling phases [1–4]. In the inflammatory phase, immune cells (particularly macrophages) are recruited into the wound [3,5]. Inflammatory cells not only sterilize the wound; they also generate a finely balanced assortment of factors that promotes the rapid healing in the proliferative phase [3,5], which includes angiogenesis [6]. The topical wound treatments that are currently available target some of these factors (e.g., prostaglandin E1 and basic fibroblast growth factor). Recent studies have shown that fatty acids and their G protein-coupled receptors may also be important targets of novel wound healing treatments: several studies showed that the fatty acid receptors GPR40 and GPR120 play important roles in wound healing processes such as cell migration [7,8]. In addition, natural products such as honey, alkaloids, flavonoids, tannins, saponins, and polyphenols have been shown to promote wound healing [9,10]. We speculate here that additional emerging therapeutic targets in skin wound healing may be the sphingolipids and their biogenic enzymes.

Sphingosine-1-phosphate (S1P) is generated by sphingosine kinase-1 (SphK1) and -2 (SphK2), which are located in the cytosol and nucleus, respectively. Only SphK1-generated S1P is transported out of the cell [11]. It then binds in a paracrine or autocrine manner to S1P-specific G protein-coupled receptors (S1PR), of which there are five forms.

This binding event regulates various physiological processes in the S1P-binding cell [12], as follows. First, the binding of S1P to S1PR regulates lymphocyte trafficking, including the recruitment of inflammatory cells into inflamed tissues [13–15]. This effect is mediated by the S1P concentration gradient between various tissues: this gradient shapes the egress of S1PR1-expressing lymphocytes from secondary lymphoid organs into the blood or lymphatic vessels [16,17]. This mechanism has been targeted for the treatment of multiple sclerosis: Fingolimod (FTY720), which is a functional agonist of S1PR, induces lymphocytes to sequester in lymph nodes, thereby preventing them from contributing to the autoimmune reaction that causes the disease [12]. S1P-S1PR binding also acts to retain inflammatory cells in inflamed tissues, which produce high levels of S1P [13,18–20].

Second, S1P-S1PR binding plays key regulatory roles in vasculogenesis, angiogenesis, and blood vessel permeability [13,18–20]. Specifically, S1P regulates angiogenesis by binding to S1PR1 and S1PR3 on vascular endothelial cells, thereby inducing them to form capillary-like networks [18]. Moreover, S1P (and its functional analog FTY720) increases adherens junction assembly in endothelial cells: as a result, S1P treatment potently inhibits VEGF-induced endothelial cell transmonolayer permeability in vitro and vascular permeability in mice [21]. Since there are high levels of S1P in the blood, this vascular permeability-related activity of S1P also helps maintain the endothelial barrier integrity of specific vascular beds. This function of S1P is mediated by endothelial cell S1PR1 [22]. By contrast, S1P binding to S1PR2 disrupts endothelial barrier permeability [23]. These disparate effects of the S1PRs are due to the fact that S1PR1 couples solely with Gi/o whereas S1PR2 couples with Gq, G12, and G13 as well as Gi/o. The activation of G12 and G13 stimulates the small GTPase Rho, which induces cortical actin destabilization, stress-fiber formation, and endothelial barrier disruption [22,24].

Given that S1P promotes lymphocyte recruitment to and retention in inflamed tissues along with vasculogenesis and angiogenesis, we hypothesized that S1P is involved in the skin wound healing process by enhancing the local recruitment of the inflammatory cells that produce various wound healing-related factors in the wound. The aim of this study was to clarify the roles of the SphK1/S1P axis in the wound healing process.

2. Results

2.1. Longitudinal SphKs and S1PRs Expression during Mouse Wound Healing

To test our hypothesis, we first investigated S1P signaling during wound healing using the murine excisional wound splinting model [25]. SphK1 expression in the wound started increasing on Day 2 and peaked on Day 5 (88.6-fold increase compared with immediately after the wounds were generated) (Figure 1A). SphK2 expression did not change (Figure 1B). Interestingly, the expression of S1PR2 (which inhibits S1PR1 and S1PR3 signaling [12]) gradually increased towards the end of the wound healing process. S1PR1 expression did not change significantly (Figure 1C). S1PR3 expression was not detected at any time point. Thus, SphK1, but not S1PR1, is massively upregulated in the proliferative phase of wound healing.

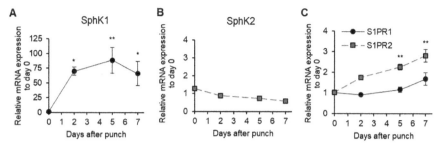

Figure 1. Longitudinal sphingosine-1-phosphate (S1P) production during mouse wound healing. Splinted excisional wounds (*n* = 4–6) were generated in C57BL/6J mice, and the mRNA expression of (**A**) sphingosine kinase-1 (SphK1), (**B**) sphingosine kinase -2 (SphK2), and (**C**) sphingosine-1-phosphate reseptor-1/2 (S1PR1/2) in the wound during wound healing was measured. All values shown in this figure represent the mean ± s.e.m. * $p < 0.05$, ** $p < 0.01$.

2.2. Effect of SphK1 Gene Knockout on Wound Healing, Vasculogenesis, and Cell Proliferation

Compared with littermate wild-type (WT) mice, SphK1$^{-/-}$ mice had significantly delayed wound healing, as determined by two-factor repeated measures ANOVA (Figure 2A,B; $p = 0.010$). This reflects the tendency of the SphK1$^{-/-}$ mice to have larger wound sizes on Days 5, 7, and 9 after injury, as determined by Student's *t*-test ($p = 0.056$, 0.262, and 0.068, respectively). We investigated vasculogenesis on Day 5 by immunohistochemistry against CD34, which is an early marker of vasculogenesis [26]. The SphK1$^{-/-}$ mice exhibited significantly less angiogenesis than the WT mice (Figure 2C–E). Immunohistochemistry with Ki67 showed that SphK1 knockout also had similar suppressive effects on the proliferation of both the fibroblasts in the wound (Figure 2F) and the keratinocytes at the wound edge (Figure 2G). The Ki67^{+} cells in the latter analyses are expressed as the percentage of Ki67^{+} cells/total cells per field.

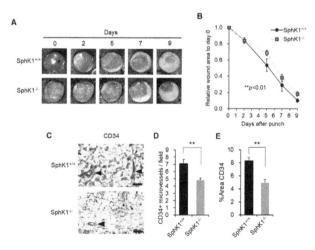

Figure 2. *Cont.*

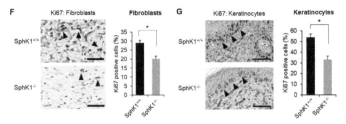

Figure 2. Effect of SphK1 knockout on wound healing, vasculogenesis, and cell proliferation. (**A**) Splinted excisional wounds were generated in SphK1$^{-/-}$ and SphK1$^{+/+}$ mice. Representative images of the closing wounds are shown. (**B**) Change in wound area over time ($n = 6$–10). (**C**) Representative images of CD34 expression on immunohistochemistry are shown. Arrowheads indicate positive findings (scale bars: 50 μm). (**D**) The numbers of CD34-positive microvessels per 200-fold magnified field are graphed ($n = 4$). (**E**) The percentage of the wound area that is occupied by CD34$^+$ cells is graphed ($n = 4$). (**F**) Representative images of Ki67 expression in fibroblasts on immunohistochemistry are shown. Arrowheads indicate positive findings (scale bars: 50 μm). The frequencies of Ki67$^+$ fibroblasts are graphed ($n = 4$). (**G**) Representative images of Ki67 expression in keratinocytes on immunohistochemistry are shown. Arrowheads indicate positive findings (scale bars: 50 μm). The frequencies of Ki67$^+$ keratinocytes are graphed ($n = 4$). All values shown in this figure represent the mean ± s.e.m. * $p < 0.05$, ** $p < 0.01$.

2.3. Effect of SphK1 Gene Knockout on Inflammatory Cell Recruitment during Wound Healing

Immunohistochemistry showed that the SphK1$^{-/-}$ mice exhibited significantly decreased macrophage numbers compared to the WT mice on Day 5 (Figure 3A–C). Flow cytometric analyses confirmed that the SphK1$^{-/-}$ mice had significantly lower frequencies of T cells in the wound five days after injury (Figure 3D,E).

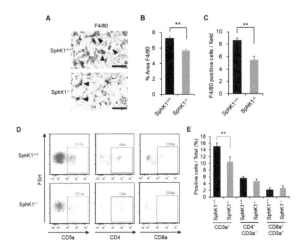

Figure 3. Effect of SphK1 knockout on inflammatory cell recruitment during wound healing. (**A**) Representative images of F4/80 expression on immunohistochemistry are shown. Arrowheads indicate positive findings (scale bars: 50 μm). (**B**) The percentage of the wound area that is occupied by F4/80$^+$ cells is graphed ($n = 4$). (**C**) The number of F4/80$^+$ cells per field is graphed ($n = 4$). (**D,E**) Representative flow cytometric plots (D) and frequency of the indicated T cell populations (E) on Day 5 after wounding, as determined by flow cytometry ($n = 5$–8). All values shown in this figure represent the mean ± s.e.m. ** $p < 0.01$.

2.4. Effect of Nanoparticle-Mediated Topical SphK1 Gene Delivery on Wound Healing, Vasculogenesis, and Cell Proliferation

We generated control and SphK1-expressing plasmids that were encapsulated with super carbonate apatite (sCA). sCA is a nanoparticle that is safe for in vivo gene delivery. The in vitro and in vivo safety of sCA-mediated gene delivery has been reported [27]. When mixed with sCA, the control and SphK1-expressing plasmids transfected mouse dermal fibroblast NIH3T3 cell lines in vitro with high efficiency (Figure 4A). Ointments containing the sCA-encapsulated plasmids were then generated and applied topically to the wounds of wound splinting model mice (Figure 4B). V5-tag protein expression analysis showed that the plasmids had a high transfection rate in vivo (Figure 4C). Compared with the vector, the SphK1 plasmid significantly accelerated wound closure, as determined by two-factor repeated measures ANOVA ($p < 0.0001$, Figure 4D,E). This reflected significantly greater closure on Days 7 and 9 after injury ($p = 0.003$ and 0.0002, respectively), as shown by Student's t-test (the vector and SphK1 plasmid did not differ significantly in terms of Day 5 closure rate; $p = 0.122$). We then investigated vasculogenesis and cell proliferation on Day 5 by immunohistochemistry. The SphK1 plasmid ointment significantly accelerated vasculogenesis (Figure 4F–H). Immunohistochemistry with Ki67 showed that the SphK1 plasmid ointment had corresponding positive effects on the proliferation of both the fibroblasts in the wound (Figure 4I) and the keratinocytes at the wound edge (Figure 4J). The Ki67$^+$ cells in the latter analyses are expressed as the percentage of positive cells/total cells per field.

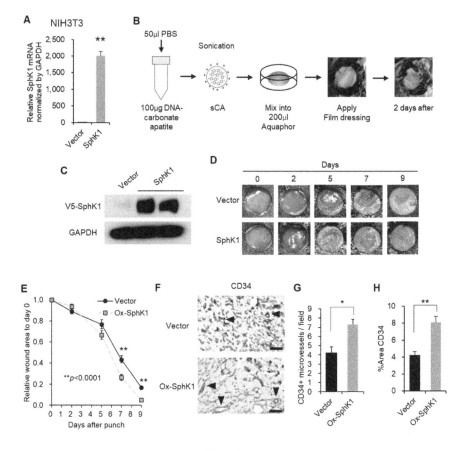

Figure 4. *Cont.*

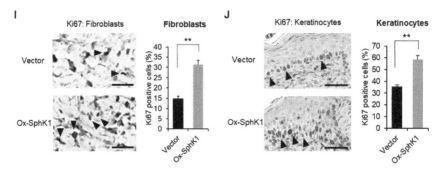

Figure 4. Effect of SphK1 overexpression on wound healing, vasculogenesis, and cell proliferation. (**A**) In vitro transfection efficiency with SphK1-expressing plasmid using super carbonate apatite (sCA) in NIH3T3 cells. (**B**) An ointment containing a SphK1-expressing plasmid encapsulated with sCA was prepared. (**C**) In vivo transfection efficiency of the sCA-encapsulated plasmid, as shown by immunoblots of V5-SphK1 expression in the wound surface tissues two days after application. (**D**) Representative images of the closing wounds are shown. (**E**) Effect of the plasmid ointment on wound closure. The change in wound area over time is graphed ($n = 12$). (**F**) Representative images of CD34 expression on immunohistochemistry are shown. Arrowheads indicate positive findings (scale bars: 50 μm). (**G**) The numbers of CD34-positive microvessels per 200-fold magnified field are graphed ($n = 4$). (**H**) The percentage of the wound area that is occupied by CD34$^+$ cells is graphed ($n = 4$). (**I**) Representative images of Ki67 expression in fibroblasts on immunohistochemistry are shown. Arrowheads indicate positive findings (scale bars: 50 μm). The frequencies of Ki67$^+$ fibroblasts are graphed ($n = 4$). (**J**) Representative images of Ki67 expression in keratinocytes on immunohistochemistry are shown. Arrowheads indicate positive findings (scale bars: 50 μm). The frequencies of Ki67$^+$ keratinocytes are graphed ($n = 4$). All values shown in this figure represent the mean ± s.e.m. * $p < 0.05$, ** $p < 0.01$.

2.5. Effect of Nanoparticle-Mediated Topical SphK1 Gene Delivery on Inflammatory Cell Recruitment during Wound Healing

Immunohistochemistry showed that the SphK1 plasmid-treated wounds had significantly higher macrophage numbers on Day 5 (Figure 5A–C). Moreover, the SphK1 plasmid ointment increased the recruitment of total T cells, CD4 T cells, and CD8a T cells in the wound five days after injury (Figure 5D,E). It should be noted that uninjured SphK1$^{-/-}$ mice exhibit normal lymphocyte trafficking despite the fact that their blood S1P levels are about half of those in WT mice [28]. Thus, our experiments suggest that SphK1 participates in the recruitment of inflammatory cells to the wound, and that this is needed for the normal progression of the proliferative phase of wound healing. These results are consistent with our hypothesis that after wounding, S1P generated by SphK1 promotes vasculogenesis and recruits inflammatory cells, including lymphocytes and macrophages, and that this facilitates the wound healing process during the proliferative phase. Furthermore, immunoblot analyses showed that the SphK1 plasmid ointment increased expression of the well-known wound healing-related factors VEGF, FGF-2, and IGF-1 [29–31] in the wound on Day 5 (Figure 5F,G). These findings suggest that these wound-related factors were secreted by the recruited lymphocytes and macrophages.

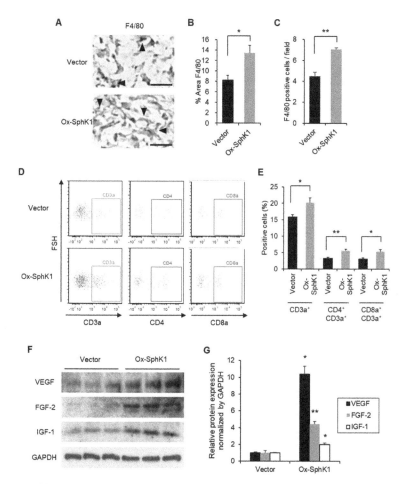

Figure 5. Effect of SphK1 overexpression on inflammatory cell recruitment and enhanced wound-related factors. (**A**) Representative images of F4/80 expression on immunohistochemistry are shown. Arrowheads indicate positive findings (scale bars: 50 µm). (**B**) The percentage of the wound area that is occupied by F4/80[+] cells is graphed (*n* = 4). (**C**) The number of F4/80[+] cells per field is graphed (*n* = 4). (**D,E**) Representative flow cytometric plots (D) and frequency of the indicated T cell populations (E) on Day 5 after wounding, as determined by flow cytometry (*n* = 5–8). (**F**) Effect of the plasmid ointment on the expression of the indicated wound healing-related factors on Day 5 after wounding, as determined by immunoblot analysis. (**G**) The immunoblots were quantified and the data were graphed (*n* = 3). All values shown in this figure represent the mean ± s.e.m. * *p* < 0.05, ** *p* < 0.01.

2.6. Effect of SphK1 Overexpression on Granuloma Formation

When we injected sponge granulomas in mice with the sCA-encapsulated vector or SphK1 plasmid every other day, as described previously [32], the SphK1 plasmid generated clearer collagen bundles, higher fibroblast density, and less dead cell accumulation in the center of the sponge on Day 14 (Figure 6A). Moreover, on Day 14 after injury, the SphK1 plasmid associated with significantly more granulation than the control plasmid (Figure 6B).

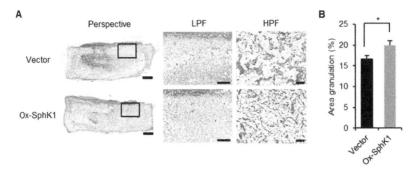

Figure 6. Topical SphK1 gene delivery promotes granulation. (**A**) Representative images of the hematoxylin and eosin (HE)-stained sponge granulomas treated with sCA-encapsulated plasmid injection on Day 14 are shown. The black boxes are shown magnified. (scale bars: Perspective: 1 mm; LPF: 400 μm; HPF: 50 μm). (**B**) Percentage of granulated area is graphed ($n = 8$). All values in this figure represent the mean ± s.e.m. * $p < 0.05$.

2.7. Effect of SphK1 and S1PR2 Gene Expression on Scar Thickness, the Interaction between Transforming Growth Factor (TGF)-β1 and S1P

We treated the dermal fibroblast line NIH3T3 with SphK1 plasmid or exogenous S1P. We found that exogenous S1P, but not the SphK1 plasmid, suppressed the transcription of Collagen1a1 and Collagen3a1 in the cells (Figure 7A,B). Thus, exogenous S1P, but not endogenously produced S1P, prevents the collagen deposition of dermal fibroblasts. Notably, when the exogenous S1P-stimulated cells were treated with the S1PR1 and S1PR3 inhibitor VPC23019 or the S1PR2 inhibitor JTE013, their collagen production was restored (Figure 7C). Thus, exogenous S1P suppresses the collagen deposition of dermal fibroblasts via S1PR signaling. Transforming growth factor (TGF)-β1, which is produced during the proliferative phase of wound healing, induces fibroblasts to produce granulation tissue in vivo and extracellular matrix in vitro [33,34]. Our finding that endogenous S1P, but not exogenous S1P, also promotes granulation and participates in the proliferative phase of wound healing led us to examine the effect of TGF-β1 treatment on S1PR expression by NIH3T3 cells. We found that this treatment significantly suppressed transcription of S1PRs (Figure 7D). This suggests that TGF-β1 is a key modulator of the ability of S1P to promote the proliferative phase of wound healing. Given that S1PR2 expression in the wound increased around the end of wound closure (Figure 1C), S1PR2$^{-/-}$ mice had significantly smaller wounds on Day 12 after injury (Figure 7E,F). This suggests that S1PR2 signaling negatively regulates SphK1-S1PR1 signaling, thereby slowing down wound closure at the end of the proliferative phase and allowing the wound to prepare for the remodeling phase. Interestingly, we discovered that when the wounds in the mouse excisional wound splinting model were treated with SphK1-sCA ointment, the scars that formed when epithelization was completed were much thinner than the scars of the vector-sCA-treated mice. The SphK1-sCA-treated wounds also had much thinner collagen bundles, as shown by high power field images (Figure 7G,H).

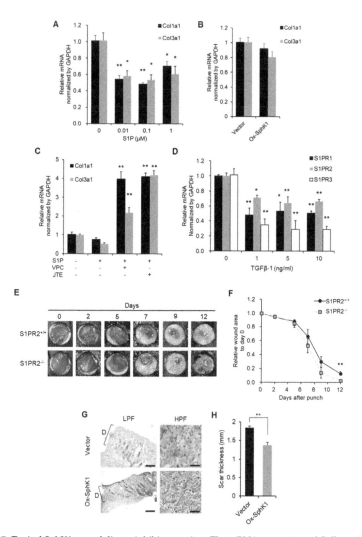

Figure 7. Topical SphK1 gene delivery inhibits scarring. The mRNA expression of Collagen1a1 and Collagen3a1 in NIH3T3 cells (**A**) stimulated with the indicated concentration of S1P for 24 h ($n = 4$) or (**B**) transfected with SphK1-expressing plasmid or vector plasmid ($n = 4$). (**C**) The mRNA expression of Collagen1a1 and Collagen3a1 in NIH3T3 cells stimulated with 1 µM S1P for 24 h with or without 10 µM VPC23019 (inhibitor of S1PR1 and S1PR3) or JTE013 (inhibitor of S1PR2) ($n = 3$). (**D**) The mRNA expression of the indicated S1PRs in NIH3T3 cells stimulated with the indicated concentration of transforming growth factor (TGF)-β1 for 18 h ($n = 3$). (**E**) Splinted excisional wounds were generated in S1PR2$^{-/-}$ and S1PR2$^{+/+}$ mice. Representative images of the closing wounds are shown. (**F**) The wound area over time was measured ($n = 6$). (**G**) Representative images of Masson's trichrome-stained scars at the point of epithelization after treatment with sCA-encapsulated plasmid ointment (the scale bars are LPF: 400 µm; HPF: 50 µm). "D" indicates the scar thickness. (**H**) The scar thickness was measured and graphed ($n = 4$–6). All values in this figure represent the mean ± s.e.m. * $p < 0.05$, ** $p < 0.01$.

3. Discussion

The present study demonstrates that there were high levels of SphK1 expression after wounding and that high endogenous production of S1P via SphK1 plasmid transfection accelerated wound closure and induced less scarring. It also suggested that the scarless healing induced by the SphK1 plasmid is due to the anti-fibrotic effect of S1P-S1PR signaling in the early phase of wound healing. This is supported by the fact that S1P treatment of dermal fibroblasts suppressed their production of collagens and that this effect was reversed by S1PR inhibitors. These observations together suggest that since the SphK1 plasmid transfection increases S1P levels, it may prolong the anti-fibrotic effects of S1P-S1PR signaling during the proliferative phase of wound healing. This in turn limits the deposition of extracellular matrix, thus generating minimal granulation tissue and very thin scars when epithelialization is complete.

We found that SphK1 knockout significantly decreased the recruitment to the wound of CD3a$^+$ T cells but not CD4$^+$CD3a$^+$ and CD8a$^+$CD3a$^+$ T cells. By contrast, topical overexpression of SphK1 significantly increased the CD4$^+$CD3a$^+$ and CD8a$^+$CD3a$^+$ T cell populations as well as the total CD3a$^+$ T cell population in the wound. This apparent discrepancy may reflect the different methods involved: SphK1 knockout has systemic effects whereas the SphK1 ointment has direct local effects. It will be of interest to further examine the profile of the T cells that are recruited to the wound (including NK cells and $\gamma\delta$ T cells) when SphK1 is systemically knocked out: this may help elucidate the mechanisms by which the SphK1/S1P axis recruits T cells. Our finding that altering SphK1/S1P signaling shapes not just wound healing but also T cell recruitment suggests that T cells participate in wound healing. This notion is supported by multiple lines of evidence. For example, CD3 T cell numbers in the wound bed increase during the proliferation phase, particularly in the regenerating epidermis [35], and total T cell depletion impairs wound healing [36]. Moreover, burn injuries activate $\gamma\delta$ T cells at the injury site. This initiates extensive infiltration by $\alpha\beta$ T cells, which facilitate the transition from the inflammatory phase to the proliferative phase [37]. In addition, wound healing is associated with activation of epidermal T cells and their production of growth factors [38].

Overexpression of SphK1 increases recruitment of lymphocytes and macrophages while at the same time enhancing retention; this strengthens subsequent fibroblast activation. Therefore, granulation is promoted. However, fibroblasts activated by TGFβ-1 find it difficult to respond to S1P stimulation as S1PRs are down-regulated (Figure 7D). This phenomenon should decrease as wound healing proceeds towards epithelialization. The anti-fibrotic effect mediated by S1PR signaling occurs with epithelialization. Treatment with the SphK1 plasmid strengthens the dynamic transition from the proliferative phase to the remodeling phase, resulting in inhibited scarring (Figure 7F).

TGF-β1 is likely to play a key role in S1P-S1PR1 signaling-induced less scarring. This cytokine is produced during the proliferative phase of wound healing and induces granulation [33,34]. Fibroblasts activated by TGFβ-1 find it difficult to respond to S1P stimulation as S1PRs are down-regulated (Figure 7A,D). This phenomenon should decrease as wound healing proceeds towards epithelialization. The anti-fibrotic effect mediated by S1PR signaling occurs with epithelialization. Treatment with the SphK1 plasmid strengthens the dynamic transition from the proliferative phase to the remodeling phase, resulting in inhibited scarring (Figure 7F). The expression of TGF-β1 during the proliferative phase of wound healing postpones S1PR2 expression in the wound. Thus, when high S1P levels are generated by SphK1 plasmid transfection, the S1PR2 that is eventually produced is less able to suppress anti-fibrotic S1P-S1PR1 signaling. This limits the production of extracellular matrix and thereby inhibits excessive scar formation.

Immune responses play important roles in skin wound healing [39], and the present study suggests that increased expression of SphK1 also improves wound healing by strengthening these responses. These responses result in the production of multiple wound healing factors; they also have an anti-bacterial effect [40,41]. Since all currently available wound healing agents either target angiogenesis or fibroblast function [42–44], SphK1 plasmid treatment constitutes a novel approach to wound healing. Moreover, SphK1 plasmid treatment is simple. By contrast, other wound healing agents must be applied in a stepwise fashion: first, infections or necrotic tissues must be removed, followed by treatment with agents that support fibroblast function and/or angiogenesis. Notably, macrophage polarization was suggested recently to participate in wound healing [45,46]. Further studies exploring the effect of the systemic or local SphK1/S1P axis on macrophage polarization may expand the potential usefulness of these molecules in wound management.

In summary, we found that the SphK1/S1P axis accelerated wound healing by increasing angiogenesis and the recruitment of T cells and macrophages, which secreted various wound-related factors. It was also involved in inhibiting excessive scarring because it promoted the anti-fibrotic effect of S1P signaling. This finding suggests that the SphK1/S1P axis may be a novel therapeutic agent that could help limit scarring after surgery and trauma and aid chronic wound management. However, studies that further elucidate the role of the SphK1/S1P axis in wound healing are needed to determine its full clinical potential.

4. Material and Methods

4.1. Animal Models and Wound Area Analysis

C57BL/6J mice were purchased from Jackson Laboratory. SphK1 KO and S1PR2 KO mice were from Dr. Richard Proia (The National Institute of Diabetes and Digestive and Kidney Diseases (NIDDK) of National Institutes of Health (NIH)). All animal procedures were approved by the Institutional Animal Care and Use Committee of the Virginia Commonwealth University on 1 July 2015 (AD20100) and the Animal Experimental Ethical Review Committee of Nippon Medical School on 7 September 2016 (28-054). The murine excisional wound splinting model was generated as described previously [25]. Mice were anesthetized with isoflurane, and their dorsal hair was removed. Two 5 mm-diameter full-thickness skin punches were generated symmetrically on either side of the midline. Circular 12 mm-diameter silicon rubber splints were punched in the center to generate 6 mm-diameter holes. They were then fixed with instant-bonding adhesive and sutures around the punch wounds. After applying the required ointment, the wounds were dressed with Tegaderm (3M, Maplewood, MN, USA). The wounds were photographed at the indicated time points. The digital photos were analyzed using GIMP 2.8 software. The pixels of the wound area were normalized to the pixels of the inside of the silicon splint. The wound areas at the indicated time points were expressed as ratios relative to the wound area immediately after wounding.

4.2. Cells and S1P Preparation

Murine dermal fibroblast NIH3T3 cells, human cervix epithelioid carcinoma HeLa cells, and human embryo kidney HEK293 were cultured in Dulbecco's modified eagle medium (DMEM) containing 10% fetal bovine serum (FBS). To analyze collagen production, ascorbic acid 2-phosphate (Sigma-Aldrich, Carlsbad, CA, USA) was added to the culture medium to a concentration of 0.2 mM. S1P was purchased from Sigma-Aldrich and 1 mM was sonicated in 4% bovine serum albumin (BSA). Recombinant human TGFβ-1 was purchased from R&D systems (Minneapolis, MN, USA). VPC23019 was purchased from Avanti (Alabaster, AL, USA). JTE013 was purchased from Cayman Chemical (Ann Arbor, MI, USA).

4.3. Plasmid Construction, In Vitro Transfection with sCA-Encapsulated Plasmids, and Preparation of Plasmid-sCA Ointment

The murine SphK1 gene was amplified using TaKaRa Ex Taq Hot Start Version (TaKaRa, Kusatsu, Japan). The SphK1-expressing plasmid was then constructed using the pcDNA3.1/V5-His TOPO TA Expression Kit (Invitrogen, Carlsbad, CA, USA). sCA-encapsulated plasmids were prepared as described previously [27,47]. Thus, 4 μL of 1 M $CaCl_2$ was incubated at 37 °C for 30 min with 2 μg of plasmid DNA in 1 mL of an inorganic solution ($NaHCO_3$, 44 mM; NaH_2PO_4, 0.9 mM; $CaCl_2$, 1.8 mM; pH 7.5) and then centrifuged at 12,000 rpm for 3 min. After the pellet was dissolved with DMEM, the solution was sonicated in a water bath for 10 min, thus generating sCA-encapsulated plasmids.

Cells cultured in 6-well plates for 24 h were incubated with the plasmid-sCA-DMEM solution for 6 h. The medium was then replaced with DMEM containing 10% FBS. After another 48 h, the cells were collected for total RNA isolation. The plasmid-sCA ointment was generated by dissolving the sCA pellet with 50 μL of PBS, mixing it with 100 μg of plasmid DNA, and then mixing the solution into 200 μL of Aquaphor®. The four wounds of two mice were each treated once with 250 μL of ointment.

4.4. Sponge Granulomas in Mice and Their Injection with Plasmid-sCA

Sponge granulomas were generated in two mice as described previously [32]. Thus, polyvinyl alcohol (PVA) sponges were processed to generate 10 mm-diameter 3 mm-thick sponges. The sponges were irradiated with ultraviolet light and infiltrated with saline for 48 h. The sponges were then transplanted (two per mouse) in the subcutaneous dorsal area in a symmetrical fashion. sCA was mixed with 50 μg of plasmid DNA and pelleted. The pellet was then dissolved in 100 μL of saline containing 0.5% mouse serum albumin. The two sponges on one mouse were injected every other day with 50 μL of sCA-plasmid. The two sponges on the other mouse were injected with sCA-vector. The samples were harvested 14 days after transplantation and subjected to histological analysis. The percentage of total area that was occupied by eosin-positive area in the sponges were analyzed by using ImageJ. Four fields per sponge were analyzed and the averages were calculated.

4.5. Flow Cytometry

Cells were isolated from the wound tissues as described previously [6]. Thus, the tissues were cut into small pieces and digested at 37 °C for 90 min in DMEM containing 10% FBS, 1.2 mg/mL hyaluronidase (Sigma-Aldrich), 2 mg/mL collagenase (Sigma-Aldrich), and 0.2 mg/mL DNase I (Sigma-Aldrich). The cell pellets were resuspended in PBS containing 2% FBS and then incubated with anti-CD16/32 antibody (BioLegend, San Diego, CA, USA) for 5 min to block the Fcγ receptors. To measure inflammatory cell recruitment, the wound cell preparations were stained with phycoerythrin (PE)-conjugated anti-Gr-1, allophycocyanin (APC)-conjugated anti-CD3a, PE/CY7-conjugated anti-CD4, or fluorescein isothiocyanate (FITC)-conjugated anti-CD8a antibody (CiteAb, Bath, UK) at 4 °C for 20 min. The lymphocytes were analyzed with FACSDiva (BD, San Jose, CA, USA).

4.6. Quantitative RT-PCR

Total RNA was extracted using TRIzol® Regent (Invitrogen). cDNA was synthesized using High Capacity cDNA Reverse Transcription Kits (Applied Biosystems, Foster City, CA, USA). qRT-PCR was performed by using a CFX96 Real-Time System (Bio-Rad, Hercules, CA, USA) with PowerUp SYBR Green master mix (Bio-Rad). GAPDH served as the internal control. The primer pairs used are shown in Table 1. Relative expression was calculated using the $2^{-\Delta\Delta Ct}$ method with correction for different amplification efficiencies.

Table 1. The primers used for quantitative real-time RT-PCR.

Primer	Bio-Rad Assay ID	Forward (5'->3')	Reverse (5'->3')
Col1a1		CGATGGATTCCCGTTCGAGTA	CATTAGGCGCAGGAAGGTCA
Col3a1		GAAGTCTCTGAAGCTGATGGG	TTGCCTTGCGTGTTTGATATTC
GAPDH	qMmuCEP0039581		
S1PR1	qMmuCID0020925		
S1PR2	qMmuCED0004722		
S1PR3	qMmuCIP0028162		
SphK1	qMmuCED0040475		
SphK2	qMmuCED0039969		

4.7. Immunohistochemistry, Western Blot Analysis, and Scar Thickness Analysis

Paraffin-embedded sections were stained with H&E or Masson's trichrome stain and primary antibodies against F4/80, Ki67, and CD34. The immunostained sections were developed with

VECTASTAIN Universal Elite ABC Kit (Vector, Burlingame, CA, USA). All antibodies were from Abcam (Cambridge, UK). The sections were analyzed using ImageJ. The excised wound tissue was homogenized with liquid nitrogen. Total protein was isolated using 1% NP-40. Equal amounts of protein were separated by SDS-PAGE and then transferred to a nitrocellulose membrane. The membranes were incubated with primary antibodies against V5 (Invitrogen), VEGF, FGF-2 (Santa Cruz Biotechnology, Dallas, TX, USA), IGF-1 (Abcam), or GAPDH (Cell Signaling Technology, Danvers, MA, USA), followed by horseradish peroxidase-conjugated IgG against mouse, rabbit, or goat antibodies (Jackson ImmunoResearch, West Grove, PA, USA). The membranes were developed by using SuperSignal Chemiluminescent Substrates (Thermo Fisher Scientific, Cambridge, MA, USA). The antibodies used are summarized in Table 2. The quantification was performed by using ImageJ. Scar thickness was measured by photographing the sectioned tissues after Masson's trichrome staining and then using ImageJ.

Table 2. The primary antibodies used for this study.

Antigen	Company	Application	Concentration
F4/80	Abcam	Immunohistochemistry	1:100
Ki67	Abcam	Immunohistochemistry	1:100
CD34	Abcam	Immunohistochemistry	1:100
V5	Invitrogen	Western blot	1:5000
VEGF	Santa Cruz	Western blot	1:200
FGF-2	Santa Cruz	Western blot	1:200
IGF-1	Abcam	Western blot	1:500
GAPDH	Cell Signaling Technology	Western blot	1:1000

4.8. Statistical Analysis

Wound groups were compared using two-factor repeated measures ANOVA. If three or more wound groups were compared, ANOVA was followed by post-hoc Tukey's test. Two wound groups were compared using Student's t-test or Welch's t-test after F test. $p < 0.05$ was considered significant. All statistical analyses were performed using Statcel2 software (OMS, Saitama, Japan).

Author Contributions: Conceptualization, M.A. and K.T.; methodology, M.A., H.Y. and K.T.; validation, M.A., H.A., P.M., T.T., N.M.M., E.T. and Y.O.; formal analysis, M.A.; investigation, M.A., H.A., P.M., T.T., N.M.M., E.T. and Y.O.; data curation, M.A.; writing—original draft preparation, M.A.; writing—review and editing, R.O. and K.T.; supervision, K.T.; project administration, K.T.; funding acquisition, M.A., T.T., and K.T.

Funding: This study was supported by R01 CA160688 from the National Institute of Health (NIH) and grants (Nos. JP16K20371 and JP17K17037) from the Japan Society for the Promotion of Science (JSPS).

Conflicts of Interest: The authors declare no conflict of interest.

Abbreviations

S1P	Sphingosine-1-phosphate
S1PRs	Sphingosine-1-phosphate receptors
SphKs	Sphingosine kinases
TGF-β1	Transforming growth factor-β1

References

1. Waldorf, H.; Fewkes, J. Wound healing. *Adv. Dermatol.* **1995**, *10*, 77–96.
2. Boyce, D.E.; Jones, W.D.; Ruge, F.; Harding, K.G.; Moore, K. The role of lymphocytes in human dermal wound healing. *Br. J. Dermatol.* **2000**, *143*, 59–65. [CrossRef] [PubMed]
3. Ploeger, D.T.; Hosper, N.A.; Schipper, M.; Koerts, J.A.; de Rond, S.; Bank, R.A. Cell plasticity in wound healing: paracrine factors of M1/M2 polarized macrophages influence the phenotypical state of dermal fibroblasts. *Cell Commun. Signal.* **2013**, *11*, 29. [CrossRef] [PubMed]

4. Stein, C.; Küchler, S. Targeting inflammation and wound healing by opioids. *Trends Pharmacol. Sci.* **2013**, *34*, 303–312. [CrossRef] [PubMed]

5. Hofmann, U.; Beyersdorf, N.; Weirather, J.; Podolskaya, A.; Bauersachs, J.; Ertl, G.; Kerkau, T.; Frantz, S. Activation of CD4 + T lymphocytes improves wound healing and survival after experimental myocardial infarction in mice. *Circulation* **2012**, *125*, 1652–1663. [CrossRef] [PubMed]

6. Liu, M.; Saeki, K.; Matsunobu, T.; Okuno, T.; Koga, T.; Sugimoto, Y.; Yokoyama, C.; Nakamizo, S.; Kabashima, K.; Narumiya, S.; et al. 12-Hydroxyheptadecatrienoic acid promotes epidermal wound healing by accelerating keratinocyte migration via the BLT2 receptor. *J. Exp. Med.* **2014**, *211*, 1063–1078. [CrossRef] [PubMed]

7. Oh, S.Y.; Lee, S.J.; Jung, Y.H.; Lee, H.J.; Han, H.J. Arachidonic acid promotes skin wound healing through induction of human MSC migration by MT3-MMP-mediated fibronectin degradation. *Cell Death Dis.* **2015**, *6*, e1750. [CrossRef] [PubMed]

8. Chao, C.Y.; Lii, C.K.; Ye, S.Y.; Li, C.C.; Lu, C.Y.; Lin, A.H.; Liu, K.L.; Chen, H.W. Docosahexaenoic acid inhibits vascular endothelial growth factor (VEGF)-induced cell migration via the GPR120/PP2A/ERK1/2/eNOS signaling pathway in human umbilical vein endothelial cells. *J. Agric. Food Chem.* **2014**, *62*, 4152–4158. [CrossRef]

9. Majtan, J. Honey: An immunomodulator in wound healing. *Wound Repair Regen.* **2014**, *22*, 187–192. [CrossRef]

10. 'Izzah Ibrahim, N.; Wong, S.K.; Mohamed, I.N.; Mohamed, N.; Chin, K.Y.; Ima-Nirwana, S.; Shuid, A.N. Wound healing properties of selected natural products. *Int. J. Environ. Res. Public Health* **2018**, *15*, 2360. [CrossRef]

11. Takabe, K.; Kim, R.H.; Allegood, J.C.; Mitra, P.; Ramachandran, S.; Nagahashi, M.; Harikumar, K.B.; Hait, N.C.; Milstien, S.; Spiegel, S. Estradiol induces export of sphingosine 1-phosphate from breast cancer cells via ABCC1 and ABCG2. *J. Biol. Chem.* **2010**, *285*, 10477–10486. [CrossRef] [PubMed]

12. Takabe, K.; Paugh, S.W.; Milstien, S.; Spiegel, S. "Inside-out" signaling of sphingosine-1-phosphate: Therapeutic targets. *Pharmacol. Rev.* **2008**, *60*, 181–195. [CrossRef] [PubMed]

13. Aoki, M.; Aoki, H.; Ramanathan, R.; Hait, N.C.; Takabe, K. Sphingosine-1-phosphate signaling in immune cells and inflammation: roles and therapeutic potential. *Mediat. Inflamm.* **2016**, *2016*, 8606878. [CrossRef]

14. Matloubian, M.; Lo, C.G.; Cinamon, G.; Lesneski, M.J.; Xu, Y.; Brinkmann, V.; Allende, M.L.; Proia, R.L.; Cyster, J.G. Lymphocyte egress from thymus and peripheral lymphoid organs is dependent on S1P receptor 1. *Nature* **2004**, *427*, 355–360. [CrossRef] [PubMed]

15. Schwab, S.R.; Cyster, J.G. Finding a way out: lymphocyte egress from lymphoid organs. *Nat. Immunol.* **2007**, *8*, 1295–1301. [CrossRef]

16. Schwab, S.R.; Pereira, J.P.; Matloubian, M.; Xu, Y.; Huang, Y.; Cyster, J.G. Lymphocyte sequestration through S1P lyase inhibition and disruption of S1P gradients. *Science* **2005**, *309*, 1735–1739. [CrossRef] [PubMed]

17. Pappu, R.; Schwab, S.R.; Cornelissen, I.; Pereira, J.P.; Regard, J.B.; Xu, Y.; Camerer, E.; Zheng, Y.-W.; Huang, Y.; Cyster, J.G.; et al. Promotion of lymphocyte egress into blood and lymph by distinct sources of sphingosine-1-phosphate. *Science* **2007**, *316*, 295–298. [CrossRef]

18. Lee, M.J.; Thangada, S.; Claffey, K.P.; Ancellin, N.; Liu, C.H.; Kluk, M.; Volpi, M.; Sha'afi, R.I.; Hla, T. Vascular endothelial cell adherens junction assembly and morphogenesis induced by sphingosine-1-phosphate. *Cell* **1999**, *99*, 301–312. [CrossRef]

19. Allende, M.L.; Proia, R.L. Sphingosine-1-phosphate receptors and the development of the vascular system. *Biochim. Biophys. Acta* **2002**, *1582*, 222–227. [CrossRef]

20. Ledgerwood, L.G.; Lal, G.; Zhang, N.; Garin, A.; Esses, S.J.; Ginhoux, F.; Merad, M.; Peche, H.; Lira, S.A.; Ding, Y.; et al. The sphingosine 1-phosphate receptor 1 causes tissue retention by inhibiting the entry of peripheral tissue T lymphocytes into afferent lymphatics. *Nat. Immunol.* **2008**, *9*, 42–53. [CrossRef]

21. Sanchez, T.; Estrada-Hernandez, T.; Paik, J.; Wu, M.; Venkataraman, K.; Brinkmann, V.; Claffey, K.; Hla, T. Phosphorylation and action of the immunomodulator FTY720 inhibits vascular endothelial cell growth factor-induced vascular permeability. *J. Biol. Chem.* **2003**, *278*, 47281–47290. [CrossRef] [PubMed]

22. Marsolais, D.; Rosen, H. Chemical modulators of sphingosine-1-phosphate receptors as barrier-oriented therapeutic molecules. *Nat. Rev. Drug Discov.* **2009**, *8*, 297–307. [CrossRef] [PubMed]

23. Sanchez, T.; Skoura, A.; Wu, M.T.; Casserly, B.; Harrington, E.O.; Hla, T. Induction of vascular permeability by the sphingosine-1-phosphate receptor-2 (S1P2R) and its downstream effectors ROCK and PTEN. *Arterioscler. Thromb. Vasc. Biol.* **2007**, *27*, 1312–1318. [CrossRef] [PubMed]

24. Sanchez, T.; Hla, T. Structural and functional characteristics of S1P receptors. *J. Cell. Biochem.* **2004**, *92*, 913–922. [CrossRef] [PubMed]

25. Wang, X.; Ge, J.; Tredget, E.E.; Wu, Y. The mouse excisional wound splinting model, including applications for stem cell transplantation. *Nat. Protoc.* **2013**, *8*, 302–309. [CrossRef] [PubMed]

26. Ferreras, C.; Cole, C.L.; Urban, K.; Jayson, G.C.; Avizienyte, E. Segregation of late outgrowth endothelial cells into functional endothelial CD34− and progenitor-like CD34+ cell populations. *Angiogenesis* **2015**, *18*, 47–68. [CrossRef] [PubMed]

27. Wu, X.; Yamamoto, H.; Nakanishi, H.; Yamamoto, Y.; Inoue, A.; Tei, M.; Hirose, H.; Uemura, M.; Nishimura, J.; Hata, T.; et al. Innovative Delivery of siRNA to Solid Tumors by Super Carbonate Apatite. *PLoS ONE* **2015**, *10*, e0116022. [CrossRef] [PubMed]

28. Allende, M.L.; Sasaki, T.; Kawai, H.; Olivera, A.; Mi, Y.; Van Echten-Deckert, G.; Hajdu, R.; Rosenbach, M.; Keohane, C.A.; Mandala, S.; et al. Mice deficient in sphingosine kinase 1 are rendered lymphopenic by FTY720. *J. Biol. Chem.* **2004**, *279*, 52487–52492. [CrossRef] [PubMed]

29. Canesso, M.C.C.; Vieira, A.T.; Castro, T.B.R.; Schirmer, B.G.A.; Cisalpino, D.; Martins, F.S.; Rachid, M.A.; Nicoli, J.R.; Teixeira, M.M.; Barcelos, L.S. Skin Wound Healing Is Accelerated and Scarless in the Absence of Commensal Microbiota. *J. Immunol.* **2014**, *193*, 5171–5180. [CrossRef]

30. Tang, Q.L.; Han, S.S.; Feng, J.; Di, J.Q.; Qin, W.X.; Fu, J.; Jiang, Q.Y. Moist exposed burn ointment promotes cutaneous excisional wound healing in rats involving VEGF and bFGF. *Mol. Med. Rep.* **2014**, *9*, 1277–1282. [CrossRef] [PubMed]

31. Aghdam, S.Y.; Eming, S.A.; Willenborg, S.; Neuhaus, B.; Niessen, C.M.; Partridge, L.; Krieg, T.; Bruning, J.C. Vascular endothelial insulin/IGF-1 signaling controls skin wound vascularization. *Biochem. Biophys. Res. Commun.* **2012**, *421*, 197–202. [CrossRef] [PubMed]

32. Kyriakides, T.R.; Zhu, Y.H.; Yang, Z.; Huynh, G.; Bornstein, P. Altered extracellular matrix remodeling and angiogenesis in sponge granulomas of thrombospondin 2-null mice. *Am. J. Pathol.* **2001**, *159*, 1255–1262. [CrossRef]

33. Schmid, P.; Kunz, S.; Cerletti, N.; Mcmaster, G.; Cox, D. Injury induced expression of TGF-β1 mRNA is enhanced by exogenously applied TGF-βS. *Biochem. Biophys. Res. Commun.* **1993**, *194*, 399–406. [CrossRef] [PubMed]

34. Haroon, Z.A.; Raleigh, J.A.; Greenberg, C.S.; Dewhirst, M.W. Early wound healing exhibits cytokine surge without evidence of hypoxia. *Ann. Surg.* **2000**, *231*, 137–147. [CrossRef] [PubMed]

35. Agaiby, A.D.; Dyson, M. Immuno-inflammatory cell dynamics during cutaneous wound healing. *J. Anat.* **1999**, *195*, 531–542. [CrossRef] [PubMed]

36. Efron, J.; Frankel, H.; Lazarou, S.; Wasserkrug, H.; Barbul, A. Wound healing and T-lymphocytes. *J. Surg. Res.* **1990**, *48*, 460–463. [CrossRef]

37. Rani, M.; Zhang, Q.; Scherer, M.R.; Cap, A.P.; Schwacha, M.G. Activated skin γδ T-cells regulate T-cell infiltration of the wound site after burn. *Innate Immun.* **2015**, *21*, 140–150. [CrossRef] [PubMed]

38. Havran, W.L.; Jameson, J.M. Epidermal T Cells and Wound Healing. *J. Immunol.* **2010**, *184*, 5423–5428. [CrossRef] [PubMed]

39. Jun, J.; Kim, K.; Lau, L.F. The matricellular protein CCN1 mediates neutrophil efferocytosis in cutaneous wound healing. *Nat. Commun.* **2015**, *6*, 7386. [CrossRef]

40. Dreymueller, D.; Denecke, B.; Ludwig, A.; Jahnen-Dechent, W. Embryonic stem cell-derived M2-like macrophages delay cutaneous wound healing. *Wound Repair Regen.* **2013**, *21*, 44–54. [CrossRef]

41. Zheng, X.F.; Hong, Y.X.; Feng, G.J.; Zhang, G.F.; Rogers, H.; Lewis, M.A.O.; Williams, D.W.; Xia, Z.F.; Song, B.; Wei, X.Q. Lipopolysaccharide-induced M2 to M1 macrophage transformation for IL-12p70 production is blocked by candida albicans mediated up-regulation of EBI3 expression. *PLoS ONE* **2013**, *8*, 4–13. [CrossRef] [PubMed]

42. Kämpfer, H.; Bräutigam, L.; Geisslinger, G.; Pfeilschifter, J.; Frank, S. Cyclooxygenase-1-coupled prostaglandin biosynthesis constitutes an essential prerequisite for skin repair. *J. Investig. Dermatol.* **2003**, *120*, 880–890. [CrossRef] [PubMed]

43. Toyota, T.; Hirata, Y.; Ikeda, Y.; Matsuoka, K.; Sakuma, A.; Mizushima, Y. Lipo-PGE1, a new lipid-encapsulated preparation of prostaglandin E1: placebo-and prostaglandin E1-controlled multicenter trials in patients with diabetic neuropathy and leg ulcers. *Prostaglandis* **1993**, *46*, 453–468. [CrossRef]

44. Barrientos, S.; Brem, H.; Stojadinovic, O.; Tomic-Canic, M. Clinical application of growth factors and cytokines in wound healing. *Wound Repair Regen.* **2014**, *22*, 569–578. [CrossRef] [PubMed]

45. Hesketh, M.; Sahin, K.B.; West, Z.E.; Murray, R.Z. Macrophage Phenotypes Regulate Scar Formation and Chronic Wound Healing. *Int. J. Mol. Sci.* **2017**, *18*, 1545. [CrossRef]

46. He, R.; Yin, H.; Yuan, B.; Liu, T.; Luo, L.; Huang, P.; Dai, L.; Zeng, K. IL-33 improves wound healing through enhanced M2 macrophage polarization in diabetic mice. *Mol. Immunol.* **2017**, *90*, 42–49. [CrossRef]

47. Chowdhury, E.; Akaike, T. High performance DNA nano-carriers of carbonate apatite: Multiple factors in regulation of particle synthesis and transfection efficiency. *Int. J. Nanomed.* **2007**, *2*, 101–106. [CrossRef]

International Journal of
Molecular Sciences

Article

Defect of Interferon γ Leads to Impaired Wound Healing through Prolonged Neutrophilic Inflammatory Response and Enhanced MMP-2 Activation

Emi Kanno [1,*], Hiromasa Tanno [1], Airi Masaki [2], Ayako Sasaki [2], Noriko Sato [2], Maiko Goto [1], Mayu Shisai [1], Kenji Yamaguchi [2], Naoyuki Takagi [2], Miki Shoji [2], Yuki Kitai [3], Ko Sato [4], Jun Kasamatsu [4], Keiko Ishii [3], Tomomitsu Miyasaka [5], Kaori Kawakami [5], Yoshimichi Imai [2], Yoichiro Iwakura [6], Ryoko Maruyama [1], Masahiro Tachi [2] and Kazuyoshi Kawakami [3,4]

[1]   Department of Science of Nursing Practice, Tohoku University Graduate School of Medicine, 2-1 Seiryo-cho, Aoba-ku, Sendai 9808575, Japan; hiromasa-tanno@med.tohoku.ac.jp (H.T.); skn.kdr.oor.325@gmail.com (M.G.); ambystomatmexicanum@gmail.com (M.S.); maruyama@med.tohoku.ac.jp (R.M.)
[2]   Department of Plastic and Reconstructive Surgery, Tohoku University Graduate School of Medicine, 2-1 Seiryo-cho, Aoba-ku, Sendai 9808575, Japan; masaki.a.m.825@gmail.com (A.M.); ssayakoss812@gmail.com (A.S.); surry310630@yahoo.co.jp (N.S.); jupiter1212@icloud.com (K.Y); takagi-prs@med.tohoku.ac.jp (N.T.); miki_shouji_0121@yahoo.co.jp (M.S.); yo-imai@med.tohoku.ac.jp (Y.I.); tachi@med.tohoku.ac.jp (M.T.)
[3]   Department of Medical Microbiology, Mycology and Immunology, Tohoku University Graduate School of Medicine, 2-1 Seiryo-cho, Aoba-ku, Sendai 9808575, Japan; kawakami@med.tohoku.ac.jp (K.K); yuki.m4058@gmail.com (Y.K.); ishii-k@med.tohoku.ac.jp (K.I.)
[4]   Department of Intelligent Network for Infection Control, Tohoku University Graduate School of Medicine, 2-1 Seiryo-cho, Aoba-ku, Sendai 9808575, Japan; ko-sato@med.tohoku.ac.jp (K.S.); kasamatsu@med.tohoku.ac.jp (J.K)
[5]   Division of Pathophysiology, Department of Pharmaceutical Sciences, Faculty of Pharmaceutical Sciences, Tohoku Medical and Pharmaceutical University, Sendai 9818558, Japan; t-miya13@tohoku-mpu.ac.jp (T.M.); fl.nikomako.dr@gmail.com (K.K.)
[6]   Division of Laboratory Animals, Research Institute for Biomedical Sciences, Tokyo University of Science, 2669 Yamazaki, Noda, Chiba 2788510, Japan; iwakura@rs.tus.ac.jp
[*]   Correspondence: ekanno@med.tohoku.ac.jp; Tel.: +81-22-717-8675

Received: 27 September 2019; Accepted: 10 November 2019; Published: 12 November 2019

Abstract: Interferon (IFN)-γ is mainly secreted by CD4+ T helper 1 (Th1), natural killer (NK) and NKT cells after skin injury. Although IFN-γ is well known regarding its inhibitory effects on collagen synthesis by fibroblasts in vitro, information is limited regarding its role in wound healing in vivo. In the present study, we analyzed how the defect of IFN-γ affects wound healing. Full-thickness wounds were created on the backs of wild type (WT) C57BL/6 and IFN-γ-deficient (KO) mice. We analyzed the percent wound closure, wound breaking strength, accumulation of leukocytes, and expression levels of *COL1A1*, *COL3A1*, and matrix metalloproteinases (MMPs). IFN-γKO mice exhibited significant attenuation in wound closure on Day 10 and wound breaking strength on Day 14 after wound creation, characteristics that are associated with prolonged neutrophil accumulation. Expression levels of *COL1A1* and *COL3A1* mRNA were lower in IFN-γKO than in WT mice, whereas expression levels of *MMP-2* (gelatinase) mRNA were significantly greater in IFN-γKO than in WT mice. Moreover, under neutropenic conditions created with anti-Gr-1 monoclonal antibodies, wound closure in IFN-γKO mice was recovered through low *MMP-2* expression levels. These results suggest that IFN-γ may be involved in the proliferation and maturation stages of wound healing through the regulation of neutrophilic inflammatory responses.

Keywords: interferon-γ; wound healing; neutrophils; matrix metalloproteinase-2

Int. J. Mol. Sci. **2019**, *20*, 5657

1. Introduction

Wound healing is a complex process involving inflammation, cell proliferation, matrix deposition, and tissue remodeling [1,2]. During the inflammatory phase, infiltrating neutrophils and macrophages play an important role in the defense against bacterial infections and debridement of necrotic tissue [2]. In the proliferation phase, fibroblasts and myofibroblasts interact and produce extracellular matrix (mainly collagen), resulting in granulation tissue formation. The tissue remodeling process is associated with tissue maturation and collagen degradation by matrix metalloproteinases (MMPs), which are mainly derived from leukocytes and dermal fibroblasts [3]. Previously, several MMPs including MMP-2, -8, -9 and -13 have been reported to be involved in wound healing [4–7].

Neutrophils are the first infiltrating cells to appear within 24 h after wound creation and are necessary for host defense responses [8,9]. However, prolonged neutrophil infiltration is involved in the degradation of collagen by the production of proteinases such as MMPs. In-vitro collagen synthesis by fibroblasts is induced by transforming growth factor-β (TGF-β) [10,11] and inhibited by interferon (IFN)-γ [12,13].

IFN-γ is mainly secreted by CD4+ helper T cells, NK cells, and NKT cells and contributes to the activation of immune cells [14]. IFN-γ is also associated with both neutrophil recruitment and cell clearance through apoptosis [15]. Indeed, in the thrombus resolution process, which resembles wound healing, the absence of IFN-γ accelerates thrombus resolution by enhancing MMP-9 but not MMP-2 [16]. As for IFN-γ's role in wound healing, in a mouse acute open wound model [14] and a post-scald burn injury model [17], IFN-γKO mice exhibited accelerated healing and enhanced TGF-β expression compared with WT mice, suggesting that IFN-γ makes a negative contribution to the skin wound healing process. While treatment with TNF-α plus IFN-γ-stimulated monocytes/macrophages in diabetic rat wounds improved the delay in wound healing [18], IFN-γ's role in wound healing remains controversial.

With this background, we focused on the effects of IFN-γ deficiency on the proliferation phase of skin wound healing using a mouse model with full-thickness wounds. Here, we show that IFN-γ is required for the repair of skin wounds in the proliferation phase due to its regulation of neutrophilic inflammatory responses, including the activation of MMP-2 (Gelatinase A) which is mainly derived from neutrophils.

2. Results

2.1. Delayed Wound Healing in IFN-γ-Deficient Mice in the Proliferative Phase

To examine the possible contribution of IFN-γ to wound healing, the rate of wound closure in IFN-γKO mice was compared with that in WT mice. Wound closure on Day 10 was significantly delayed in IFN-γKO mice compared with WT mice (Figure 1A,B). To confirm this effect, wound breaking strength was examined. Wound breaking strength on Day 14 was significantly delayed in IFN-γKO mice compared with WT mice (Figure 1C). As an alternate indicator of wound healing, we also evaluated α-SMA, which indicates myofibroblast differentiation. As shown in Figure 1D, the number of α-SMA$^+$ cells was significantly decreased in IFN-γKO mice. In addition, IFN-γKO mice exhibited lower *COL1A1*, *COL3A1*, and *TGF-β1* expression compared with WT mice on Day 14 (Figure 1E).

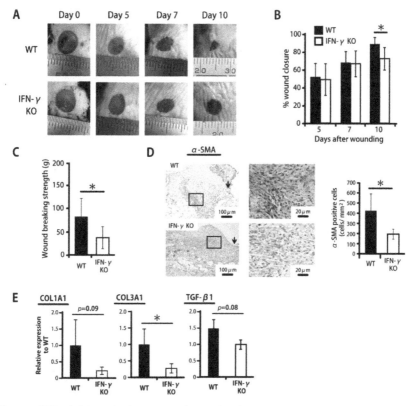

Figure 1. IFN-γ deficiency leads to impaired wound healing in skin. Wounds were created on the backs of WT or IFN-γKO mice. (**A**) Wound photographs in WT or IFN-γKO mice. (**B**) Percentage of wound closure was evaluated on Days 5, 7, and 10. (**C**) Wound breaking strength was measured on day 14. (**D**) The number of myofibroblasts stained with anti-α-SMA antibody on Day 10. The myofibroblast density/mm2 was determined by counting the positive cells within six visual fields (*n* = 6). Arrows indicate the re-epithelialized leading edges. (**E**) Real-time PCR was performed to detect *COL1A1*, *COL3A1*, and *TGF-β* mRNA isolated from the wound. Each column represents the mean ± SD. * *p* < 0.05.

2.2. Prolonged Accumulation of Neutrophils in IFN-γKO Mice

To define the role of inflammatory leukocytes during the wound healing process in IFN-γKO mice, wounded skin tissues were histologically examined in IFN-γKO and WT mice. As shown in Figure 2A, the former genotype exhibited prolonged accumulation of inflammatory leukocytes at the wound sites on Day 7. In the WT mice, in contrast, mainly fibroblasts were accumulated at the wound sites. Next, Ly6G, a marker specific to neutrophils, given that accumulated macrophages and eosinophils at the wound sites did not express Ly6G [19], was evaluated histologically. As shown in Figure 2B, the number of Ly6G$^+$ cells on Day 7 was significantly greater in IFN-γKO mice. Consistent with these results, *CXCL1* (KC) and *CXCL2* (MIP-2) expression levels were also significantly higher in IFN-γKO mice than in WT mice on Day 7 (Figure 2C).

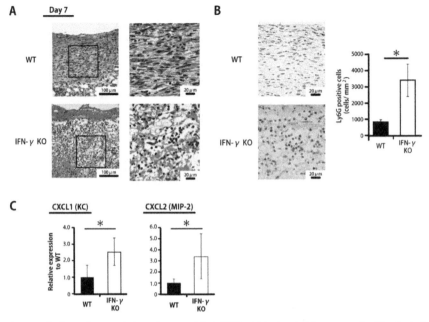

Figure 2. Prolonged accumulation of neutrophils in IFN-γ-KO mice. (**A**) Representative histological views of skin wounds on Day 7 are shown. (**B**) The number of neutrophils stained with anti-Ly6G antibody on Day 7. The Ly6G+ cell density/mm2 was determined by counting the positive cells in six visual fields (*n* = 6). (**C**) Real-time PCR was performed to detect *CXCL1* (KC) and *CXCL2* (MIP-2) mRNA isolated from the wound. Each column represents the mean ± SD. * *p* < 0.05.

2.3. Inhibited MMP-2 Activation by IFN-γ

To define the mechanisms underlying IFN-γ-associated reductions in breaking strength and in *COL1A1* and *COL3A1* expression as well as IFN-γ-associated prolonged neutrophil accumulation, we examined mRNA expression levels of the collagen degradation-associated factors *MMP-2* and *MMP-9* in the wounded tissue. *MMP-2* mRNA expression on Day 14 was significantly increased in IFN-γKO mice compared with WT mice; with regard to *MMP-9* expression, in contrast, there was no significant difference between WT and IFN-γKO mice (Figure 3A). As shown in Figure 3B, from a morphological perspective, *MMP-2* is mainly expressed in neutrophils in IFN-γKO mice in contrast to WT mice. Next, because *MMP-2* expression was significantly increased in IFN-γKO mice, we examined the involvement of IFN-γ in the activity of neutrophil-derived MMP-2 and pro-MMP-2 activity by gelatin zymography. As shown in Figure 3C,D, pro-MMP-2 activity level was significantly suppressed by IFN-γ in a concentration-dependent manner, while MMP-2 activity, in contrast, was not detected in any experimental groups.

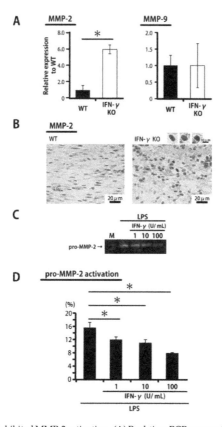

Figure 3. IFN-γ leads to inhibited MMP-2 activation. (**A**) Real-time PCR was performed to detect *MMP-2* and *MMP-9* mRNA isolated from the wound. (**B**) Representative histological views of wounded skin stained with MMP-2 antibody on Day 7. Red indicates MMP-2 positive cells. (**C**) Thioglycolate-elicited peritoneal neutrophils were treated with IFN-γ and lipopolysaccharide (LPS) for 24 h. The conditioned medium samples were analyzed for pro-MMP-2 activation by gelatin zymography. (**D**) The levels of pro-MMP-2 activation in (C) were analyzed using Image J image analysis software. Each column represents the mean ± SD. * $p < 0.05$. M—marker.

2.4. Wound Healing and MMP-2 Expression after Neutrophil Depletion Induced by Anti-Gr-1 Monoclonal Antibody in IFN-γKO Mice

As histological findings have revealed, MMP-2 derived mainly from neutrophils is involved in the delayed wound healing in IFN-γKO mice, as described above. Accordingly, we examined the effect of neutropenia induced by means of the anti-Gr-1 monoclonal antibody on wound closure and *MMP-2* expression. As shown in our recent study [20], the neutrophils in peripheral blood are completely depleted by this treatment. Wound closure on Day 10 was significantly accelerated in anti-Gr-1 antibody-treated mice compared with control IgG-treated mice (Figure 4A). As shown in Figure 4B,C, the accumulation of Ly6G$^+$ neutrophils had almost completely disappeared on Day 10 after anti-Gr-1 antibody administration at the wound sites. In addition, *MMP-2* expression was significantly decreased in anti-Gr-1 antibody-treated mice (Figure 4D). In the control group, interestingly, *MMP-2* was mainly detected in infiltrating leukocytes, whereas *MMP-2*-expressing fibroblasts were frequently detected in the anti-Gr-1 antibody-treated group (Figure 4E).

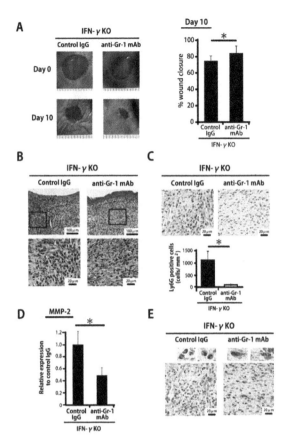

Figure 4. Neutrophil depletion by means of anti-Gr-1 monoclonal antibody leads to decreased MMP-2. (**A**) IFN-γKO mice were injected intraperitoneally with anti-Gr-1 monoclonal antibody or control rat IgG 5 and 7 days after wound creation. Percentage of wound closure was evaluated on Day 10. (**B**) Representative histological views of skin wounds on Day 10 are shown. (**C**) The number of neutrophils stained with anti-Ly6G antibody on Day 10. The Ly6G+ cell density/mm² was determined by counting the positive cells in six visual fields ($n = 6$). (**D**) Real-time PCR was performed to detect *MMP-2* mRNA isolated from the wound. (**E**) Representative histological views of wounded skin stained with MMP-2 antibody on Day 10. Each column represents the mean ± SD. * $p < 0.05$.

3. Discussion

In the current study, IFN-γKO mice exhibited significant attenuation in wound closure, wound breaking strength, and myofibroblast differentiation in the proliferation phase compared with WT mice through prolonged neutrophil accumulation and enhanced MMP-2 activation.

IFN-γ contributes to macrophage activation [14], neutrophil recruitment, and cell clearance by apoptosis [15]. Yet the question of how IFN-γ contributes to wound healing, especially in the proliferative phase, remains controversial and poorly understood. Regarding the role of IFN-γ in skin wounds, we previously reported that IFN-γ plays a key role in the early phase of the wound healing process in a study on mice deficient in invariant natural killer T (*i*NKT) cells, which are major IFN-γ-producing cells [21]. In addition, IFN-γ-treated LEPCs, which initiate blood vessel regeneration [22], or TNF-α- and IFN-γ-treated monocytes/macrophages [18] have been reported to be involved in the promotion of wound healing. In the current study, IFN-γKO mice exhibited significant attenuation in wound closure on Day 10 in association with prolonged neutrophil accumulation. In contrast to this, Ishida and Kondo et al. [14] demonstrated that IFN-γ deficiency accelerated the wound healing process in association with an early-phase reduction in the infiltration of myeloperoxidase (MPO)$^+$ neutrophils, F4/80$^+$ macrophages, and CD3$^+$ T cells.

Our murine wound model was at low risk for microbial infection as we used a clean procedure for the wounding and occlusive dressings for the wounds (closed wounds) until tissue collection. The model used by Ishida and Kondo et al. [14], in contrast, analyzed open wounds, i.e., wounds that had not been covered with occlusive dressings. This difference may have affected the different results of our two studies as a variation in environmental moisture and the microbial load at the wound site may have affected the findings. This possibility is strengthened by our previous finding that, compared with WT mice, IL-17AKO mice exhibited accelerated wound healing under closed-wound conditions but delayed wound healing under open-wound conditions [23].

In the present study, IFN-γKO mice exhibited diminished wound breaking strength, reduced myofibroblast differentiation, and low levels of *COL1A1* and *COL3A1* expression. Although several reports have demonstrated that IFN-γ can inhibit collagen synthesis by fibroblasts in vitro [12,13], in wound sites, IFN-γ can contribute to collagen deposition [21]. Previously, Hata et al. reported that TGF-β1 induces myofibroblast differentiation and collagen synthesis in the proliferation phase [24]. In this study, TGF-β1 expression was decreased in IFN-γKO mice compared with WT mice. Thus, our results are likely to be related to a delay in collagen synthesis.

In the current study, IFN-γKO mice exhibited delayed wound repair in the proliferative phase along with an increased neutrophil count, suggesting that accumulated neutrophils may suppress the healing process. In normal acute wounds, neutrophils are infiltrated immediately after skin injury and initially play a key role in antimicrobial activity; later, these cells undergo apoptosis and are engulfed by macrophages [25]. In non-healing wounds, however, prolonged neutrophil accumulation often leads to persistent inflammation through the production of proteases such as MMPs [26]. The functions of *MMP-2* [6], *MMP-8* [5], and *MMP-9* [27] have been studied with regard to the wound healing process. MMP-2 is not considered to play a critical role in normal acute murine wounds [6]. In non-healing wounds in humans, however, high levels of *MMP-2* activity have been detected [28]. In the current study, IFN-γKO mice exhibited delayed wound healing associated with a significant increase in *MMP-2* expression on recruited neutrophils at the wound sites. We also confirmed that pro-*MMP-2* activity levels in peritoneal neutrophils were significantly suppressed by IFN-γ stimulation. In fact, our current results demonstrate that delayed wound healing in IFN-γKO mice can be recovered under neutropenic conditions induced by treatment with the anti-Gr-1 monoclonal antibody, and that this recovery is associated with low levels of MMP-2. Previously, Qin et al. [29] reported the transcriptional suppression of *MMP-2* gene expression in human astroglioma cells by IFN-γ administration. Our skin wound model likewise suggests that IFN-γ could be involved in *MMP-2* expression.

MMP-2 has been reported to involve tissue remodeling by degrading extracellular matrix components such as type III collagen, type IV collagen, fibronectin and elastin [30,31]. At wound sites, upregulation of *MMP-2* expression has been observed in both granulation and scar tissues after skin injury [32]: during normal wound repair, *MMP-2* expression reached peak levels on Day 3 after wound creation and declined thereafter to the baseline level [33]. In this study, we showed that IFN-γKO mice exhibited decreased wound breaking strength along with upregulated *MMP-2* activity, suggesting that MMP-2 in the proliferative phase may reduce the strength of wounded skin. Thus, MMP-2 is likely to contribute positively in the early phase of wound healing, and negatively from the proliferative phase onward.

In this study, our in vitro gelatin zymography experiment detected pro-*MMP-2* activity but not MMP-2 itself in peritoneal neutrophils. It has previously been reported that MMP-2 is secreted as a zymogen (pro-MMP-2), and that membrane-bound MMP-14 (MT-1-MMP), which is mainly expressed on fibroblasts and cancer cells, activates secreted MMP-2 by cleaving its pro-domain [34]. Thus, the absence of MMP-14-expressing cells such as fibroblasts may be related to the absence of detectable MMP-2 in our in vitro analysis.

In conclusion, the present study demonstrated that IFN-γ plays an important role in the proliferation phase of skin wound healing and in the neutrophilic inflammatory response at the wound site. To date, little was known about IFN-γ's function in the proliferation phase; here, we have shown that it contributes significantly to wound strength and the suppression of inflammation. Inflammation is deeply involved in wound healing [35], but little is known about therapy for inflammatory responses at the wound sites. IFN-γ therapy has already been used as a treatment for pulmonary fibrosis [36] and may also be useful in a novel approach to the treatment of augmented fibrosis in the skin, such as hypertrophic scarring, keloid scarring and scleroderma. However, we did not confirm the effects of IFN-γ administration in this study. Further investigation is necessary to clarify the effects of IFN-γ therapy on augmented fibrosis in skin as well as its optimal dose and route.

4. Materials and Methods

4.1. Animals

IFN-γ gene-disrupted (knockout (KO)) mice were generated and established as described previously [37] and backcrossed to C57BL/6 mice for more than eight generations. Wild-type (WT) C57BL/6 mice, purchased from CLEA Japan (Tokyo, Japan), were used as controls. Male or female mice at 7 to 10 weeks of age were used in the experiments. Food and water were available ad libitum. All mice were kept under specific pathogen-free conditions in the Institute for Animal Experimentation, Tohoku University Graduate School of Medicine (Sendai, Japan). All experimental protocols described in the present study were approved by the Ethics Review Committee for Animal Experimentation of Tohoku University (2016MdA-279-3, 19 July 2016; 2016MdLMo-138-3, 7 July 2016). All experiments were performed under anesthesia, and all efforts were made to minimize suffering of the animals.

4.2. Wound Creation and Tissue Collection

All handling of the animals was performed under anesthesia induced by an intraperitoneal injection of 40 mg/kg sodium pentobarbital (Somnopentyl, Kyoritsu Seiyaku Corporation, Tokyo, Japan) and sustained by inhalation anesthesia of isoflurane (Isoflurane, Mairan Pharma, Osaka, Japan). The dorsal hair was shaved to fully expose the n skin, which was then rinsed with 70% ethanol. Four full-thickness wounds extending to the panniculus carnosus were created using a 6 mm diameter biopsy punch (Biopsy Punch, Kai industries Co., Ltd., Gifu, Japan) under sterile conditions. The injured areas were covered with a polyurethane film (Tegaderm Transparent Dressing, 3M Health Care, St. Paul, MN, USA) and an elastic adhesive bandage (Hilate, Iwatsuki, Tokyo, Japan) as an occlusive dressing. The day on which the wounds were made was designated as Day 0. At various time points, mice were sacrificed, and the wound tissue was collected by excising a 1 cm square section of skin using scissors and a surgical knife.

4.3. Administration of Anti-Gr-1 Antibody and the Effect of Neutrophil Depletion Induced by This Means

Anti-Gr-1 monoclonal antibody was purified from hybridoma culture supernatants (clones RB6-8C5) using a protein G column kit (Kirkegaard & Perry Laboratories, Gaithersburg, MD, USA). To neutralize the biological activity of neutrophils, mice were injected intraperitoneally with 400 µg of mAb on Days 5 and 7 after wounding. Rat IgG (ICN Pharmaceuticals, Aurora, OH, USA) was used as a control antibody. Immediately prior to injection and on Days 1, 2 and 5 after injection, mouse blood was collected via the tail vein and reacted with 0.83% ammonium chloride and Tris-HCl (pH 7.2), then washed three times with 1% FCS RPMI 1640 medium, yielding the blood cells used in our flow cytometric analysis. These blood cells were stained with PE-CD11b (BioLegend, San Diego, CA, USA) and APC/Cy7-anti-Ly6G mAb (clone 1A8; BioLegend). Isotype-matched irrelevant IgG was used for control staining. The stained cells were analyzed using a BD FACS Canto II flow cytometer (BD Bioscience, San Jose, CA, USA).

4.4. Measurement of the Wound Area

Morphometric analysis was performed on digital images obtained using a digital camera (CX4; Ricoh, Tokyo, Japan). After the wounds were created, photographs were taken of each wound before dressing. At various time points, the polyurethane films were gently removed from the experimental mice, and the wounds were photographed. Each wound area was quantified by tracing its margin and calculating the pixel area using AxioVision imaging software Release 4.6 (Carl Zeiss Micro Imaging Japan, Tokyo, Japan). Percentage of wound closure was calculated using the following formula: % wound closure = (1 − wound area at the indicated time point/wound area on Day 0) × 100.

4.5. Wound Breaking Strength

Wounded skin tissue was harvested from WT and *IFN-γ*KO mice on Day 14 after wound creation. A strip of this tissue located 5 mm from the center of the wound was excised with a no. 15 surgical blade (Feather Safety Razor Co., Ltd., Osaka, Japan). Wound breaking strength was measured using an IMS-001 (Keisei Medical Industrial Co., Ltd., Tokyo, Japan) as previously described [38]. Briefly, each side of the strip was pinched in a clip and the two clips were pulled apart at a constant speed of 3 cm/min until the strip broke. The result was expressed as the tensile force necessary to break the repaired wounds. Tensile force is characterized as tissue fragility and delay of collagen synthesis.

4.6. Histology and Immunohistochemistry

The tissues were fixed with 4% paraformaldehyde-phosphate buffer solution and embedded in paraffin. Sections were taken from the central portion of the wound and stained with hematoxylin-eosin (HE) according to the standard method.

For immunohistochemical analysis, after endogenous peroxidase was blocked with methanol/hydrogen peroxide, the sections were incubated with 10% normal rabbit serum for 20 min to block non-specific binding and then stained with anti-α-smooth muscle actin (α-SMA) antibody (dilution 1:200; Vector Laboratories, Inc., Burlingame, CA, USA), anti-Ly6G Ab (clone 1A8; dilution 1:100; BioLegend), or anti-MMP-2 (dilution 1:200; Chemicon, Darmstadt, Germany). The sections were incubated with peroxidase-conjugated secondary Ab (4 µg/mL; Histofine Simple Stain MAX-PO, Nichirei Bioscience, Tokyo, Japan), then reacted with 3, 3-diaminobenzidine (DAB) (Nichirei Bioscience) or Alkaline Phosphatase (Dako, Bettingen, Switzerland). The number of myofibroblasts and neutrophils in six random fields (each 0.2 mm^2) was determined by counting the number of α-SMA-positive cells or the number of Ly6G-positive cells, respectively. All analyses were performed under blinded conditions.

4.7. RNA Extraction and Quantitative Real-Time RT-PCR

Total RNA was extracted from the wound tissues using ISOGEN (Nippon Gene Co. Ltd., Tokyo, Japan), and first-strand cDNA was synthesized using the PrimeScript first-strand cDNA synthesis kit (TaKaRa Bio Inc., Otsu, Japan) according to the manufacturer's instructions. Quantitative real-time PCR was performed in a volume of 20 µL using gene-specific primers and FastStart essential DNA green master mix (Roche Applied Science, Penzburg, Germany) in a Step One™ (Thermo Fisher Scientific, Waltham, MA, USA). Primers were as follows: 5'- TGT TCA GCT TTG ACC TCC G -3' (Forward) and 5'- TAC CTC GGG TTT CCA CGT CTC A -3' (Reverse) for COL1A1, 5'- GGA CCA GGC AAT GAT GGA AAA CC -3' (Forward) and 5'- ACC AGG GAA ACC CAT GAC ACC -3' (Reverse) for COL3A1, 5'-CCG CGC CTA TCG CCA ATG AGC TGC GC-3' (Forward) and 5'-CTT GGG GAC ACC TTT TAG CAT CTT TTG G-3' (Reverse) for CXCL1 (KC), 5'-CTG AAC AAA GGC AAG GCT AAC TG -3' (Forward) and 5'-CAC ATC AGG TAC GAT CCA GGC TT -3' (Reverse) for CXCL2 (MIP-2), 5'- CCC CTG ATG TCC AGC AAG TAG A -3' (Forward) and 5'- AGT CTG CGA TGA GCT AGG GGA AA-3' (Reverse) for MMP-2, 5'- CCC TGG AAC TCA CAC GAC ATC TTC-3' (Forward) and

5′- GGT CCA CCT TGT TCA CCT CAT TTT -3′ (Reverse) for MMP-9 and 5′-GCT TCC TCC TCA GAC CGC TT-3′ (Forward) and 5′-TCG CTA ATC ACG ACG CTG GG-3′ (Reverse) for β-actin (ACTB). The reaction efficiency with each primer set was determined using standard amplifications. Target gene expression levels and that of ACTB as a reference gene were calculated for each sample using the reaction efficiency. The results were analyzed using a relative quantification procedure and are presented as expression levels relative to that of ACTB.

4.8. Isolation of Peritoneal Neutrophils

Thioglycolate-elicited peritoneal neutrophils were obtained from WT mice by a previously described method [39]. WT mice were intraperitoneally injected with 1.5 mL of sterile 4% thioglycolate; 12–15 h later, peritoneal lavages were performed with 10 mL PBS in each mouse. The proportion of neutrophils in the lavages was over 90% as assessed by FACS analysis of anti-CD45, anti-CD11b, and anti-Ly6G expression. Peritoneal neutrophils were recovered by centrifugation and suspended in RPMI 1640 medium supplemented with 10% FCS, 100 U/mL penicillin G, 100 μg/mL streptomycin, and 50 μM 2-mercaptoethanol. The obtained cells were cultured at 1×10^6/mL with various doses of IFN-γ or lipopolysaccharide (LPS) (Sigma-Aldrich, St. Louis, MO, USA) for 24 h at 37 °C.

4.9. Pro-MMP-2 Assay

Pro-MMP-2 activation in the culture supernatants, peritoneal neutrophils and IFN-γ or LPS were measured using a gelatin zymography kit (Cosmo Bio, Tokyo, Japan) according to the manufacturer's instructions. The gelatin zymography products were electrophoresed on 2% agarose gels, stained with 0.5 mg/mL ethidium bromide and observed with a ultraviolet transilluminator. Images were analyzed using Image J version 1.51 (National Institutes of Health, MD, USA).

4.10. Statistical Analysis

Data are expressed as the mean ± standard deviation (SD). Data analysis was performed using Welch's *t*-test. A *p* value less than 0.05 was considered to indicate significance.

Author Contributions: In the present study, E.K., H.T., A.M. and A.S. performed the research, M.T. and K.K. designed the research study, N.S., M.G., M.S., K.Y., N.T., M.S., Y.K., K.S., J.K., K.I., T.M., K.K., Y.I. and R.M. analyzed the data, Y.I. contributed the knockout mice for the study, and E.K. and K.K. wrote the paper.

Funding: This work was supported in part by a Grant-in-aid for Scientific Research (B) (19H03918), a Grant-in-aid for Challenging Exploratory Research (17K19710) and a Grant-in-Aid for Young Scientists (19K19494) from the Ministry of Education, Culture, Sports, Science and Technology of Japan.

Conflicts of Interest: The authors have declared no conflicts of interest. The funders had no role in the design of the study; in the collection, analyses, or interpretation of data; in the writing of the manuscript, or in the decision to publish the results.

Abbreviations

α-SMA	α-smooth muscle actin
IFN-γ	Interferon-gamma
KO	Knock out
MMP	Matrix metalloproteinase
NK cell	Natural killer cell
NKT cell	Natural killer T-cell
TGF-β	Transforming growth factor beta
WT	Wild type
Th1	T helper 1

References

1. Eming, S.A.; Krieg, T.; Davidson, J.M. Inflammation in wound repair: Molecular and cellular mechanisms. *J. Investig. Dermatol.* **2007**, *127*, 514–525. [CrossRef] [PubMed]
2. Martin, P.; Nunan, R. Cellular and molecular mechanisms of repair in acute and chronic wound healing. *Br. J. Dermatol.* **2015**, *173*, 370–378. [CrossRef] [PubMed]
3. Yamaguchi, Y.; Yoshikawa, K. Cutaneous wound healing: An update. *J. Dermatol.* **2001**, *28*, 521–534. [CrossRef] [PubMed]
4. Hattori, N.; Mochizuki, S.; Kishi, K.; Nakajima, T.; Takaishi, H.; D'Armiento, J.; Okada, Y. MMP-13 plays a role in keratinocyte migration, angiogenesis, and contraction in mouse skin wound healing. *Am. J. Pathol.* **2009**, *175*, 533–546. [CrossRef] [PubMed]
5. Gutiérrez-Fernández, A.; Inada, M.; Balbín, M.; Fueyo, A.; Pitiot, A.S.; Astudillo, A.; Hirose, K.; Hirata, M.; Shapiro, S.D.; Noël, A.; et al. Increased inflammation delays wound healing in mice deficient in collagenase-2 (MMP-8). *FASEB J.* **2007**, *21*, 2580–2591. [CrossRef] [PubMed]
6. Frøssing, S.; Rønø, B.; Hald, A.; Rømer, J.; Lund, L.R. Skin wound healing in MMP2-deficient and MMP2/plasminogen double-deficient mice. *Exp. Dermatol.* **2010**, *19*, e234–e240. [CrossRef] [PubMed]
7. Mäkelä, M.; Larjava, H.; Pirilä, E.; Maisi, P.; Salo, T.; Sorsa, T.; Uitto, V.J. Matrix metalloproteinase 2 (gelatinase A) is related to migration of keratinocytes. *Exp. Cell Res.* **1999**, *251*, 67–78. [CrossRef] [PubMed]
8. Park, J.E.; Barbul, A. Understanding the role of immune regulation in wound healing. *Am. J. Surg.* **2004**, *187*, 11S–16S. [CrossRef]
9. Dovi, J.V.; Szpaderska, A.M.; DiPietro, L.A. Neutrophil function in the healing wound: Adding insult to injury? *Thromb. Haemost.* **2004**, *92*, 275–280. [CrossRef] [PubMed]
10. Palumbo-Zerr, K.; Zerr, P.; Distler, A.; Fliehr, J.; Mancuso, R.; Huang, J.; Mielenz, D.; Tomcik, M.; Fürnrohr, B.G.; Scholtysek, C.; et al. Orphan nuclear receptor NR4A1 regulates transforming growth factor-β signaling and fibrosis. *Nat. Med.* **2015**, *21*, 150–158. [CrossRef] [PubMed]
11. Barrientos, S.; Brem, H.; Stojadinovic, O.; Tomic-Canic, M. Clinical application of growth factors and cytokines in wound healing. *Wound Repair Regen.* **2014**, *22*, 569–578. [CrossRef] [PubMed]
12. Higashi, K.; Inagaki, Y.; Fujimori, K.; Nakao, A.; Kaneko, H.; Nakatsuka, I. Interferon-γ interferes with transforming growth factor-beta signaling through direct interaction of YB-1 with Smad3. *J. Biol. Chem.* **2003**, *278*, 43470–43479. [CrossRef] [PubMed]
13. Harrop, A.R.; Ghahary, A.; Scott, P.G.; Forsyth, N.; Uji-Friedland, A.; Tredget, E.E. Regulation of collagen synthesis and mRNA expression in normal and hypertrophic scar fibroblasts in vitro by interferon-γ. *J. Surg. Res.* **1995**, *58*, 471–477. [CrossRef] [PubMed]
14. Ishida, Y.; Kondo, T.; Takayasu, T.; Iwakura, Y.; Mukaida, N. The essential involvement of cross-talk between IFN-γ and TGF-β in the skin wound-healing process. *J. Immunol.* **2004**, *172*, 1848–1855. [CrossRef] [PubMed]
15. McLoughlin, R.M.; Witowski, J.; Robson, R.L.; Wilkinson, T.S.; Hurst, S.M.; Williams, A.S.; Williams, J.D.; Rose-John, S.; Jones, S.A.; Topley, N. Interplay between IFN-γ and IL-6 signaling governs neutrophil trafficking and apoptosis during acute inflammation. *J. Clin. Investig.* **2003**, *112*, 598–607. [CrossRef] [PubMed]
16. Nosaka, M.; Ishida, Y.; Kimura, A.; Kuninaka, Y.; Inui, M.; Mukaida, N.; Kondo, T. Absence of IFN-γ accelerates thrombus resolution through enhanced MMP-9 and VEGF expression in mice. *J. Clin. Investig.* **2011**, *121*, 2911–2920. [CrossRef] [PubMed]
17. Shen, H.; Yao, P.; Lee, E.; Greenhalgh, D.; Soulika, A.M. Interferon-γ inhibits healing post scald burn injury. *Wound Repair Regen.* **2012**, *20*, 580–591. [CrossRef] [PubMed]
18. Gu, X.; Shen, S.; Huang, C.; Liu, Y.; Chen, Y.; Luo, L.; Zeng, Y.; Wang, A. Effect of activated autologous monocytes/macrophages on wound healing in a rodent model of experimental diabetes. *Diabetes Res. Clin. Pract.* **2013**, *102*, 53–59. [CrossRef] [PubMed]
19. Daley, J.M.; Thomay, A.A.; Connolly, M.D.; Reichner, J.S.; Albina, J.E. Use of Ly6G-specific monoclonal antibody to deplete neutrophils in mice. *J. Leukoc. Biol.* **2008**, *83*, 64–70. [CrossRef] [PubMed]
20. Miura, T.; Kawakami, K.; Kanno, E.; Tanno, H.; Tada, H.; Sato, N.; Masaki, A.; Yokoyama, R.; Kawamura, K.; Kitai, Y.; et al. Dectin-2-mediated signaling leads to delayed skin wound healing through enhanced neutrophilic inflammatory response and neutrophil extracellular trap formation. *J. Investig. Dermatol.* **2019**, *139*, 702–711. [CrossRef] [PubMed]

21. Tanno, H.; Kawakami, K.; Ritsu, M.; Kanno, E.; Suzuki, A.; Kamimatsuno, R.; Takagi, N.; Miyasaka, T.; Ishii, K.; Imai, Y.; et al. Contribution of invariant natural killer T cells to skin wound healing. *Am. J. Pathol.* **2015**, *185*, 3248–3257. [CrossRef] [PubMed]

22. Lee, B.N.R.; Chang, H.-K.; Son, Y.S.; Lee, D.; Kwon, S.-M.; Kim, P.-H.; Cho, J.-Y. IFN-γ enhances the wound healing effect of late EPCs (LEPCs) via BST2-mediated adhesion to endothelial cells. *FEBS Lett.* **2018**, *592*, 1705–1715. [CrossRef] [PubMed]

23. Takagi, N.; Kawakami, K.; Kanno, E.; Tanno, H.; Takeda, A.; Ishii, K.; Imai, Y.; Iwakura, Y.; Tachi, M. IL-17A promotes neutrophilic inflammation and disturbs acute wound healing in skin. *Exp. Dermatol.* **2017**, *26*, 137–144. [CrossRef] [PubMed]

24. Hata, S.; Okamura, K.; Hatta, M.; Ishikawa, H.; Yamazaki, J. Proteolytic and non-proteolytic activation of keratinocyte-derived latent TGF-β1 induces fibroblast differentiation in a wound-healing model using rat skin. *J. Pharmacol. Sci.* **2014**, *124*, 230–243. [CrossRef] [PubMed]

25. Wilgus, T.A.; Roy, S.; McDaniel, J.C. Neutrophils and wound repair: Positive actions and negative reactions. *Adv. Wound Care* **2013**, *2*, 379–388. [CrossRef] [PubMed]

26. Wetzler, C.; Kämpfer, H.; Stallmeyer, B.; Pfeilschifter, J.; Frank, S. Large and sustained induction of chemokines during impaired wound healing in the genetically diabetic mouse: Prolonged persistence of neutrophils and macrophages during the late phase of repair. *J. Investig. Dermatol.* **2000**, *115*, 245–253. [CrossRef] [PubMed]

27. Mohan, R.; Chintala, S.K.; Jung, J.C.; Villar, W.V.L.; McCabe, F.; Russo, L.A.; Lee, Y.; McCarthy, B.E.; Wollenberg, K.R.; Jester, J.V.; et al. Matrix metalloproteinase gelatinase B (MMP-9) coordinates and effects epithelial regeneration. *J. Biol. Chem.* **2002**, *277*, 2065–2072. [CrossRef] [PubMed]

28. Wysocki, A.B.; Staiano-Coico, L.; Grinnell, F. Wound fluid from chronic leg ulcers contains elevated levels of metalloproteinases MMP-2 and MMP-9. *J. Investig. Dermatol.* **1993**, *101*, 64–68. [CrossRef] [PubMed]

29. Qin, H.; Moellinger, J.D.; Wells, A.; Windsor, L.J.; Sun, Y.; Benveniste, E.N. Transcriptional suppression of matrix metalloproteinase-2 gene expression in human astroglioma cells by TNF-α and IFN-γ. *J. Immunol.* **1998**, *161*, 6664–6673. [PubMed]

30. Itoh, T.; Matsuda, H.; Tanioka, M.; Kuwabara, K.; Itohara, S.; Suzuki, R. The role of matrix metalloproteinase-2 and matrix metalloproteinase-9 in antibody-induced arthritis. *J. Immunol.* **2002**, *169*, 2643–2647. [CrossRef] [PubMed]

31. Page-McCaw, A.; Ewald, A.J.; Werb, Z. Matrix metalloproteinases and the regulation of tissue remodelling. *Nat. Rev. Mol. Cell Biol.* **2007**, *8*, 221–233. [CrossRef] [PubMed]

32. Okada, A.; Tomasetto, C.; Lutz, Y.; Bellocq, J.P.; Rio, M.C.; Basset, P. Expression of matrix metalloproteinases during rat skin wound healing: Evidence that membrane type-1 matrix metalloproteinase is a stromal activator of pro-gelatinase A. *J. Cell Biol.* **1997**, *137*, 67–77. [CrossRef] [PubMed]

33. Soo, C.; Shaw, W.W.; Zhang, X.; Longaker, M.T.; Howard, E.W.; Ting, K. Differential expression of matrix metalloproteinases and their tissue-derived inhibitors in cutaneous wound repair. *Plast. Reconstr. Surg.* **2000**, *105*, 638–647. [CrossRef] [PubMed]

34. Oblander, S.A.; Zhou, Z.; Gálvez, B.G.; Starcher, B.; Shannon, J.M.; Durbeej, M.; Arroyo, A.G.; Tryggvason, K.; Apte, S.S. Distinctive functions of membrane type 1 matrix-metalloprotease (MT1-MMP or MMP-14) in lung and submandibular gland development are independent of its role in pro-MMP-2 activation. *Dev. Biol.* **2005**, *277*, 255–269. [CrossRef] [PubMed]

35. Beyer, S.; Koch, M.; Lee, Y.H.; Jung, F.; Blocki, A. An in vitro model of angiogenesis during wound healing provides insights into the complex role of cells and factors in the inflammatory and proliferation phase. *Int. J. Mol. Sci.* **2018**, *19*, 2913. [CrossRef] [PubMed]

36. Christmann, R.B.; Sampaio-Barros, P.; Stifano, G.; Borges, C.L.; de Carvalho, C.R.; Kairalla, R.; Parra, E.R.; Spira, A.; Simms, R.; Capellozzi, V.L.; et al. Association of Interferon- and transforming growth factor β-regulated genes and macrophage activation with systemic sclerosis-related progressive lung fibrosis. *Arthritis Rheumatol.* **2014**, *66*, 714–725. [CrossRef] [PubMed]

37. Tagawa, Y.; Sekikawa, K.; Iwakura, Y. Suppression of concanavalin A-induced hepatitis in IFN-γ(-/-) mice, but not in TNF-α(-/-) mice: Role for IFN-γ in activating apoptosis of hepatocytes. *J. Immunol.* **1997**, *159*, 1418–1428. [PubMed]

Int. J. Mol. Sci. **2019**, *20*, 5657

38. Chen, L.; Mehta, N.D.; Zhao, Y.; DiPietro, L.A. Absence of CD4 or CD8 lymphocytes changes infiltration of inflammatory cells and profiles of cytokine expression in skin wounds, but does not impair healing. *Exp. Dermatol.* **2014**, *23*, 189–194. [CrossRef] [PubMed]

39. Baruah, S.; Murthy, S.; Keck, K.; Galvan, I.; Prichard, A.; Allen, L.-A.H.; Farrelly, M.; Klesney-Tait, J. TREM-1 regulates neutrophil chemotaxis by promoting NOX-dependent superoxide production. *J. Leukoc. Biol.* **2019**, *105*, 1195–1207. [CrossRef] [PubMed]

International Journal of
Molecular Sciences

Article

Local Growth Hormone Therapy for Pressure Ulcer Healing on a Human Skin Mouse Model

Lara Cristóbal [1,2,3], Nerea de los Reyes [1], Miguel A. Ortega [2,3,4], Melchor Álvarez-Mon [2,3,5], Natalio García-Honduvilla [2,3,4,6], Julia Buján [2,3,4] and Andrés A. Maldonado [2,3,7,*]

1   Department of Plastic and Reconstructive Surgery and Burn Unit. University Hospital of Getafe, 28905 Madrid, Spain
2   Department of Medicine and Medical Specialties, Faculty of Medicine and Health Sciences, University of Alcalá, 28801 Madrid, Spain
3   Ramón y Cajal Institute of Sanitary Research (IRYCIS), 28801 Madrid, Spain
4   Networking Biomedical Research Center on Bioengineering, Biomaterials and Nanomedicine (CIBER-BBN), 28801 Madrid, Spain
5   Immune System Diseases-Rheumatology and Oncology Service and Internal Medicine Department, University Hospital Príncipe de Asturias, Alcalá de Henares, 28805 Madrid, Spain
6   University Center of Defense of Madrid (CUD-ACD), 28047 Madrid, Spain
7   Department of Plastic, Hand and Reconstructive Surgery, BG Unfallklinik Frankfurt, 60389 Frankfurt am Main, Germany
*   Correspondence: mail@andresmaldonado.es; Tel.: +49-(0)-69-4753079

Received: 10 August 2019; Accepted: 20 August 2019; Published: 26 August 2019

Abstract: The growth hormone is involved in skin homeostasis and wound healing. We hypothesize whether it is possible to improve pressure ulcer (PU) healing by locally applying the recombinant human growth hormone (rhGH) in a human skin mouse model. Non-obese diabetic/severe combined immunodeficient mice ($n = 10$) were engrafted with a full-thickness human skin graft. After 60 days with stable grafts, human skin underwent three cycles of ischemia-reperfusion with a compression device to create a PU. Mice were classified into two groups: rhGH treatment group ($n = 5$) and control group ($n = 5$). In the rhGH group for local intradermal injections, each had 0.15 mg (0.5IU) applied to the PU edges, once per week for four weeks. Evaluation of the wound healing was conducted with photographic and visual assessments, and histological analysis was performed after complete wound healing. The results showed a healing rate twice as fast in the rhGH group compared to the control group (1.25 ± 0.33 mm2/day versus 0.61 ± 0.27 mm2/day; p-value < 0.05), with a faster healing rate during the first 30 days. The rhGH group showed thicker skin (1953 ± 457 µm versus 1060 ± 208 µm; p-value < 0.05) in the repaired area, with a significant decrease in collagen type I/III ratio at wound closure (62 days, range 60–70). Local administration of the rhGH accelerates PU healing in our model. The rhGH may have a clinical use in pressure ulcer treatment.

Keywords: growth hormone; human skin graft; pressure ulcer treatment; wound healing

---

1. Introduction

Despite the implementation of prevention strategies, the incidence and prevalence of pressure ulcers (PU) in today's society is high. Because of population aging and medical advances, this disease has become a health problem, which also entails social and economic impact. [1] Research on the pathogenesis and mechanisms involved in PU and wound healing is crucial. However, research in this field has been hindered by a lack of experimental animal models [2].

Regarding the etiology of PUs, external pressure is viewed as the main factor. Other patient-specific factors leading to derangement in tissue perfusion may account for an observed development of a pressure ulcer. It is well known that ischemia–reperfusion injury contributes to the pathophysiology of PUs more significantly than a single, prolonged ischemic insult [3,4]. Previously published PU models have been developed using animal skin, which imposes limitations when studying the wound healing process and the extrapolation of results and the effect of treatments on humans.

Once a pressure ulcer has developed, its course becomes insidious and its evolution towards healing is prolonged. The management of these patients needs a comprehensive and multidisciplinary team approach, involving plastic surgeons, nurses, nutritionists, rehabilitation therapists, etc. The goal in these chronic wounds is prompt tissue recovery. [1,5] Treatments that accelerate wound closure are of vital importance and interest for its potential benefits for these patients. The available evidence supports the use of different therapeutic options based on patient and wound characteristics, but none preponderates as the gold standard. Tissue engineering applied to wound healing, and specifically to PU, and approaches incorporating cellular therapy and growth factors are an expanding field in this issue. According to the American and European Pressure Ulcer Advisory Panel guidelines, Platelet-Derived Growth Factor (PDGF) can be used for Category/Stage III and IV pressure ulcers that have delayed healing. However, the evidence is not sufficient to recommend or refute the routine use of other growth factors in the treatment of pressure ulcers. [6] Rees et al. [7] published a randomized double blind, placebo-controlled study in which the efficacy of becaplermin gel (recombinant human PDFG-BB) in the treatment of chronic full thickness pressure ulcers was compared to that of placebo gel. The authors concluded that within the setting of a comprehensive wound management program, becaplermin gel once daily increases the incidence of complete healing and ≥90% healing in patients with full thickness pressure ulcers. Another randomized double blinded study [8] suggested that treatment with PDGF-BB before surgery enhances the ability to achieve a closed wound over surgery alone.

The growth hormone (GH), anabolic hormone, regulates growth through hypertrophy, hyperplasia, and as a result of tissue differentiation, cell proliferation and protein synthesis. It can exert its effects directly on the tissues, or indirectly through mediators: the so-called insulin-like growth factors IGF-I and IGF-II. [9,10] GH activity, sometimes mediated via IGF-I, is involved in skin homeostasis and wound healing acting at different stages and including dermal–epidermal communication [11]. During the inflammatory phase of healing, macrophages deliver growth factors that attract fibroblasts and facilitate the proliferative phase. GH promotes the release of some of these factors, such as EGF, VEGF, and FGF. Furthermore, IGF-I and II mRNAs are modulated during the healing process. The highest levels of IGF-I are seen in human wound fluids within 24 h after injury, and they return to their baseline when healing ends. [12,13] Animal models reveal that systemic GH promotes cellular proliferation, especially fibroblasts; granulation tissue formation; increases collagen formation and extracellular matrix; and enhances keratinocyte migration, shortening the time for healing, as well as providing increased mechanical strength of the wounds. [14–23] GH is also an inducer of the immune system. It mainly acts on macrophages and T-lymphocytes, that also play a key role in wound healing. [24] Studies in burns show that rhGH treatment could result in improved wound healing and reduced length of hospital stay. [25] Most of the studies have been developed applying systemic GH, and adverse effects cannot be ignored. [26]

The aim of this study is to compare the healing rate and different histological parameters on a previously described PU human skin model with and without the application of the recombinant human growth hormone (rhGH). We hypothesize that the local administration of the rhGH should increase the healing rate of PU and improve the quality of the human skin.

2. Results

Five mice received local treatment with the growth hormone (rhGH group) and five did not receive it (control group). Two paired mice (one of each group) died during the surgical procedure. Local administration of the rhGH was well tolerated. No local reactions or adverse effects were observed in the rhGH group.

2.1. Macroscopic Evaluation

The healing pattern was similar among all mice. The macroscopic evolution of the PU was comparable between the rhGH group and the control group. The evolution was towards a retracted and elevated crusty lesion. This crust was giving off progressively from the periphery toward the center as the ulcer was healing. Fully recovered dermoepidermal tissue then emerged. The evolution of PU in the rhGH group and the control group can be observed in Figures 1 and 2 respectively.

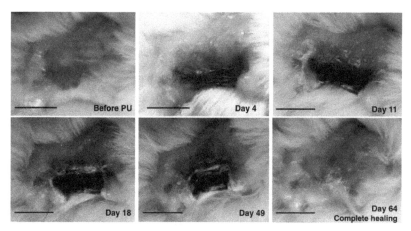

Figure 1. Macroscopic evolution of pressure ulcer healing in the recombinant human growth hormone rhGH group. The healing rate was 1.03 mm^2 per day in this mouse. Bar = 10 mm.

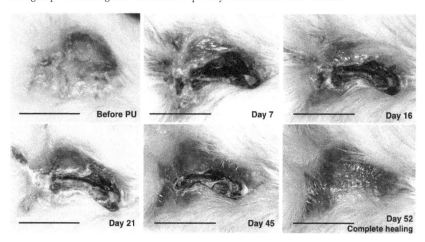

Figure 2. Macroscopic evolution of pressure ulcer healing in the control group. The healing rate was 0.75 mm^2 per day in this mouse. Bar = 10 mm.

The healing rate was twice as fast in mice subjected to treatment with the growth hormone—rhGH group (1.25 ± 0.33 mm^2 per day) compared to those which did not receive it—control group (0.61 ± 0.27 mm^2 per day), with a statistically significant difference (p-value = 0.03). Kinetics was compared between groups, with faster healing for the first 30 days in the rhGH group (1.27 mm^2 vs. 0.37 mm^2), time in which the hormone was administered once per week. The daily PU mean size in both groups until complete healing can be observed in Figure 3.

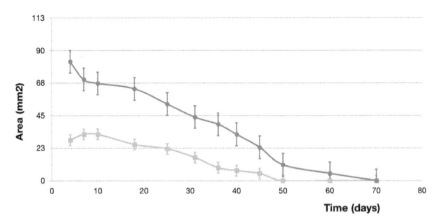

Figure 3. Daily pressure ulcer mean size (mm^2) until complete healing in the rhGH group (blue line) and the control group (green line).

Mean body weight in the rhGH group before PU formation and after PU healing was 29.38 ± 0.48 g and 30.2 ± 0.3 g respectively. Mean body weight in the control group before PU formation and after PU healing was 29.8 ± 1.9 g and 30.5 ± 2.1 g respectively. No statistically significant difference in body weight was found before and after PU healing in both groups (p-value > 0.05) (Figure 4).

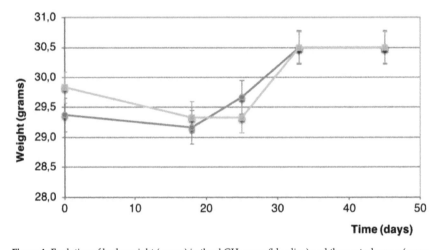

Figure 4. Evolution of body weight (grams) in the rhGH group (blue line) and the control group (green line). No statistically significant difference was found between both groups (p-value > 0.05).

2.2. Microscopic Evaluation

Epidermis maintained a normal architecture in both groups (Figure 5). No histological signs of malignancy were observed. The rhGH group showed thicker skin compared to the control group (1953 ± 457 μm versus 1060 ± 208 μm; p-value = 0.03) in the repaired area (Figure 6). This increase in the dermal layer was mainly due to a higher number of cells and the increase of extracellular matrix (rich in amorphous material). An increased in collagen deposition and a greater number of inflammatory cells were observed in the rhGH group.

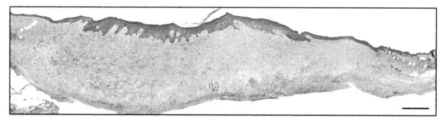

rhGH group

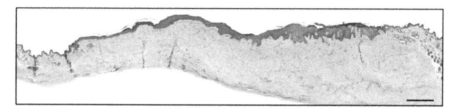

Control group

Figure 5. Histological analysis (H&E at 50 ×, panoramic view) of the rhGH group and the control group after complete healing of the pressure ulcer. Bar = 200 μm.

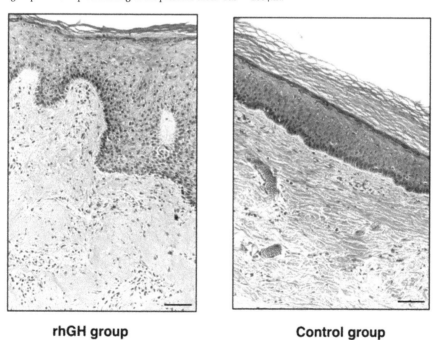

rhGH group   Control group

Figure 6. Histological analysis (Masson's trichrome at 200 ×) of the rhGH group (left) and the control group (right) after complete healing of the pressure ulcer. Note the thicker dermis in the rhGH group. Bar = 50 μm.

The rhGH group presented an important decrease of collagen type I compared to the control group (16.8 % ± 4.4 versus 76.8 % ± 16.5; *p*-value < 0.01) and an increase in collagen type III (64.4 % ± 3.8 versus 70.8 % ± 2.8; *p*-value = 0.04) at wound closure (62 days, range 60–70) (Figure 7, Table 1).

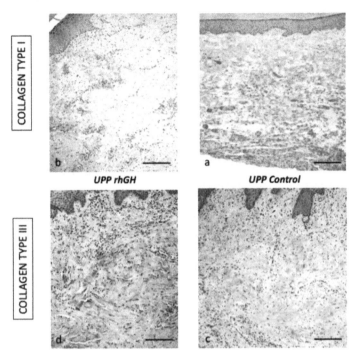

Figure 7. Immunohistochemical expression of collagen type I (160 ×) and III (250 ×) in the rhGH group (left, **a** and **c**) and the control group (right, **b** and **d**). Bar = 50 μm.

Table 1. Percentage of protein expression (collagen type I and III) in the total area of tissue samples (the rhGH(recombinant human growth hormone) group and the control group).

	Collagen type I	Collagen type III
rhGH group	16.8 % ± 4.4	70.8 % ± 2.8
Control group	76.8 % ± 16.5	64.4 % ± 3.8
p-value	<0.01	<0.05

3. Discussion

Wound therapies acting on a molecular and cellular level, such as growth factors, have a main role in wound healing. [27–29] The human GH, as an anabolic agent, stimulates growth and mitosis in a number of cell types by acting both directly and indirectly through the insulin-like growth factor (IGF)-I. Its effects have been proved in a variety of tissues, including skin, nerve, muscle, bone, cornea, etc. [11,14,17,19,22,23,30–34] and animal models reveal that systemic GH promotes granulation tissue and collagen formation, increases extracellular matrix, and enhances keratinocyte migration, shortening the time for healing. [14,17,19,22,23] Our findings show a statistically significant difference in healing rates between the rhGH group and control group, the healing rate being twice as fast in mice subjected to treatment with the rhGH. The faster healing was for the first 30 days in the rhGH group, time in which the hormone was administered once per week.

In our histological analysis, we found a thicker skin, increased cellularity and decreased collagen type I in the dermis of the rhGH group. An increase in collagen type III with a decrease in collagen type I are indicators of a delay in the maturation period of collagen. All these characteristics are typical of an active prolongation of the dermal proliferation and secretion period (facilitating the sliding of the keratinocytes), and they should accelerate and improve the re-epithelialization process. This effect was observed in previous studies on diabetic rats with a polymeric GH delivery system. [18] Epidermis maintained a normal architecture and keratinocyte differentiation, showing no histological signs of malignancy. These data are consistent with the results published by Rudman et al. [35], Jorgensen et al. [36], and Conte et al. [37]. A recent study in mice published by Messias de Lima et al. [38], topical treatment with GH resulted in faster wound closure rates. The GH accelerates the closure of skin wounds by resolving the inflammatory phase faster, accelerating reepithelialization, collagen deposition, and stimulating angiogenesis.

The extracellular matrix (ECM) defines the mechanical properties of the skin. Collagens are a principal component, and type I and III collagens (fibrillar collagens) are the major determinants of the strength and stiffness of the tissue. [39] Both types of collagens have a very similar biochemical composition, and they are secreted as procollagens, containing a non-collagenous C-teminal propetide and a N-teminal propeptide. Propeptide processing may be complete in collagen I and incomplete in collagen III, leaving a C-telopeptide and a partially processed N-propeptide domain. These domains have been implicated in the regulation of fibrillogenesis [40]. In human skin, the ratio of collagen I/III is 1 for adolescent, increasing up to 2.5 in adult skin. This ratio depends on age, increasing in old age and decreasing in fetuses. The presence of a high content of collagen III could provide more flexibility and tensility. During wound healing the content of this type of collagens could modulate the scar formation. There is a direct relationship between a high secretion of collagen type I and hypertrophic scar formation. [41] Other authors have shown the importance of collagen type III in fibrinogenesis compare to collagen type I [42]. The authors mentioned how collagen type III was present in distensible organs, reducing the mechanical stiffness. The alteration of the ratio of both collagens can be indicative of a tissue response process to an adverse event, such as an abdominal hernia. [43] In situations of chronic stress and injury, tissues are able to react with a change in the ratio of collagens, increasing the gene and protein expression of collagen type III [44]. The ECM protein profiles and distributions were examined in our model. The injury caused by the compression device is slightly different from other types of damage with heavy bleeding. Our model presents a progressive ischemia and necrosis formation, with progressive tissue regeneration from the healthy edges, showing an increase in the protein expression of collagen I and III in the human skin [45].

It is well known that GH is one of those molecules with pleiotropic actions on skin cells, and it participates in inflammatory, proliferative, and maturation phases of wound healing. During the inflammatory phase, macrophages deliver growth factors that attract fibroblasts and facilitate the next phase. GH promotes the release of (a) EGF, responsible for stimulating fibroblasts; (b) VEGF, which promotes angiogenesis in the wound; (c) FGF, which stimulates macrophages, mast cells, and T-lymphocytes, and facilitates granulation and epithelization [12]. Angiogenesis plays a key role during the granulation phase and tissue remodeling, as new vessels are required for the progression of wound healing. Endothelial cells express the GH receptor (GHR) [46] and produce the participation of GH in the latter process. In our PU model, the local treatment of the PU with rhGH produced changes in the ratio of the protein's expression (collagen type I/III). A significant increase of collagen type III protein expression was observed after wound closure (62 days, range 60–70). This finding could be interpreted as a delay in the process of consolidation of the scar tissue, keeping the immature tissue longer. However, we hypothesize that these changes increase the tissue effectiveness, favoring the response capacity to cover the damaged area. This fibrillar collagen could potentially be able to mature and generate a skin with greater tone.

Studies in patients who present delayed wound healing and/or catabolic states, such as diabetes or burns, showed that systemic GH treatment improves skin healing and reduces time required for wound healing. These patients present catabolic responses, with negative nitrogen balance and reduction in serum levels of GH and IGF. [47–50] A review of randomized controlled trials showed that people with

Int. J. Mol. Sci. **2019**, *20*, 4157

large burns could benefit from using systemic rhGH because of faster healing of the wound and donor site and reduced length of hospital stay, without increased mortality or scarring. However, it seems to be related to an increased risk of hyperglycemia. [25] Patients with PU are patients with multiple comorbidities. In the case of the elderly, especially in hospitals, they are usually malnourished or have catabolic states that worsen the tissue repair processes, resembling the situation of burn or diabetic patients. Therefore, the rhGH could potentially have an important role in accelerating the PU healing in this population. We think that our immunosuppressed model resembles the general condition that many patients with PU present in clinical practice. Since pressure ulcers are not just a problem of pressure, many of the patients are characterized by advanced age, malnutrition, systemic diseases such as diabetes, etc. with delayed wound healing, altered levels of cytokines and inflammatory cells, decreased reepithelialization, and of course immunosuppression. Furthermore, chronic wounds, such as PU, usually present dysregulation of cytokines and growth factors. A critical step for treatments may be to target these factors. [51] Several studies [52,53] have reported that GH, PRL, and IGF-I have a direct influence on cells involved with immunity (high-affinity PRL and GH receptors have been observed on a number of these cells) and modulate humoral and cellular immune functions.

Other anabolic agents, such as anabolic steroids (derivates of testosterone, i.e., oxandrolone), might be useful in promoting healing of PU. A comprehensive review of the literature found one trial in which oxandrolone administered orally was compared with a dose of placebo on pressure ulcer healing in people with spinal cord injuries [54]. The authors were uncertain whether oxandrolone is better than placebo in promoting complete healing of pressure ulcers at 24 weeks of treatment, and it could not draw conclusions about the potential benefits or harms of this treatment on treating PU. Well-designed studies are necessary to provide evidence as to whether anabolic steroids are beneficial or not in treating pressure ulcers.

We are concerned about the adverse effects of systemic GH treatment. Most side effects of GH treatment are local reactions at the injection site, such as pain, erythema, nodules, bruising, lipoatrophy, or swelling. However, different side-effects (i.e., hypoglycemia, changes in mental status, edema, fatigue, and headache) have been reported after systemic GH treatment and they are dependent on dose and time of administration. [26] Therefore, we developed our study for local administration of rhGH into ulcer edges. Several animal studies support the use of local GH in order to accelerate the wound healing process. Rasmussen et al. [55] injected different doses of GH into the back of 36 rats and compared it to a control group. They concluded that the optimal doses to increase the granulation tissue were between 0.2 to 0.7 UI. Kim et al. [56] demonstrated that the wound healing was faster after applying local rhGH in the back of five micro-pigs. A study by Lee et al. [22] described how the GH enhances the local formation of IGF-1, which activates fibroblast proliferation and keratinocyte migration—which highlight the potential of the topical application of GH. Andreassen et al. [32] reported bone formation without an increase in muscle mass, weight, or contralateral bone dimensions after the local injection of GH at the surface of tibial diaphyses in rats. Similar results were found in our study: mice did not present significant weight gain or changes in the usual behavior. Based on these data, we think that local application of GH should be the selected route of administration in future studies.

There is a lack of controlled clinical trials on humans to prove that GH can accelerate the PU healing process. There are a few case reports in the literature using the GH to treat PU. In 1955 Ravina et al. [57] reported the use of systemic GH to treat ulcers of diverse etiology. Six patients received intramuscular administration of the hormone. He reported complete healing after 1 to 3 months in a mixed cohort of patients with no control group and with different doses of GH. In 1987, Waago [58] administered GH topically in a diabetic patient with two recalcitrant ulcers. Four IU were administered topically twice per day, and 8 IU afterward. The author observed faster wound healing and noticeable decreased size of the ulcers. Due to logical ethical considerations, there was not histological analysis in all these cases to prove an improvement of the quality of the skin. The main advantages of our model are the possibility of having a matched control group and performing histological analysis without the previous ethical considerations.

As in most studies, this article has its limitations. A limitation of this study is the animal model. It is not clear how mouse cells could influence the ulcer healing process. Special care was taken to keep healthy human skin around the ulcer. The clip was placed in the center of the skin graft, maintaining healthy human skin around the ulcer, and injecting the rhGH into human skin, so that the healing and re-epithelialization were carried out by surrounding human cells (without the involvement of mouse skin). The human tissue over the mouse was assessed using fluorescence in situ hybridization (FISH) for chromosomes XX and XY, as previously described in *Maldonado* et al. [59]. We took advantage of the condition that the model was performed on male mice (XY chromosomes), and the human skin graft came from human female donors (chromosomes XX). Chromosomes XX were found in the areas of human skin graft. We think this model provides the opportunity to test different therapeutic strategies directly on human skin in the context of a living organism, without the ethical considerations involved in human research. A second bias is the initial pressure ulcer sizes: the control group presented smaller ulcers compared to the rhGH group. However, it is reported that wound contraction is 0.6–0.75 mm/day and keratinocyte migration up to 0.5 mm/day, regardless of the wound size [60], and therefore the initial size of the ulcer was not considered in the process of randomization. Finally, there are other histological techniques that could have provided useful information (i.e., the Fontana Masson Picrosirius technique [61] for identification of pigmented melanocytic lesions and the correlation between normal and neoplastic pigmented cells). Future studies will have to developed new observations and ideas. In spite of these limitations, we think our model opens up prospects for expanding knowledge about multiple fields such as skin wound healing, mechanisms of tolerance and immunological rejection, skin diseases, and carcinogenesis, among others. As we did in this study, cell therapy, growth factors, and other therapeutic strategies can be tested directly on damaged human skin through our ulcer model, without the ethical considerations involved in human research. Advances in skin healing and skin regeneration performed on our model could be potentially applied in clinical practice.

4. Materials and Methods

4.1. Animals

Three-week-old, male, non-obese diabetic/severe combined immunodeficiency (NOD/Scid-NOD.CB17-Prkdscid/NCrHsd) mice ($n = 10$) (Harlan Laboratories S.r.l. Barcelona, Spain) were used in this study. These mice present immunological multidysfunction, including absence of mature T and B cells, reductions in macrophage function, complement-dependent hemolytic activity, and NK cell activity. [62] All mice were caged under standard light and temperature conditions with free access to food and water throughout the study. All efforts were made to minimize suffering and all animals were sacrificed at the end of the study.

All experimental procedures were approved and regulated by the Animal Experimentation Ethics Committee—University of Alcalá and University Hospital of Getafe (IRB: PROEX reference 237/15, 9 October, 2015), in accordance with the Royal Decree 53/2013 and the European Community Council Directive.

4.2. PU model on Human Skin

Ten NOD/Scid mice were engrafted under general anesthesia (Ohmeda, BOC Health Care) with female human skin. All human skin ($n = 5$) came from abdominoplasty procedures. Written informed consent was obtained from all patients. The skin was immediately stored after haverst in D-MEM (Dulbecco/Vogt modified Eagle's minimal essential medium) at a temperature of 4 °C. Skin grafting was performed during the first 24 h after extraction. Human full-thickness skin grafts (FTSGs) were placed onto a 4 × 3 cm wound. Mice skin was incised down to the muscle and removed, exposing muscular layer. FTSGs were sutured in place with 4/0 nylon. A tie-over bolster dressing was placed for the first 5 days. The same skin donor was used to graft two mice (in order to pair two mice with the same human skin donor). After 60 days, a compression device was applied to the human skin graft, as previously described. [59] The clip exerted a pressure of 150 mmHg, measured with a dynamometer. Three cycles of compression–release (8 h of clamping after 16 h of no compression) were applied to simulate a pressure ulcer, based on the method described by Stadler et al. [63].

4.3. Recombinant Human Growth Hormone (rhGH)

Genotonorm Kabipen 5.3 mg (Pfizer, Madrid, Spain), solution for injection in a pre-filled pen, was provided by the Department of Pharmacy of the University Hospital of Getafe and stored at a temperature between 2 and 8 °C. The use of the rhGH is restricted to the hospital setting, and its use was approved and regulated by the Animal Experimentation Ethics Committee University Hospital of Getafe (PROEX reference 237/15) in accordance with the Royal Decree 53/2013 and the European Community Council Directive.

4.4. Local Treatment of the PU with rhGH

PU formation was confirmed by visual assessment after the last cycle of compression–release. Paired mice were assigned randomly to the rhGH group ($n = 5$) or to the control group ($n = 5$). We designed a protocol for local administration of the hormone. The concentration of GH was determined based on previous studies. [55] In the rhGH group, the five mice were treated with four local rhGH intradermal injections, each of 0.15 mg (0.5 IU), applied to the PU edges on human skin (Figure 8). The injection protocol started 24 h after the last cycle of compression–release, and the administration of the hormone was repeated once per week for four weeks, always the same day of the week at the same hour. In the control group, the five mice received the same care but without the local administration of the rhGH.

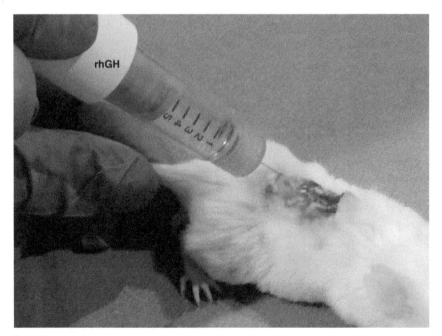

Figure 8. Local administration of the rhGH. Note the intradermal injection of the rhGH applied to the pressure ulcer edges on human skin.

4.5. Macroscopic Analysis

Evaluations were conducted with photographic and visual assessment in both groups. PU size (in mm^2) was measured every seven days until complete healing (wound closure) using the software ImageJ (National Institute of Health, USA). The healing rate was calculated in both groups as the initial size of the ulcer in mm^2 per number of days until closure. The weight in grams of all mice was recorded before creating PU, after the three cycles of ischemia-reperfusion, and once per week until wound closure. All the measurements were taken by two independent researchers.

4.6. Microscopic Evaluation

Histological analysis of the human skin was performed in both groups after wound closure by two independent histologists. Samples of skin were obtained from the two groups, and they were placed in 10% buffered formaldehyde (for histopathological studies) and Bouin (for immunohistochemical studies). Then the samples were dehydrated and embedded in paraffin. Tissue sections (5 mm thick; 50 sections for each sample) passing through the central plane of each sample were stained with hematoxylin-eosin and Masson's trichrome for morphological assessment. Tissue sections were examined under a Zeiss Axiophot light microscope (Carl Zeiss, Oberkochen, Germany). The thickness of the healed human skin was measured in micrometers with Axiovision Release 4.6.3 software (Carl Zeiss, Oberkochen, Germany). The total thickness of the skin was defined as the distance between the stratum corneum and the boundary between human dermis–host mouse tissue.

4.7. Immunohistochemistry

Samples of tissue were deparaffined, hydrated, and equilibrated in phosphate buffered saline (pH 7.4). Rabbit polyclonal anti-COL-I and anti-COL-III (Abcam, Cambridge, UK) were used as primary antibodies to study collagen type I and III. Samples were incubated with secondary antibodies, anti-rabbit immunoglobulin G (IgG) (Sigma-Aldrich, St. Louis, MO, USA). For COL-I and COL-III, the alkaline phosphatase procedure was performed. COL-I and COL-III were conjugated with avidin-alkaline phosphatase (ExtrAvidin-Alkaline Phosphatase, Sigma-Aldrich, St. Louis, MO, USA). It was used for 60 min at room temperature (Dilution 1/200 in PBS) and developed with the alkaline chromogenic substrate for 15 min (controlling the appearance of marking under the microscope). The chromogenic substrate preparation was performed immediately before development by adding 10 mL of PBS (10 mg of α-naphthol AS-BI phosphate, 10 mg of Fast Red, and 100 µL of 0.1 M levamisole) [64]. Nuclei were counterstained with Carazzi's hematoxylin (15 min). A negative control of the technique was performed without the primary antibody. Samples were mounting in aqueous medium with Plasdone. Tissue sections were examined under a Zeiss Axiophot light microscope equipped with an AxioCam HRc (Carl Zeiss, Oberkochen, Germany). A digital camera was used for observations. In order to calculate the percentage of protein expression, the German semiquantitative scoring system considering the staining intensity and area extent was used [65]. Immunostaining in the tissue was assessed by two independent histologists.

4.8. Statistical Analysis

The results were analyzed by the software SPSS 21 (SPSS, Inc., Chicago, IL, USA). Sample size estimation was performed considering a statistical power of 0.8 and alpha error of 0.05. Mean values of healing rates, thickness of the skin and collagen type I and III expression were compared between groups using Mann-Whitney's U test. Differences with p-value < 0.05 were considered statistically significant.

5. Conclusions

Based on our model, local administration of the rhGH accelerates the wound healing process and improves the quality of human skin. The healing rate was twice as fast in the rhGH group compared to the control group. In the rhGH treatment group, we found an increase in dermis regeneration tissue with a delay in the maturation period, which potentially improves the re-epithelialization process. Based on the macroscopical and histological findings and considering the human skin component of this model, the rhGH may have a clinical use in pressure ulcer treatment, and further studies remain to be performed. We think that our findings could be extrapolated to other compromised wound healing situations such as diabetic or chronic ischemia patients.

Author Contributions: conceptualization, A.A.M. and J.B.; methodology, L.C., A.A.M., N.G.-H. and M.Á.-M.; validation, L.C., N.d.l.R., M.A.O.; formal analysis, L.C., M.A.O., A.A.M.; investigation, L.C., N.d.l.R., M.A.O., A.A.M.; writing—original draft preparation, L.C.; writing—review and editing, L.C., A.A.M. and J.B.; funding acquisition, J.B., N.G.-H., A.A.M. and M.Á.-M.

Funding: This study was supported by Community of Madrid (B2017/BMD-3804 MITIC-CM) and Fundación MAPFRE (SA/11/AYU/444). The funders had no role in study design, data collection and analysis, decision to publish, or preparation of the manuscript.

Acknowledgments: We thank the Department of Plastic Surgery and Burns and the Department of Pharmacy, University Hospital of Getafe, Madrid, Spain; and Mario Arenillas (Biomedical Research Foundation of the University Hospital of Getafe, Madrid, Spain).

Conflicts of Interest: The authors declare no conflict of interest. The funders had no role in the design of the study; in the collection, analyses, or interpretation of data; in the writing of the manuscript, or in the decision to publish the results.

References

1. Lyder, C.H. Pressure ulcer prevention and management. *JAMA* **2003**, *289*, 223–226. [CrossRef] [PubMed]
2. Salcido, R.; Popescu, A.; Ahn, C. Animal models in pressure ulcer research. *J. Spinal Cord Med.* **2007**, *30*, 107–116. [CrossRef] [PubMed]
3. Thomas, D.R. Does pressure cause pressure ulcers? An inquiry into the etiology of pressure ulcers. *J. Am. Med. Dir. Assoc.* **2010**, *11*, 397–405. [CrossRef] [PubMed]
4. Tsuji, S.; Ichioka, S.; Sekiya, N.; Nakatsuka, T. Analysis of ischemia- reperfusion injury in a microcirculatory model of pressure ulcers. *Wound Repair Regen.* **2005**, *13*, 209–215. [CrossRef] [PubMed]
5. Levine, S.M.; Sinno, S.; Levine, J.P.; Saadeh, P.B. Current thoughts for the prevention and treatment of pressure ulcers: Using the evidence to determine fact or fiction. *Ann. Surg.* **2013**, *257*, 603–608. [CrossRef] [PubMed]
6. National Pressure Ulcer Advisory Panel. European Pressure Ulcer Advisory Panel and Pan Pacific Pressure Injury Alliance. In *Prevention and Treatment of Pressure Ulcers: Quick Reference Guide*; Haesler, E., Ed.; Cambridge Media: Osborne Park, Western Australia, 2014.
7. Rees, R.S.; Robson, M.C.; Smiell, J.M.; Perry, B.H. Becaplermin gel in the treatment of pressure ulcers: A phase II randomized, double-blind, placebo-controlled study. *Wound Repair Regen.* **1999**, *7*, 141–147. [CrossRef] [PubMed]
8. Kallianinen, L.K.; Hirshberg, J.; Marchant, B.; Rees, R.S. Role of platelet derived growth factor as an adjunct to surgery in the management of pressure ulcers. *Plast. Reconstr. Surg.* **2000**, *106*, 1243–1248. [CrossRef]
9. Green, H.; Morikawa, M.; Nixon, T. A dual effector theory of growth-hormone action. *Differentiation* **1985**, *29*, 195–198. [CrossRef]
10. Strobl, J.S.; Thomas, M.J. Human growth hormone. *Pharmacol. Rev.* **1994**, *46*, 1–34.
11. Edmondson, S.R.; Thumiger, S.P.; Werther, G.A.; Wraight, C.J. Epidermal homeostasis: The role of the growth hormone and insulin-like growth factor systems. *Endocr. Rev.* **2003**, *24*, 737–764. [CrossRef]
12. Bhora, F.Y.; Dunkin, B.J.; Batzri, S.; Aly, H.M.; Bass, B.L.; Sidawy, A.N.; Harmon, J.W. Effect of growth factors on cell proliferation and epithelialization in human skin. *J. Surg. Res.* **1995**, *59*, 236–244. [CrossRef] [PubMed]
13. Vogt, P.M.; Lehnhardt, M.; Wagner, D.; Jansen, W.; Krieg, M.; Steinau, H.U. Determination of endogenous growth factors in human wound fluid: Temporal presence and profiles of secretion. *Plast. Reconstr. Surg.* **1998**, *102*, 117–123. [CrossRef] [PubMed]
14. Rasmussen, L.H.; Garbarsch, C.; Schuppan, D.; Moe, D.; Horslev-Pedersen, K.; Gottrup, F.; Steenfos, H. Influence of human growth hormone on granulation tissue formation, collagen deposition, and the aminoterminal propeptide of collagen type III in wound chambers in rats. *Wound Repair Regen.* **1994**, *2*, 31–36. [CrossRef] [PubMed]

15. Jørgensen, P.H.; Bang, C.; Andreassen, T.T.; Flyvbjerg, A.; Orskov, H. Dose-response study of the effect of growth hormone on mechanical properties of skin graft wounds. *J. Surg. Res.* **1995**, *58*, 295–301. [CrossRef] [PubMed]

16. Jørgensen, P.H.; Oxlund, H. Growth hormone increases the biomechanical strength and collagen deposition rate during the early phase of skin wound healing. *Wound Repair Regen.* **1996**, *4*, 40–47. [CrossRef] [PubMed]

17. Thorey, I.S.; Hinz, B.; Hoeflich, A.; Kaesler, S.; Elmlinger, M.; Wanke, R.; Wolf, E.; Werner, S. Transgenic Mice Reveal Novel Activities of Growth Hormone in Wound Repair, Angiogenesis, and Myofibroblast Differentiation. *J. Biol. Chem.* **2004**, *279*, 26674–26684. [CrossRef] [PubMed]

18. Gimeno, M.J.; García-Esteo, F.; García-Honduvilla, N.; San Román, J.; Bellón, J.M.; Buján, J. A novel controlled drug-delivery system for growth hormone applied to healing skin wounds in diabetic rats. *J. Biomater. Sci. Polym. Ed.* **2003**, *14*, 821–835. [CrossRef]

19. García-Esteo, F.; Pascual, G.; García-Honduvilla, N.; Gallardo, A.; San Román, J.; Bellón, J.M.; Buján, J. Histological evaluation of scar tissue inflammatory response: The role of hGH in diabetic rats. *Histol. Histopathol.* **2005**, *20*, 53–57.

20. García-Esteo, F.; Pascual, G.; Gallardo, A.; San Román, J.; Buján, J.; Bellón, J.M. A biodegradable copolymer for the slow release of growth hormone expedites scarring in diabetic rats. *J. Biomed. Mater. Res. B Appl. Biomater.* **2007**, *81*, 291–304. [CrossRef]

21. Bowers, D.; McKenzie, D.; Dutta, D.; Wheeless, C.R.; Cohen, W.R. Growth hormone treatment after cesarean delivery in rats increases the strength of the uterine scar. *Am. J. Obstet. Gynecol.* **2001**, *185*, 614–617. [CrossRef]

22. Lee, S.W.; Kim, S.H.; Kim, J.Y.; Lee, Y. The effect of growth hormone on fibroblast proliferation and keratinocyte migration. *J. Plast. Reconstr. Aesthet. Surg.* **2010**, *63*, e364–e369. [CrossRef]

23. Seeger, M.A.; Paller, A.S. The roles of growth factors in keratinocyte migration. *Adv. Wound Care* **2015**, *4*, 213–224. [CrossRef]

24. Meazza, C.; Pagani, S.; Travaglino, P.; Bozzola, M. Effect of growth hormone (GH) on the immune system. *Pediatr. Endocrinol. Rev.* **2004**, *1*, 490–495.

25. Breederveld, R.S.; Tuinebreijer, W.E. Recombinant human growth hormone for treating burns and donor sites. *Cochrane Database Syst. Rev.* **2014**, *9*, CD008990. [CrossRef]

26. Krysiak, R.; Gdula-Dymek, A.; Bednarska-Czerwińska, A.; Okopien, B. Growth hormone therapy in children and adults. *Pharmacol. Rep.* **2007**, *59*, 500–516.

27. Barrientos, S.; Stojadinovic, O.; Golinko, M.S.; Brem, H.; Tomic-Canic, M. Growth factors and cytokines in wound healing. *Wound Repair Regen.* **2008**, *16*, 585–601. [CrossRef]

28. Borena, B.M.; Martens, A.; Broeckx, S.Y.; Meyer, E.; Chiers, K.; Duchateau, L.; Spaas, J.H. Regenerative skin wound healing in mammals: State-of-the-Art on growth factor and stem cell based treatments. *Cell Physiol. Biochem.* **2015**, *36*, 1–23. [CrossRef]

29. Akita, S.; Akino, K.; Imaizumi, T.; Hirano, A. Basic fibroblast growth factor accelerates and improves second-degree burn wound healing. *Wound Repair Regen.* **2008**, *16*, 635–641. [CrossRef]

30. Steenfos, H.H.; Jansson, J.O. Growth hormone stimulates granulation tissue formation and insulin-like growth factor-I gene expression in wound chambers in the rat. *J. Endocrinol.* **1992**, *132*, 293–298. [CrossRef]

31. Tuffaha, S.H.; Budihardjo, J.D.; Sarhane, K.A.; Khusheim, M.; Song, D.; Broyles, J.M.; Salvatori, R.; Means, K.R., Jr.; Higgins, J.P.; Shores, J.T.; et al. Growth hormone therapy accelerates axonal regeneration, promotes motor reinnervation, and reduces muscle atrophy following peripheral nerve injury. *Plast. Reconstr. Surg.* **2016**, *137*, 1771–1780. [CrossRef]

32. Andreassen, T.T.; Oxlund, H. Local anabolic effects of growth hormone on intact bone and healing fractures in rats. *Calcif. Tissue Int.* **2003**, *73*, 258–264. [CrossRef]

33. Wirostko, B.; Rafii, M.; Sullivan, D.A.; Morelli, J.; Ding, J. Novel therapy to treat corneal epithelial defects: A hypothesis with Growth Hormone. *Ocul. Surf.* **2015**, *13*, 204–212. [CrossRef]

34. Ding, J.; Wirostko, B.; Sullivan, D.A. Human growth hormone promotes corneal epithelial cell migration in vitro. *Cornea* **2015**, *34*, 686–692. [CrossRef]

35. Rudman, D.; Feller, A.G.; Nagraj, H.S.; Gergans, G.A.; Lalitha, P.Y.; Goldberg, A.F.; Schlenker, R.A.; Cohn, L.; Rudman, I.W.; Mattson, D.E. Effects of human growth hormone in men over 60 years old. *N. Engl. J. Med.* **1990**, *323*, 1–6. [CrossRef]

36. Jørgensen, J.O.; Pedersen, S.A.; Thuesen, L.; Jørgensen, J.; Ingemann-Hansen, T.; Skakkebaek, N.E.; Christiansen, J.S. Beneficial effects of growth hormone treatment in GH-deficient adults. *Lancet* **1989**, *1*, 1221–1225. [CrossRef]

37. Conte, F.; Diridollou, S.; Jouret, B.; Turlier, V.; Charveron, M.; Gall, Y.; Rochiccioli, P.; Bieth, E.; Tauber, M. Evaluation of cutaneous modifications in seventy-seven growth hormone-deficient children. *Horm. Res.* **2000**, *54*, 92–97. [CrossRef]

38. Messias de Lima, C.F.; De Araujo Vieira, L.F.; de Carvalho Wanderley, L.A.; de Souza Ferro, J.N.; Smaniotto, S. Topical Growth Hormone Accelerates Wound Healing in Mice. *Wounds* **2017**, *29*, 387–392.

39. Theocharidis, G.; Connelly, J.T. Minor collagens of the skin with not so minor functions. *J. Anat.* **2019**, *235*, 418–429. [CrossRef]

40. Mecham, R.P. *The Extracellullar Matrix: An Overview*; Springer: Berlin/Heidelberg, Germany, 2011. [CrossRef]

41. Cheng, W.; Yan-hua, R.; Fang-gang, N.; Guo-an, Z. The content and ratio of type I and III collagen in skin differ with age and injury. *Afr. J. Biotechnol.* **2011**, *10*, 2524–2529.

42. Asgari, M.; Latifi, N.; Heris, H.K.; Vali, H.; Mongeau, L. In vitro fibrillogenesis of tropocollagen type III in collagen type I affects its relative fibrillar topology and mechanics. *Sci. Rep.* **2017**, *7*, 1392. [CrossRef]

43. Peeters, E.; De Hertogh, G.; Junge, K.; Klinge, U.; Miserez, M. Skin as marker for collagen type I/III ratio in abdominal wall fascia. *Hernia* **2014**, *18*, 519–525. [CrossRef]

44. Ortega, M.A.; Asúnsolo, A.; Álvarez-Rocha, M.J.; Romero, B.; De León-Luis, J.; Álvarez-Mon, M.; Buján, J.; García-Honduvilla, N. Remodelling of collagen fibres in the placentas of women with venous insufficiency during pregnancy. *Histol. Histopathol.* **2018**, *33*, 567–576.

45. Cristóbal, L.; Ortega, M.A.; Asúnsolo, Á.; Romero, B.; Álvarez-Mon, M.; Buján, J.; Maldonado, A.A.; García-Honduvilla, N. Human skin model for mimic dermal studies in pathology with a clinical implication in pressure ulcers. *Histol. Histopathol.* **2018**, *33*, 959–970.

46. Thum, T.; Hoeber, S.; Froese, S.; Klink, I.; Stichtenoth, D.O.; Galuppo, P.; Jakob, M.; Tsikas, D.; Anker, S.D.; Poole-Wilson, P.A.; et al. Age-dependent impairment of endothelial progenitor cells is corrected by growth hormone mediated increase of insulin-like growth factor-1. *Circ. Res.* **2007**, *100*, 434–443. [CrossRef]

47. Herndon, D.N.; Barrow, R.E.; Kunkel, K.R.; Broemeling, L.; Rutan, R.L. Effects of recombinant human growth hormone on donor-site healing in severely burned children. *Ann. Surg.* **1990**, *212*, 424. [CrossRef]

48. Massey, K.A.; Blakeslee, C.; Pitkow, H.S. Possible therapeutic effects of growth hormone on wound healing in the diabetic patient. *J. Am. Podiatr. Med. Assoc.* **1998**, *88*, 25–29. [CrossRef]

49. Barret, J.P.; Dziewulski, P.; Jeschke, M.G.; Wolf, S.E.; Herndon, D.N. Effects of recombinant human growth hormone on the development of burn scarring. *Plast. Reconstr. Surg.* **1999**, *104*, 726–729. [CrossRef]

50. Branski, L.K.; Herndon, D.N.; Barrow, R.E.; Kulp, G.A.; Suman, O.E.; Przkora, R.; Meyer, W., 3rd; Huang, T.; Lee, J.O.; Chinkes, D.L.; et al. Randomized controlled trial to determine the efficacy of long-term growth hormone treatment in severely burned children. *Ann. Surg.* **2009**, *250*, 514–523. [CrossRef]

51. Gantwerker, E.A.; Hom, D.B. Skin: Histology and Physiology of Wound Healing. *Clin. Plast. Surg.* **2012**, *39*, 85–97. [CrossRef]

52. Auernhammer, C.J.; Strasburger, C.J. Effects of growth hormone and insulin-like growth factor I on the immune system. *Eur. J. Endocrinol.* **1995**, *133*, 635–645. [CrossRef]

53. Gala, R.R. Prolactin and growth hormone in the regulation of the immune system. *Proc. Soc. Exp. Biol. Med.* **1991**, *198*, 513–527. [CrossRef]

54. Naing, C.; Whittaker, M.A. Anabolic steroids for treating pressure ulcers. Cochrane Wounds Group, editor. *Cochrane Database Syst. Rev.* **2017**, *158*, 718–735.

55. Rasmussen, L.H.; Garbarsch, C.; Schuppan, D.; Moe, D.; Horslev-Pedersen, K.; Gottrup, F.; Steenfos, H. Dose response profiles of human growth hormone in subcutaneous wound chambers in rats. *Eur. J. Surg.* **1995**, *161*, 157–162.

56. Kim, S.H.; Heo, E.J.; Lee, S.W. The effect of topically applied recombinant human growth hormone on wound healing in pigs. *Wounds* **2009**, *21*, 158–163.

57. Ravina, A.; Pestel, M.; Dayras, J.C. Action de l'hormone somatotrope sur les escarres de decubitus et les troubles neurotrophiques. *Presse Med.* **1955**, *63*, 305–308.

58. Waago, H. Local treatment of ulcers in diabetic foot with human growth hormone. *Lancet* **1987**, *1*, 1485. [CrossRef]

59. Maldonado, A.A.; Cristóbal, L.; Martín-López, J.; Mallén, M.; García-Honduvilla, N.; Buján, J. A novel model of human skin pressure ulcers in mice. *PLoS ONE* **2014**, *9*, e109003. [CrossRef]

60. Gerbault, O. Cicatrización cutánea. In *Enciclopedia Médico-Quirúrgica. Técnicas Quirúgicas—Cirugía Plástica Reconstructiva y Estética*; Elsevier: Paris, France, 2000.

61. Carriel, V.S.; Aneiros-Fernandez, J.; Arias-Santiago, S.; Garzón, I.J.; Alaminos, M.; Campos, A. A novel histochemical method for a simultaneous staining of melanin and collagen fibers. *J. Histochem. Cytochem.* **2011**, *59*, 270–277. [CrossRef]

62. Shultz. Multiple Defects in Innate and Adaptive Immunologic Function in NOD/LtSz-scid Mice'. *J. Immunol.* **1995**, *154*, 180–191.

63. Stadler, I.; Zhang, R.Y.; Oskoui, P.; Whittaker, M.B.S.; Lanzafame, R.J. Development of a Simple, Noninvasive, Clinically Relevant Model of Pressure Ulcers in the Mouse. *J. Investig. Surg.* **2004**, *17*, 221–227. [CrossRef]

64. Ortega, M.A.; Asúnsolo, Á.; Leal, J.; Romero, B.; Alvarez-Rocha, M.J.; Sainz, F.; Álvarez-Mon, M.; Buján, J.; García-Honduvilla, N. Implication of the PI3K/Akt/mTOR Pathway in the Process of Incompetent Valves in Patients with Chronic Venous Insufficiency and the Relationship with Aging. *Oxid. Med. Cell Longev.* **2018**, *2018*, 1495170. [CrossRef]

65. Remmele, W.; Schicketanz, K.H. Immunohistochemical determination of estrogen and progesterone receptor content in human breast cancer. Computer-assisted image analysis (QIC score) vs. subjective grading (IRS). *Pathol. Res. Pract.* **1993**, *189*, 862–866. [CrossRef]

International Journal of
Molecular Sciences

Article

Matrisome Properties of Scaffolds Direct Fibroblasts in Idiopathic Pulmonary Fibrosis

Linda Elowsson Rendin [1,*,†], Anna Löfdahl [1,†], Emma Åhrman [2], Catharina Müller [1],
Thomas Notermans [3], Barbora Michaliková [1], Oskar Rosmark [1], Xiao-Hong Zhou [4],
Göran Dellgren [5], Martin Silverborn [5], Leif Bjermer [6], Anders Malmström [1],
Anna-Karin Larsson-Callerfelt [1], Hanna Isaksson [3], Johan Malmström [2] and
Gunilla Westergren-Thorsson [1]

1   Lung Biology, Department of Experimental Medical Sciences, Lund University, BMC C12,
     Lund 221 84, Sweden
2   Division of Infection Medicine Proteomics, Department Clinical Sciences, Lund University,
     Lund 221 84, Sweden
3   Department of Biomedical engineering, Lund University, Lund 221 84, Sweden
4   Bioscience Department, Respiratory, Inflammation and Autoimmunity, IMED Biotech Unit,
     AstraZeneca, Mölndal 431 53, Sweden
5   Department of Cardiothoracic Surgery and Transplant Institute, Sahlgrenska University Hospital,
     Gothenburg 413 45, Sweden
6   Department of Respiratory Medicine and Allergology, Skåne University Hospital, Lund University,
     Lund 221 85, Sweden
*   Correspondence: linda.elowsson_rendin@med.lu.se
†   These authors contributed equally to this work.

Received: 12 July 2019; Accepted: 15 August 2019; Published: 17 August 2019

Abstract: In idiopathic pulmonary fibrosis (IPF) structural properties of the extracellular matrix (ECM) are altered and influence cellular responses through cell-matrix interactions. Scaffolds (decellularized tissue) derived from subpleural healthy and IPF lungs were examined regarding biomechanical properties and ECM composition of proteins (the matrisome). Scaffolds were repopulated with healthy fibroblasts cultured under static stretch with heavy isotope amino acids (SILAC), to examine newly synthesized proteins over time. IPF scaffolds were characterized by increased tissue density, stiffness, ultimate force, and differential expressions of matrisome proteins compared to healthy scaffolds. Collagens, proteoglycans, and ECM glycoproteins were increased in IPF scaffolds, however while specific basement membrane (BM) proteins such as laminins and collagen IV were decreased, nidogen-2 was also increased. Findings were confirmed with histology, clearly showing a disorganized BM. Fibroblasts produced scaffold-specific proteins mimicking preexisting scaffold composition, where 11 out of 20 BM proteins were differentially expressed, along with increased periostin and proteoglycans production. We demonstrate how matrisome changes affect fibroblast activity using novel approaches to study temporal differences, where IPF scaffolds support a disorganized BM and upregulation of disease-associated proteins. These matrix-directed cellular responses emphasize the IPF matrisome and specifically the BM components as important factors for disease progression.

Keywords: scaffold; decellularization; lung fibroblast; proteomics; extracellular matrix

---

1. Introduction

In idiopathic pulmonary fibrosis (IPF) the biomechanics and composition of the extracellular matrix (ECM) are altered causing a pathological phenotype associated with increased tissue stiffness and disorganized structures of the lung [1]. Today there is no real effective treatment for IPF with poor long-term survival, although there are treatments that may slow progression of IPF somewhat. Lung transplantation remains the most valid option for some patients, however, not all patients can be offered this treatment due to recipient co-morbidities or donor shortage. Although largely unknown, a combination of factors is believed to play a role in IPF, including ageing, epigenetic modifications, dysfunctional alveolar epithelium, along with persistent activation of lung fibroblasts that contributes to an increased accumulation of ECM with subsequent detrimental remodeling resulting in the loss of lung function and eventually end-stage lung disease [2–4]. Local signals from the ECM, e.g., stiffness and bound growth factors and cytokines, have been shown to influence cellular behavior such as migration, differentiation and proliferation, activities that are altered due to changes in the local microenvironment [5–7]. In a fibrotic lung, there is an imbalance in the turnover of ECM proteins causing excessive production and deposition of ECM proteins, forming a disease-specific organization and composition of the matrix [8–10]. The pathological mechanism underlying the initiation and progression of IPF is not fully understood, and there are no effective treatment options, highlighting the need to identify effective molecular targets for therapeutic interventions [11]. Lung tissue slices, decellularized for cellular removal, can serve as human structural matrices to study the important and complex interaction between cells and matrix [12,13]. In comparison to other cell culture systems, decellularized tissue (scaffolds) comprise a unique ex vivo system that more closely mimics the original intricate 3D milieu of the lung. Through this ex vivo model a better understanding of unknown key cellular mechanisms can be obtained in order to understand which ECM properties drive the formation of fibrotic tissue and which role the ECM of IPF scaffolds has in disease progression. The matrisome protein classification system defined by Naba et al., clearly describes the ECM components, subgrouping ECM matrisome core proteins (collagens, glycoproteins and proteoglycans) and ECM associated proteins such as ECM-affiliated proteins, ECM regulators, and secreted factors [14]. Distal lung tissue is mainly composed of fibrillar collagens I, III, V, and VI and the basement membrane (BM) collagen type IV [7]. Intertwined with collagen type IV are nidogens, perlecan, and laminins, which comprise the BM network, a protein complex facilitating epithelial and endothelial cell attachment and regulating cellular behavior [15]. Alterations of the BM structure and other ECM components affect both morphology and biomechanical properties of the tissues, identifying matrix stiffness as an important biomechanical signal for cell responses [16]. Tissue stiffening of the lung, caused by increased ECM deposition in the alveoli that leads to a loss in tissue elasticity, induces differentiation of fibroblasts into myofibroblasts, a response that in part could be de-activated when changing culture conditions in vitro from stiff to softer substrates [17]. In IPF, fibroblasts demonstrate an increased cellular stiffness, perhaps functioning as a positive feedback loop contributing to the formation of a non-compliant stiff lung tissue [18].

In this study we focused on the distal parenchymal matrisome properties of lung scaffolds derived from healthy donors and IPF patients in a unique 3D-ex vivo setting, mimicking pulmonary physiological conditions. Our hypothesis was that the matrisome properties, i.e., biomechanical properties and matrisome composition, of the ECM have a fundamental impact on cellular responses and may act as a mechanism in disease progression.

2. Results

2.1. Morphology and Biomechanical Properties of Native Tissue and Scaffolds Derived from Healthy and IPF Lung Tissue

The schematic layout of the study and scaffold preparation is illustrated in Figure 1A. Macroscopic characterization of healthy and IPF lung tissue slices, using scanning electron microscopy (SEM), displayed an evident difference in tissue morphology, with a dense meshwork of matrix and compact lung architecture in IPF tissue (Figure 1B), which correspond to the end stage of long-term IPF. After decellularization, the scaffolds maintained original tissue integrity and characteristics in both IPF and healthy decellularized lung tissue, examined by SEM and in histology (Figure 1B–E). Overview images of scaffolds with SEM illustrated the heterogeneity in the IPF patient material with more or less dense tissue. The decellularized scaffolds from IPF and healthy individuals showed no signs of visible cells in the tissue, as seen with hematoxylin/eosin staining (Figure 1C). Furthermore, the cellular content was examined in decellularized IPF derived scaffolds, measuring dsDNA. In support of our previous study on healthy lung tissue by Rosmark et al. [13], dsDNA content was efficiently removed following decellularization showing only 1.5% residual dsDNA per mg tissue in IPF derived scaffolds (data not shown). In the stress–strain measurements, the native lung tissues from IPF patients showed significantly higher tensile stiffness in comparison to healthy individuals ($p = 0.0003$), as well as higher ultimate force ($p = 0.0097$) ($n = 4$) (Figure 1D). One duplicate of native lung tissue from one patient examined for stiffness was excluded and regarded as an outlier with a value (115.39) exceeding more than three standard deviations from the mean. These properties remained in the decellularized IPF scaffolds. The healthy scaffolds, on the other hand, showed a higher stiffness ($p = 0.0485$) and ultimate force ($p = 0.0146$) compared to the native tissue, although with a larger variability. Within the scaffold groups, differences in stiffness ($p = 0.06676$) and ultimate force ($p = 0.0594$) were maintained compared to difference in between native tissue groups. We did not observe any differences in stress-relaxation behavior for native lung tissue and the decellularized scaffolds for neither the healthy nor the IPF samples (Figure S1A). Force to failure curves revealed a clear shift towards higher tensile strength, with increased force to tissue displacement in IPF tissue (Figure S1B,C). Despite high patient variability, tissue density (mg/mm^3) was significantly higher ($p = 0.0022$) in IPF scaffolds in comparison to healthy scaffolds (Figure 1E).

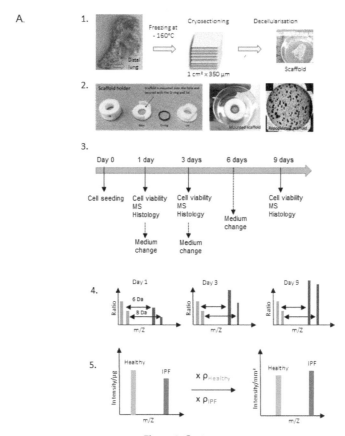

Figure 1. *Cont.*

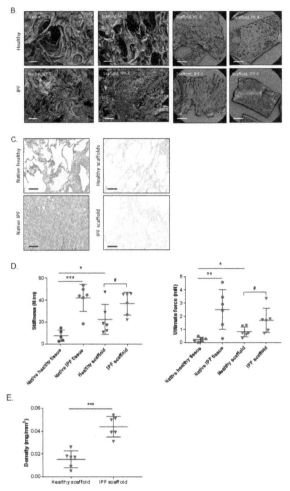

Figure 1. Characterization of native lung tissue and scaffolds (**A**) Schematic of experimental layout. Dissection and decellularization of 350 μm human lung tissue slices (1). Mounting of repopulated scaffolds pre-cultured in SILAC medium (2). Schematics of culture conditions and sample extractions (3). Mass spectrometry (MS) analysis on light (green bars) and heavy (purple bars) protein intensities (m/Z, protein mass/protein charge) illustrating the mass shift of 6 Da (Arg) or 8 Da (Lys) between pre-existing (scaffold extracellular matrix (ECM)) and newly produced matrisome proteins (4). Intensity/μg was adjusted for tissue density resulting in intensity/mm^3 (5). (**B**) Representative scanning electron microscopy (SEM) images with the same magnification (scale bar = 100 μm) of native tissue (left) and decellularized tissue (scaffold) (middle) and scaffolds at an overview (right, scale bar = 1 mm) for illustration of sample variability (right). (**C**) Hematoxylin and eosin staining of native lung tissue and corresponding scaffold after decellularization of the tissue (scale bar = 100 μm). (**D**) Stiffness and ultimate force measurements of biological replicates (*n* = 3, with two technical replicates except for native healthy tissue) from native healthy and idiopathic pulmonary fibrosis (IPF) lung tissue and corresponding scaffolds (*n* = 4, with two technical replicates) derived from healthy and IPF tissue. (**E**) Density measurements of healthy and IPF scaffolds (*n* = 2, with three technical replicates). Unpaired *t*-test for significance between patient groups with *p*-values * $p < 0.05$, ** $p < 0.01$, *** $p < 0.001$. Stiffness # $p = 0.068$, Ultimate force # $p = 0.059$.

2.2. Proteomic Profiling of Lung Scaffolds

In the next step, we used quantitative mass spectrometry to determine the ECM composition using a matrisome classification system [14,19,20] to investigate if the molecular composition of the scaffolds could be explained by the differences in matrisome properties between healthy and IPF scaffolds. Each group, healthy and IPF, was analyzed in triplicates from each donor, with two donors per group (Figure S2). The analysis showed protein groups containing comparable numbers of identified matrisome proteins in both healthy and IPF derived scaffolds, indicative of an equivalent protein extraction from each type of scaffold (Figure 2A). However, the number of identified non-ECM proteins (other) were higher in IPF scaffolds (530 proteins) in comparison to healthy derived scaffolds (417 proteins), a difference that could be explained by slightly increased cellular remnants in the compact decellularized IPF tissue. Nonetheless, the low content of dsDNA in IPF scaffolds verified the matrices as decellularized tissue with > 98% DNA removal [21].

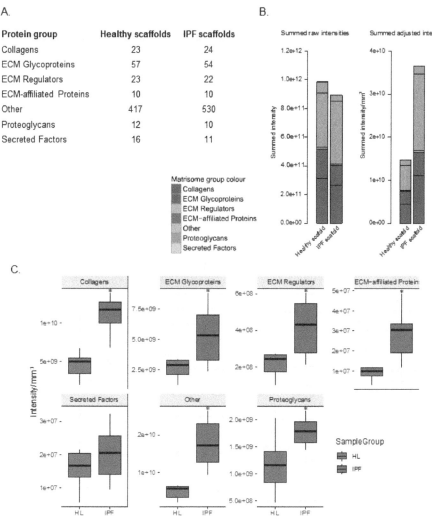

Figure 2. *Cont.*

D. Z-score

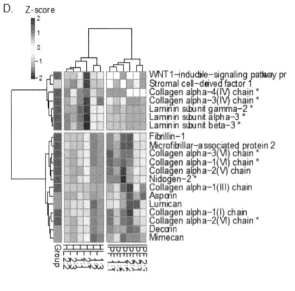

E.

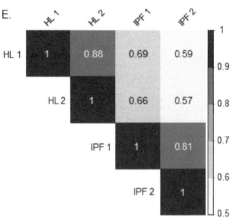

F.

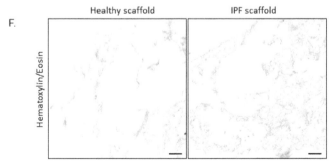

Figure 2. *Cont.*

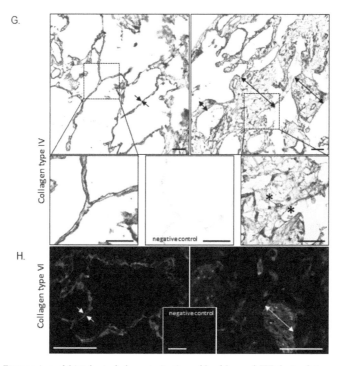

Figure 2. Proteomic and histological characterization of healthy and IPF derived tissue scaffolds. (**A**) Number of identified proteins in decellularized scaffolds derived from healthy individuals (biological replicates $n = 2$, technical replicates $n = 3$) and IPF patients ($n = 2$, $n = 3$). Protein groups assigned to matrisome affiliation. (**B**) Matrisome grouped summed raw intensities for proteins in healthy and IPF derived scaffolds, left panel. Matrisome grouped summed intensities after density adjustment in healthy and IPF scaffolds, right panel. Mean values for groups presented. (**C**) Statistics for summed matrisome groups. Student's *t*-test with Benjamini-Hochberg corrected *p*-values * $p < 0.05$. (**D**) Unsupervised hierarchical clustering of significantly different matrisome proteins characteristic for the scaffold types using Z-scored values. Basement membrane proteins marked with *. (**E**) Spearman correlation between scaffold groups. (**F**) Histological verification and spatial tissue distribution of selected matrisome (or basement membrane) proteins. Hematoxylin/Eosin staining showing distinct morphological differences between thin, alveolar septa (healthy scaffold) compared to thickened, fibrotic remodeled septa (IPF scaffold). (**G**) This is accentuated (arrows) by staining for collagen type IV (brown), indicating clear basement membrane staining lining the alveolar septa in the healthy scaffold compared to disorganized fragments in the IPF scaffold, with large areas devoid of collagen type IV signal or reduced intensity (*). (**H**) Inversely, collagen type VI showed accumulation in these fibrotic structures in the IPF scaffold. Scale bar 50 μm.

The distributions of proteins in the two types of scaffolds were presented as summed intensities by matrisome groups (Figure 2B). To compensate for the discrepancy in tissue morphology between healthy and IPF derived scaffolds, the summed intensity (intensity/μg) of all proteins was adjusted for tissue density (mg/mm^3) (Figure 1A:5). Data showed a distinct difference in intensity of matrisome groups between IPF and healthy derived scaffolds following density adjustment. The summed intensity of each matrisome group was increased in IPF scaffolds, in comparison to healthy derived scaffolds, reflecting the difference in matrisome composition. Further examination of matrisome group intensities showed a significantly higher amount of nearly all matrisome groups in IPF scaffolds compared to healthy scaffolds, seen as intensity/mm^3 (Figure 2C). To select matrisome proteins significant for respective scaffold group we used a threshold of fold change 2 and a Benjamini-Hochberg corrected *p*-value below 0.05 between the healthy and diseased group. Visualization of significantly different matrisome proteins using unsupervised hierarchical clustering of Z-scored values, identified matrisome proteins characteristic for healthy and IPF derived scaffolds respectively (Figure 2D). The top cluster in the heatmap depicts matrisome proteins that were less abundant in IPF scaffolds, while the bottom cluster showed proteins more abundant in IPF scaffolds, as compared to healthy scaffolds (Figure 2D). Despite recognized lung tissue heterogeneity coupled to IPF patients [22] and limited number of patient samples, IPF derived scaffolds showed high correlation in matrisome composition, seen both in biological replicates and in between donors (rank = 0.81) (Figure 2E). Healthy derived scaffolds showed similar matrisome correlation (rank = 0.88) within its group. Further examination of the significantly expressed matrisome proteins showed that nine out of 20 of them were assigned as BM associated proteins (Figure 2D) [20]. Nidogen-2 and Collagen type VI (α 1,2,3 chain) were clustered together as more abundant in IPF scaffolds in comparison to healthy scaffolds, whereas laminin $\gamma 2$, laminin $\beta 3$, laminin $\alpha 3$ and collagen type IV (chains $\alpha 3$ and $\alpha 4$) were significantly decreased in IPF scaffolds. Hematoxylin/eosin staining showed distinct morphological differences with thin alveolar septa in the healthy scaffolds compared to thickened and remodeled septa in the IPF scaffolds (Figure 2F). This was also clearly illustrated by immunohistochemistry (IHC) for collagen type IV (Figure 2G) and type VI (Figure 2H). In the healthy lung scaffold, the BM of both sides of the alveolar septum displayed a thin, even double-line indicating the presence of collagen type IV. In the IPF lung scaffold however, this staining was uneven and often poorly defined, with areas of decreased staining intensity and both thickened and thinned BM structures. Most obvious was the increased alveolar septum thickness, representing large areas without collagen type IV signal. Inversely, collagen type VI showed accumulation in exactly these fibrotic structures in the IPF scaffold. Furthermore, the IPF scaffolds showed disorganized BM-fragments and possibly increased microvasculature. In summary, this illustrates the loss of normal lung organizations in IPF with altered BM membrane composition and structure.

2.3. Repopulated Scaffolds

After characterization of scaffold properties, we continued to study the cellular response of primary human lung fibroblasts cultured up to 9 days on scaffolds derived from IPF patients and healthy individuals. For these experiments we seeded fibroblasts, derived from a healthy donor, on scaffolds derived from four patients for each group and cultured in duplicates for each patient (*n* = 4 per group). To start, we examined if cellular attachment and viability varied between the two types of scaffolds. Cellular viability, measured as metabolic activity, showed no difference between the two types of scaffolds after 1 day of culture, indicative of equivalent numbers of attached cells (Figure 3A), also visualized by confocal microscopy (Figure 3B).

This result was also confirmed by counting the number of cells left in the wells after cell seeding, where no difference between the groups was seen. No significant difference in cellular viability was detected in any of the scaffolds measured up to 9 days in culture (Figure 3A). SEM imaging showed differences in cell orientation between the groups, with cells densely packed on top of dense areas of the IPF scaffolds and heavily repopulated less dense structures, whereas cells cultured on healthy derived scaffolds followed and maintained open lung structures (Figure 3C). To visualize cellular attachments and organization in the scaffolds, repopulated scaffolds were antibody labeled for collagen type VI, a cell binding protein, in combination with the mesenchymal cell marker vimentin and the focal adhesion protein vinculin (Figure 3D). Results showed similar staining of collagen type VI in both types of scaffolds, again representing thin alveolar septa in the healthy scaffold compared to heavily remodeled parenchyma in the IPF scaffold. Interestingly, repopulating fibroblasts on IPF scaffolds appeared to show more intense vimentin staining compared to cells on healthy scaffolds, which is in line with other studies demonstrating a correlation between vimentin and substrates stiffness [23]. Furthermore, cells on IPF scaffolds were primarily situated in less dense tissue areas and appeared stretched and elongated, lining surface edges of pulmonary structures (Figure 3D). To further examine cellular attachments, immunofluorescence (IF) staining for vinculin was performed, an integrin involved in intracellular signaling [24] which showed no difference in cellular distribution between healthy and IPF derived scaffolds.

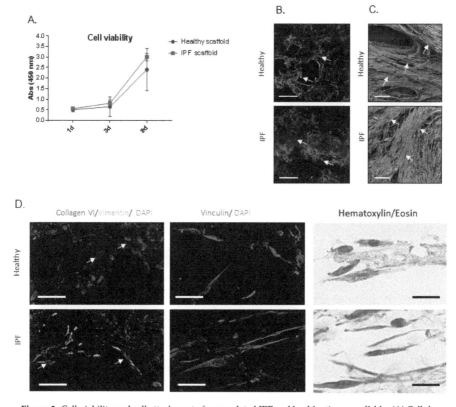

Figure 3. Cell viability and cell attachment of repopulated IPF and healthy tissue scaffolds. (**A**) Cellular viability of primary lung fibroblast repopulated on tissue scaffolds (biological replicates $n = 4$), shown as mean ± SD. (**B**) Confocal live imaging after 1 day of culture, showing equal cell attachment. Cell staining (blue), autofluorescent scaffold (green). Arrows indicate cells. Scale bar = 500 μm. (**C**) SEM after 9 days of culture, visualizing cellular differences in orientation in the scaffolds and repopulation. Arrows indicate elongated cells. Scale bar = 100 μm. (**D**) Visualization of repopulated scaffolds, showing fibroblasts attaching to the surrounding tissue (here: collagen type VI) and cytoskeleton (vimentin) and patterns of focal adhesions (vinculin). Hematoxylin/eosin staining of corresponding scaffolds shown in the right panel. Arrows: different intensities of vimentin in fibroblasts repopulating healthy vs. IPF scaffolds. Scale bar = 20 μm.

2.4. Proteomic Profiling of Matrisome Proteins in Repopulated Healthy and IPF Lung Scaffolds

Healthy primary human fibroblasts were cultured in SILAC-medium 5 days before cellular seeding and over the whole culture period on the scaffolds. In this experiment the cells take up heavy amino acids from the media and start to produce proteins with heavy amino acids that are distinguishable in the mass spectrometer from residual scaffold proteins that only contain light amino acids (Figure 1A). This enabled us to follow protein turnover over time from day 1, by differentiating between newly synthesized cell-derived proteins (heavy) and pre-existing matrisome proteins in the scaffold (light). As with the mass spectrometry (MS) data for the decellularized scaffolds, the data for the repopulated scaffolds was adjusted for differences in tissue density and a mean value was calculated for each group at each time point. Density adjustment allowed us to study an equal tissue volume and thereby the same number of cells in the two types of scaffolds. The matrisome protein differences between the groups over time were analyzed through a Spearman correlation test, which clearly demonstrated that newly synthesized proteins (Figure 4A, heavy) from cells cultured on IPF scaffolds had a different protein composition compared to healthy individuals. Scaffolds in the IPF group correlated within its group over time as did the healthy individuals (Figure 4A, light). The temporal changes of overall matrisome compositions for each type of scaffold were shown as heavy and light matrisome protein groups over time (Figure 4B). Interestingly, fibroblasts diverged in their production (heavy intensity/mm^3) of matrisome proteins, detected as early as day 1 of culture on IPF derived scaffolds. At day 1, the fibroblasts produced a significantly ($p = 0.0069$) higher level of proteoglycans compared to cells cultured on healthy scaffolds (Figure 4B). Over time, we observed a tendency of increased collagens production in repopulated IPF scaffolds, however the level of ECM glycoproteins remained unchanged. Examination of the preexisting scaffold composition (light intensity/mm^3) (Figure 4B) representing ongoing ECM remodeling, showed increased amounts of proteoglycans ($p = 0.0231$) such as perlecan and lumican in IPF scaffolds at day 1 (Figure S3). However, at day 9, IPF scaffolds showed significantly decreased amounts of ECM regulators ($p = 0.029$) (Figure 4B) e.g., TIMP-3 (Figure S3) and secreted factors ($p = 0.089$) (Figure 4B).

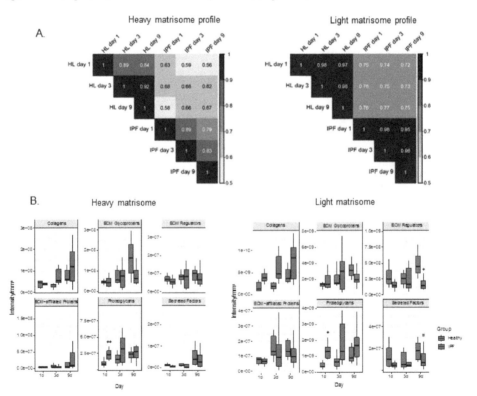

Figure 4. *Cont.*

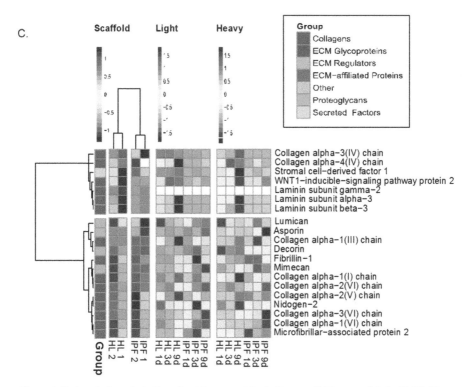

Figure 4. Proteomic characterization of matrisome proteins in tissue scaffolds repopulated with SILAC labelled fibroblasts. (**A**) Spearman correlations of matrisome proteins in repopulated healthy and IPF scaffolds at day 1, 3, and 9 after repopulation. Scaffold group mean MS-intensities for each time point presented (biological replicates $n = 4$, technical replicates $n = 2$). (**B**) Statistics for matrisome groups for repopulated healthy and IPF scaffolds over time calculated from summed matrisome groups. Student's *t*-test with Benjamin–Hochberg corrected *p*-values for significance between patient groups of the same time point with *p*-values * $p < 0.05$, ** $p < 0.01$. Light # $p = 0.089$ (Secreted Factors). (**C**) Heatmap of matrisome proteins over time. Unsupervised hierarchical clustering of Z-scored values (ward.D2). Scaffolds are presented as patient means (biological replicate $n = 2$) and repopulated scaffolds (light and heavy) are presented as patient group mean intensities for each time point ($n = 4$) with technical replicates for each group ($n = 2$). Light and heavy intensities were selected and visualized according to previous scaffold clustering.

To exclude cell number variabilities in between the two types of scaffolds after adjusting the values, we examined heavy and light labeled histones in each group over time, showing no significant difference between IPF and healthy repopulated scaffolds at any time point (data not shown). These results indicate that the identified diversity in protein synthesis was dependent on the original scaffold properties and not by variety in cellular content. To further describe this finding, we selected the matrisome proteins found to be significantly different and descriptive for the respective decellularized scaffold group, and analyzed these further showing temporal differences in repopulated scaffolds. We compared both newly synthesized matrisome proteins (Figure 4C, heavy) as well as changes in the original scaffold composition over time (Figure 4C, light) based on the significantly different matrisome proteins in the scaffolds from the starting point (Figure 4C, scaffold). The top cluster in the heat map presents the matrisome proteins that are more abundant in healthy scaffolds in comparison to IPF scaffolds. Within its own group, newly synthesized proteins from IPF and healthy scaffolds showed similar protein expressions over time (top cluster). The overall pattern of newly synthesized matrisome proteins appeared to overlap with the original scaffold composition representative for each group. These results indicate that the characteristics of the original scaffolds can influence cellular activity, stimulating scaffold specific protein production in primary fibroblasts, thus mimicking the composition found in the original scaffold.

Furthermore, to connect to our previous findings in the decellularized scaffolds, we examined how BM protein production was affected over time in each type of scaffold (Figure 5A). Most of the significantly different expressed BM proteins showed a reduced expression in IPF repopulated scaffolds (top cluster, Figure 5A) as compared to healthy scaffolds. Changes in protein intensity were analyzed over time and significantly differently expressed BM proteins (11 out of 20 BM proteins) were presented as mean heavy intensity for each group (Figure 5B). Interestingly, healthy scaffolds showed an increased production of nidogen-1 and laminins (subunit $\alpha3$, $\beta3$, and $\alpha5$) over time, whereas in the IPF scaffolds the synthesis was low or undetected. Similar responses were seen with collagen IV production of $\alpha3$ and $\alpha4$ chains. For repopulated IPF scaffolds we found an increased production of the following structural BM proteins; basement membrane-specific heparan sulfate proteoglycan core protein (perlecan), collagen type VI chains $\alpha1$, $\alpha2$, and $\alpha3$. The diverse expression and downregulation of several heavy labeled BM proteins in repopulated IPF scaffolds further supports the manifestation of a disorganized BM as previously visualized in IPF derived scaffolds. Scaffold changes over time were shown with light labeled protein intensity, showing several BM proteins with similar temporal patterns as heavy intensities (Figure S4).

Based on the quantitative data in Figure 5B and Figure S4, we show with antibody labeling, the spatial expression pattern of collagen type VI in repopulated scaffolds, showing an intensified expression level at day 9 in healthy scaffolds as compared to day 1 (Figure 5C). In IPF scaffolds, collagen VI appeared stable over time showing no distinct visual difference in antibody labeling. The overall expression of collagen VI appeared visually increased in IPF scaffold vs. healthy, which could be explained by the higher density of the tissue.

At further examination of heavy labeled proteins, we identified that the synthesis of tenascin and periostin was significantly altered in repopulated IPF scaffolds, matrix components that have been associated with the progression of IPF [25,26]. Tenascin and periostin were also found to be elevated in the original scaffold composition of IPF (Figure 6A). Fibroblasts on IPF scaffolds produced significantly higher amounts of tenascin ($p = 0.044$ at day 3, $p = 0.027$ at day 9) and periostin ($p = 0.039$ at day 1) (Figure 6A), protein expression patterns that have been implicated in fibrosis [25,27,28]. IHC staining of repopulated scaffolds visualized periostin distribution (Figure 6B). Periostin was found in certain areas of the thin alveolar septa in healthy scaffolds. IPF scaffolds, on the other hand, had a stronger staining in less remodeled areas and very low periostin signal in the heavily remodeled and fibrotic tissue areas. No apparent intracellular periostin could be detected by IHC.

A

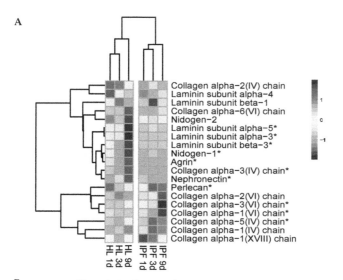

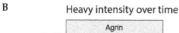

B

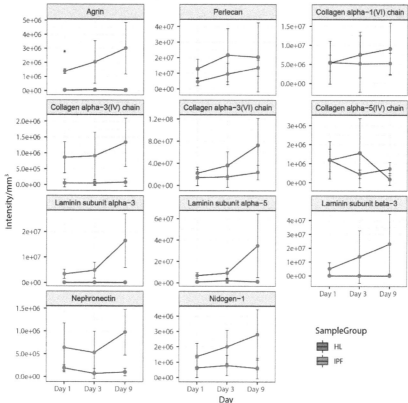

Figure 5. *Cont.*

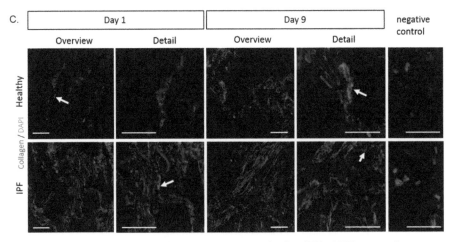

Figure 5. Synthesis of basement membrane proteins in repopulated scaffolds. (**A**) Heatmap of basement membrane (BM) proteins over time. Repopulated scaffolds as group mean heavy intensities for each time point (biological replicates $n = 4$, technical replicates $n = 2$). With Student's t-test, significantly differentially expressed proteins are marked with *. Perlecan = Basement membrane-specific heparan sulfate proteoglycan core protein. Production of significantly different basement membrane proteins in repopulated IPF and healthy scaffolds. Protein intensity shown as mean heavy intensity (**B**) over time for each group with SD. Student's t-test with Benjamin–Hochberg corrected p-values for significance between patient groups of the same time point with p-values * $p < 0.05$. Blue = Healthy, Red = IPF. (**C**) Antibody labeling of repopulated scaffolds, at day 1 and day 9 of culture, showing collagen type VI ($\alpha 1$) (red) with DAPI staining (blue). Images of collagen VI staining, illustrate newly synthesized protein and original scaffold composition, with arrows exemplifying positive staining. Scale bar = 50 μm.

Synthesis of the proteoglycan decorin was upregulated ($p = 0.043$) in fibroblasts cultured on IPF scaffolds on day 1 of repopulation (Figure 6C). Decorin labeling showed clear intracellular and periocellular staining with a general enhanced overall tissue expression in IPF derived scaffolds (Figure 6D). Interestingly, these early changes in proteoglycan production were also detected for biglycan ($p = 0.040$) and versican ($p = 0.027$), showing significantly increased levels in repopulated IPF derived scaffolds (Figure 6C). The increased production of proteoglycans was further supported with antibody labeling (Figure 6D). IPF scaffolds showed higher levels of decorin compared to healthy scaffolds, and intracellular staining of decorin in fibroblasts were found on both scaffold types. Biglycan staining showed a strong intrinsic accumulation in IPF scaffolds, whereas healthy scaffolds only had sporadic staining apart from vessels. Intracellular biglycan could be found in fibroblasts cultured on both scaffold types. As for versican, staining was largely absent in healthy scaffolds, but a distinct intrinsic accumulation in IPF scaffolds could be seen as well as prominent cellular signal in fibroblasts cultured on IPF scaffolds. No intracellular staining of versican could be seen in cells cultured on healthy scaffolds.

In summary, these results demonstrate that the material properties of the ECM affected fibroblast activity, thus supporting a profibrotic phenotype when cultured in a diseased milieu.

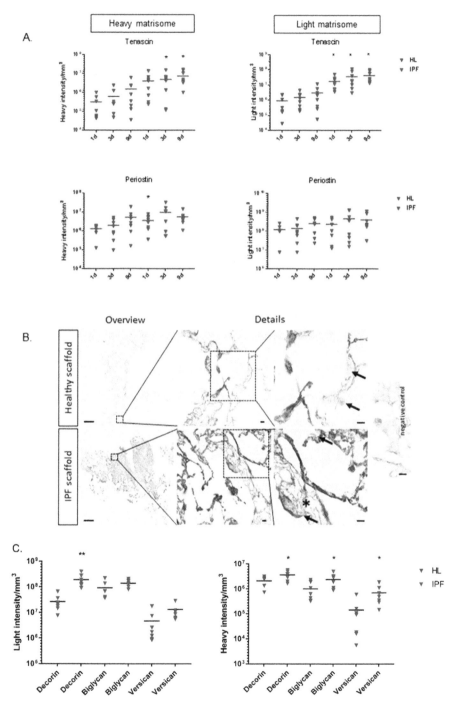

Figure 6. *Cont.*

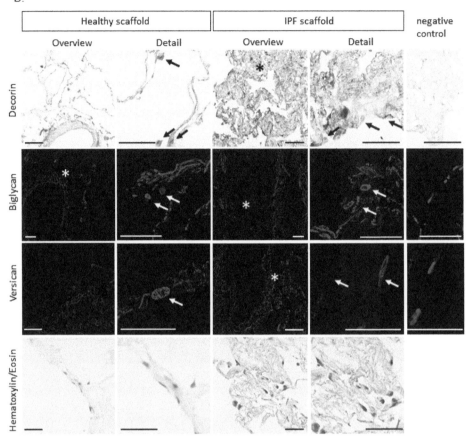

Figure 6. (**A**) Graphs of heavy and light intensity/mm^3 of tenascin and periostin of repopulated scaffolds (biological replicates $n = 4$, technical replicates $n = 2$) with calculated grand mean. Student's t-test for significance between patient groups means for each time point (* $p < 0.05$). (**B**) Periostin in repopulated scaffolds (day 1). Antibody labeling indicating periostin (brown) in certain areas in alveolar septa in the healthy scaffolds, and to a stronger degree in less remodeled tissue areas in the IPF scaffolds. Largely absent periostin staining in heavily remodeled IPF tissue areas (*). Arrows highlight differences in intracellular staining. Scale bar overview 500 μm, details 10 μm. (**C**) Graphs of original (light) and newly synthesized (heavy) proteoglycans decorin, biglycan, and versican of repopulated scaffolds (biological replicates $n = 4$, technical replicates $n = 2$) are presented with calculated grand mean of light and heavy intensity at day 1. Student's t-test for significance between patient groups (* $p < 0.05$, ** $p < 0.01$). (**D**) Antibody staining illustrating proteoglycan increase in IPF vs. healthy scaffolds (day 1) of newly synthesized proteoglycans including original scaffold composition. Decorin (brown): IPF scaffold showing intrinsically more decorin, with cellular signal in fibroblasts on both scaffold types. Biglycan (red): rare intrinsic biglycan in healthy scaffolds apart from vessels, but strong accumulation in IPF scaffolds. Cellular signal of biglycan in fibroblasts on both scaffold types were seen. Versican (red): absent intrinsic versican in healthy scaffolds, but distinct accumulation in IPF scaffolds. Prominent cellular signal in fibroblasts on IPF scaffolds, but not on healthy scaffolds. * extracellular deposition in repopulated scaffolds. Arrows highlight differences in intracellular staining. Corresponding hematoxylin/eosin staining of the repopulated scaffolds shown in bottom row. Scale bar 50 μm.

3. Discussion

The ECM has important biological functions such as regulating wound healing responses and tissue remodeling through cellular interactions [7,29]. The implementation of decellularized IPF and healthy lung tissues as scaffolds represents a promising approach to study the biological function of the ECM and how vital changes in matrisome properties, both in composition and biomechanically, influence cell behaviors [12]. In this study, we performed an in-depth characterization of the structural properties of these acellular lung matrices derived from healthy individuals and IPF patients, with regards to morphology, tissue density, and stiffness. Alterations of these important features, linked to the pathophysiological changes seen in IPF scaffolds, were sustained following decellularization. IPF is thought to be the result of an aberrant wound healing process involving abnormal deposition of matrix proteins e.g., collagens [1,30], and as seen in this study leading to almost a three-fold increase in tissue density compared to healthy, accompanied by a five-fold and 60% increase in stiffness for native IPF tissue and IPF scaffolds, respectively. Decellularization seemed to solely affect the biomechanical properties of healthy scaffolds. Essentially, collagen content is retained after the decellularization process in healthy lung tissue, while elastin content is affected to some degree and even more the proteoglycans along with the ECM glycoproteins [31]. Our data suggest that removal of these charged proteins most likely led to changes in biomechanical properties due to lost electrostatic interactions, leading to an entangled micro-structure, ultimately increasing the tensile strength of healthy scaffolds, which might influence cell-matrix interactions. The IPF scaffolds, on the contrary, had a higher content of collagens compared to healthy scaffolds and a largely absent BM along with the removal of surfactant proteins, which gives specific biomechanical properties of the scaffolds. Consistent with morphological differences of more or less fibrotic scaffold samples, the biomechanical properties of the scaffolds demonstrated large variations. Despite this, both within IPF patients and within biological replicates, the IPF scaffolds were distinctly separated from healthy scaffolds, actually exhibiting rather homogenous tissue characteristics, strengthening the results from our limited number of biological replicates (Figure S5).

One of the important findings was that there were differences in the abundance of distinct matrisome proteins between healthy and IPF scaffolds, with nine out of 20 of these being BM components. Visualized with collagen type IV antibody labeling, the BM showed large spatial differences between healthy and IPF scaffolds. The loss of BM integrity of the alveolar-capillary membrane along with an accumulation of collagen type VI, without normal structure reconstruction, causes an abnormal lung architecture, thought to promote fibrosis [30], where fibroblasts and especially myofibroblasts are known to be the main matrix producers and key players in fibrosis [4]. With that in mind, our aim was to examine how changes in ECM properties affected cellular responses in IPF. When IPF scaffolds were repopulated with healthy fibroblasts, we demonstrated a significantly reduced production of important BM complexes such as nidogens, laminins, and collagen IV in IPF scaffolds, results that are in support of a previously reported study [32]. In our study, laminin α3, α5, and β3 were not produced at the same level in IPF scaffolds as in healthy scaffolds. Data, which is in line with an in vivo study, where the loss of laminin α3 augmented the progression of lung fibrosis, is suggestive of its contribution to IPF disease progression [33]. Underlying the BM are anchoring matrix components perlecan and collagen type VI chains α1 and α3, which were elevated in repopulated IPF scaffolds, indicating an imbalance in ECM turnover with a build-up of matrix underlying the fragmented BM. Furthermore, an early induction in synthesis of proteoglycans decorin, lumican, biglycan, and versican (Figure 6C, Figure S3), as well as the ECM regulator, TIMP-3, (Figure S3) in IPF scaffolds compared to fibroblasts cultured on healthy scaffolds further strengthen the picture of a promotion of a profibrotic feedback loop. Proteoglycans are multifunctional proteins involved in wound healing responses and shown to be elevated in lungs from IPF patients [34–37]. Fibroblasts from lung fibrosis patients have shown an increased production of small proteoglycans, with decorin as the major proteoglycan produced with implications in pulmonary fibrotic responses [35,38]. These findings were replicated in our study and further support the hypothesis that fibroblast activity is modified by certain elements of the ECM.

In a previous study, where primary fibroblasts were cultured on healthy lung scaffolds freely floating in culture medium [13], cells contracted the surface area of the scaffold from approximately 1 cm^2 to 1 mm^2 in less than 9 days. To prevent this and to more closely mimic the physiological conditions, we introduced custom-made holders to mount the scaffolds in order to sustain a stretched and organized lung tissue structure during cell culture. This approach clearly demonstrated the importance of imposing a static stretch of the scaffolds, sustained by the holders, to transduce forces similar to the native situation. It has been shown that cells sense resistance to pulling as well as the local environment due to protein conformation, substrate rigidity, and architecture [39]. Repopulated scaffolds showed equivalent numbers of cells attached in both healthy and IPF scaffolds, verified by cellular viability and histone levels over time. In addition, patterns of focal adhesions, shown with vinculin staining, did not appear to be different in the groups. Although, the cell morphology appeared to be similar in both types of scaffolds, fibroblasts on IPF scaffolds seemed to have a higher accumulation of vimentin, indicating a shift in the cellular response due to an increased stiffness, also seen by others [40]. Compositional alterations of the ECM affect mechanical properties of tissues, which in turn influence how the cells perceive its local environment in terms of forces and ECM tension through integrin-ECM interactions that in turn will have an impact on the intracellular signaling [24,39]. An enhanced matrix stiffness with reduced tissue compliance is known to promote fibroblast activation and fibrosis [41]. We demonstrated an increased tissue stiffness in IPF scaffolds, as recognized in other studies of native lung tissue from IPF patients [42], which in turn had an effect on fibroblast activity. The stiffness of the ECM is increased in areas of fibrosis [43] and stimulates fibroblast migration, differentiation, and other cellular events that are associated with tissue remodeling [6]. Invasive migratory fibroblasts degrade and disrupt surrounding barriers to propagate its migration toward stiff and fibrotic areas of the lung [44]. In our study, repopulated IPF scaffolds synthesized lower amounts of the MMP (metalloproteases) inhibitor TIMP-3 (Figure S3). The shift in ECM regulators connect to our previous study by Ahrman et al. and also to other studies showing decreased levels of tissue inhibitors and increased levels of proteases in IPF [8,10,45]. Deprived balance of MMPs and TIMPs, enzymes necessary for matrix reorganization, contribute to a pathological turnover rate of the ECM [45,46]. These factors with both direct and indirect regulation of ECM structures, including activation of growth factors, cytokines, and chemokines, have been suggested to have an important role in the development of fibrosis, however, with diverse and complex functions [47]. We also saw that ECM regulators and secreted factors decreased at day 9 only in the IPF light matrisome, indicative of a high enzymatic activity in fibroblasts cultured on IPF scaffolds, thus resulting in enhanced release and/or removal of ECM components to the medium compared to fibroblasts cultured on healthy scaffolds. We saw that the fibroblasts filled up the spaces in less dense areas and covered dense areas with a compact cell sheet in the IPF scaffolds, while the alveolar structure was maintained in the healthy scaffolds. This feature may be explained by the loss of an intact BM in combination with an increased stiffness in the IPF scaffolds. Collectively, these characteristics may contribute to a dysregulated and imbalanced proteolysis of matrix proteins, changes that we saw in the temporal expression of light labeled BM proteins in between the two types of scaffolds (Figure S4).

Interestingly, when cultured on IPF scaffolds, fibroblasts showed an increased production of tenascin and periostin, proteins which are upregulated in IPF patients, with the latter recognized as a disease marker for IPF progression [25,26]. Tenascin is a large ECM glycoprotein transiently expressed during wound healing and involved in several tissue remodeling processes, which was reflected in our system where the fibroblasts responded to the altered milieu in the IPF scaffolds. This protein stimulates migration of fibroblasts and increased mechanical stiffness, seen in vitro, and is upregulated in patients with IPF, especially at fibroblastic foci [26,27,48]. The matricellular protein periostin is able to bind to tenascin facilitating its incorporation to the ECM [49]. In seemingly healthy looking areas in the IPF scaffolds we found strong staining for periostin, whereas in heavily remodeled and fibrotic areas the staining was absent. The spatial distribution of periostin may direct the progression of fibrosis by acting as an early trigger for matrix build-up, seen with an initial high production in IPF scaffolds compared to healthy, which supports our observation that fibroblast migrate to less dense areas in IPF scaffolds.

In accordance with previous transcriptome studies by Parker et al. [29], our results support the notion of the ECM being a key driver and regulator of fibrosis, causing a positive feedback loop between fibroblasts and the diseased ECM (Figure 7), which warrants further investigation. We hypothesized that the biomechanical properties and the composition of the ECM dictate the cellular response in human primary fibroblasts as reflected by the overall cellular response to a healthy and diseased matrix.

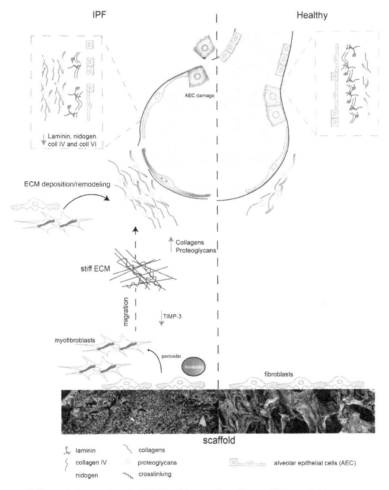

Figure 7. Cell-matrix interactions in IPF. Fibroblasts cultured on stiff IPF scaffolds secrete increased amounts of periostin, known to stimulate myofibroblast differentiation and migration. Increased synthesis of tenascin and reduced levels of metalloprotease inhibitors (TIMP-3) support migration and movement toward stiffer tissue. Fibroblasts become activated and generate increased deposition and build-up of collagens and proteoglycans (decorin, versican, and biglycan). Alveolar epithelial cell (AEC) damages causes basement membrane disruption and the loss of structural barriers. Fibroblasts on IPF scaffolds reduced their production of BM complexes (laminins, nidogens, and collagen IV), potentially hindering the rebuild of a functional BM for anchoring AEC.

We saw that fibroblasts cultured on stiff IPF scaffolds secreted increased amounts of periostin, known to stimulate myofibroblast differentiation and migration. This in combination with an increased synthesis of tenascin and reduced levels of metalloprotease inhibitors (TIMP-3) supports the migration of fibroblasts towards a stiffer ECM. The cells become activated and generate increased deposition and build-up of collagens and proteoglycans including decorin, versican, and biglycan. With the elevated levels of periostin, the incorporation of tenascin-C into the matrix may be facilitated as well as the formation of collagen fibrils, assisted by decorin. The IPF scaffolds have a clear disruption of the BM, which is thought to arise from alveolar epithelial cell (AEC) damages leading to the loss of structural barriers. This may promote transdifferentiation of epithelial cells to mesenchymal cells which in addition activates the progression of remodeling. Interestingly, fibroblasts on IPF scaffolds reduced their production of BM complexes (laminins, nidogens, and collagen IV), potentially hindering the rebuild of a functional BM for anchoring AEC. The continuation of fibroblast activation in combination with a disorganized BM seem to propagate changes in the matrisome properties, further promoting disease progression.

This study is separate from previously performed studies on pulmonary fibrotic lung tissue [12,29] as we focused on the distal lung properties of IPF, where this disease typically manifests itself with subpleural fibrotic formations. Furthermore, the advantage of our human 3D-model excludes the effect of resident cellular components of the parenchymal tissue characteristics and focuses on the cellular response of the ECM.

We have clearly demonstrated that the biomechanics and the matrisome composition of the IPF scaffolds are closely connected, which make up an intricate biological system controlling cellular behavior with the ability to sustain a profibrotic lung environment. To mimic the physiological conditions more closely and to maintain the complex structure of decellularized lung tissue during repopulation, a novel approach was implemented in this study through the application of scaffold holders, manufactured to mount lung tissue in order to impose a static stretch. By combining the biomechanical properties of a scaffold, linked with its own proteomic profile, unique matrisome properties were identified in IPF patients in comparison to healthy individuals. In a novel way of analyzing proteomic data, tissue density adjustments enabled an in-depth study of ECM turnover in IPF and healthy scaffolds by recognizing structural heterogenetic differences, which thereby separated the two types of tissues. The cellular responses studied in repopulated scaffolds identified the cell-matrix interactions as essential in the progression of IPF, emphasizing the BM and the underlying composition of ECM proteins as a possible disease mechanism in the induction of normal versus fibrotic tissue remodeling. We demonstrated that the IPF scaffolds had an enhanced content of proteoglycans and after the repopulation with healthy fibroblasts, we also distinguished a shift in the synthesis of proteoglycans, accompanied with a distinct localization of the tissue deposition. Together, these results further support that the existing cellular milieu alters fibroblast activity, promoting a profibrotic phenotype when cultured in a diseased matrix. More in-depth examinations with a larger number of patients on how specific ECM components may direct cellular activity are warranted to further elucidate how healthy cells become programed to synthesize a disease-like protein profile in a diseased ECM environment, studies which may lead to the unveiling of potential targets and biomarkers for IPF.

4. Materials and Methods

4.1. Decellularization of Lung Tissue Samples

Tissue samples for healthy controls originated from healthy human donor lungs, unusable for transplantation, or from an unaffected area in resection material (Table 1). The diagnosis of IPF was confirmed by clinicians with histological examination of explanted lungs that had reached end stage of disease, consistent with ERS and ATS criteria. Sample HL 4 showed no signs of pathological changes in the parenchymal tissue used for scaffold extraction.

Table 1. Patient and donor tissue information.

Sample ID	HL 1	HL 2	HL 3	HL 4	IPF 1	IPF 2	IPF 3	IPF 4
Group	Healthy	Healthy	Healthy	Healthy	IPF	IPF	IPF	IPF
Age	55	41	62	86	61	57	62	68
Gender	Female	Female	Male	Male	Female	Female	Female	Male
Smoking history	Yes	No	No	No	Yes	Yes	Yes	Yes
Non-lung disease				Alpha 1 anti-trypsin deficiency				
Lung disease	No	No	No	Squamous cell carcinoma *	IPF	IPF	IPF	IPF

* No COPD diagnosis. Tissue obtained from non-affected area.

Lung tissue was dissected for scaffold isolation within the first 24 h of surgical removal of explanted lungs. Adjacent to the pleura, cubic blocks (1 cm^3) of parenchymal tissue were dissected from peripheral regions of the lung (Figure 1A). Tissue blocks were immediately frozen in 2-methylbutane chilled with liquid nitrogen. After storage in −80 °C lung tissue was cryosectioned into 350 μm tissue slices with a HM-560 cryostat (Microm, Heidelberg, Germany). Antifreeze cryoprotective solution (30% v/v glycerol and 30% v/v ethylene glycol in 0.1 M sodium phosphate buffer) was used to maintain the integrity of the tissue at sectioning. Tissue slices were thawed on chilled D-PBS (Dublecco's phosphated buffer solution) (Invitrogen, Waltham, MA, USA) and treated for decellularization. Samples for histology were fixated and prepared as described below.

Tissue slices were decellularized according to Rosmark et al. [13]. In short, tissue was incubated with mild agitation in decellularization solution (8 mM CHAPS, 1 M NaCl, 25 mM EDTA in D-PBS) (1 mL/slice), with the solution replaced five times during the first 4 h of incubation. Tissue was stored overnight at +4 °C in D-PBS. The following day, tissue slices were rinsed with benzonase working buffer (20 mM Tris-HCl, 2 mM Mg^{2+}, 20 mM NaCl) prior to incubation with benzonase nuclease (Sigma-Aldrich, Saint Louis, MO, USA, cat. no. E1014) (90 U/mL, 1 mL/slice, 30 min at 37 °C). The decellularized tissue (scaffold) was rinsed and stored in D-PBS supplemented with amphotericin B (2.5 μg/mL), penicillin-streptomycin (1%) and gentamicin (50 μg/mL) at +4 °C. Randomly selected scaffolds from each tissue cube were used, which further introduced biological variability between the technical replicates.

4.2. Study Approval

Healthy donor lung tissue explants from Lund University hospital (Lund, Sweden) and lung samples from patients diagnosed with IPF were received from Sahlgrenska University hospital (Gothenburg, Sweden). The study was approved by ethical committees in Lund and Gothenburg, Sweden (Dnr. 413/2008, 2015-891, and 1026-15). Written informed consent was received from participants or the closest relative.

4.3. DNA Measurements

Decellularized lung tissue was quantified for residual double stranded DNA (dsDNA) using fluorescent nucleic acid staining (Thermo Fisher Scientific, P7589). Lung tissue slices were freeze dried and homogenized with 0.1 mm zirconia silica beads (Thermo Fisher Scientific, Waltham, MA, USA, cat.no. 3488) in a fast prep bead beater (MP fastprep96, Nordic Biolabs, Täby, Sweden). Samples were centrifuged at 6000× *g* for 3 min and supernatants were analyzed for dsDNA quantification according to manufacturer's instructions.

4.4. Tissue Density Measurements

For each individual within a group (i.e., biological replicates per group, $n = 4$), three technical replicates of scaffold samples were used. Scaffolds were first separately photographed to measure tissue area, using ImageJ software version 1.51n (NIH, Bethesda, MD, USA; http://imagej.nih.gov/ij) and subsequently freeze dried and weighed to calculate tissue density (mg/mm^3).

4.5. Mechanical Testing

Native tissue slices and decellularized scaffolds of equal size from healthy and IPF donor tissues ($n = 4$ biological replicates per group) were mounted in organ baths (emkaBATH4, emka Technologies, Paris, France) in D-PBS for mechanical testing. Tissue samples were mounted to triangular hooks with silk suture and original tissue length was measured (L_0). Tissues/scaffolds were then pre-loaded in tension with 350 mg by vertical elongation. After relaxation, the samples were loaded with a displacement corresponding to a strain of 5%, 10%, and 15% at a rate of 0.1 mm/s, and allowed to relax for 20 min between each sequential load step (sequential stress-relaxation). Finally, samples were tested in tension at a rate of 0.1 mm/s until they ruptured or reached a maximal additional 10 mm. The software iox 2.10.0.40 datanalystv2.6.1.18 was used for data acquisition. Tissue stiffness (N/m) was calculated from the linear region of the force displacement curve during the final tensile test, $k = \frac{F}{\delta}$, where F is the load [mN] and δ is the displacement. Ultimate force was the maximum load [mN] at failure i.e., physical breakage of the tissue.

4.6. Repopulation of Scaffolds with Primary Lung Fibroblasts Labeled with Heavy Arginine and Lysine

Human primary parenchymal lung fibroblasts were isolated from one healthy donor control lung as previously described [50]. Fibroblasts were expanded on regular culture flasks (Sarstedt, Nümbrecht, Germany, cat.no. 83.3910.002) in DMEM supplemented with amphotericin B (2.5 µg/mL), penicillin-streptomycin (1%), gentamicin (50 µg/mL), glutamine (1%), and 10% fetal clone serum (FCIII, Thermo Scientific) at 37 °C, 10% CO_2. Cells in passage 7 were trypsinized and resuspended in complete SILAC DMEM Flex Media (Life Technologies, Carlsbad, CA, USA, cat.no. A2493901) supplemented with 10% dialyzed serum (Gibco, A3382001), glucose (4500 µg/mL), amphotericin B (2.5 µg/mL), penicillin-streptomycin (1%), gentamicin (50 µg/mL), 1% Glutamax along with "heavy" $^{13}C_6$ labeled L-Arginine-HCl (Thermo Fisher Scientific, 88210) and "heavy" $^{13}C_6$ $^{15}N_2$-labeled L-lysine-2HCl (Thermo Fischer Scientific, 88209), as needed for optimal cell culture conditions. Fibroblasts were pre-cultured for 5 days on regular culture flasks in complete SILAC DMEM Media and scaffolds were pre-conditioned for 1 h with SILAC DMEM Media prior to re-population of scaffolds. In 24-well suspension culture plates (Sarstedt, cat.no. 83.3922.500) fibroblasts were seeded on scaffolds with mild agitation for 24 h at 10% CO_2, 37 °C. Culture media was analyzed for cellular content for the examination of cellular attachment to scaffolds. The cell seeded scaffolds were then mounted on scaffold holders (8 mm inner diameter), composed of polyoxymethylene and incubated for up to 9 days, based on previous data [13]. Culture medium was changed after 24 h, 3 days, and 6 days of incubation. Schematics of the experimental layout is provided in Figure 1A. Repopulated scaffolds were analyzed for cellular viability after 1, 3, and 9 days of incubation (biological replicates per group $n = 4$ with two technical replicates). Cell viability was analyzed with WST-1 (Roche, Basel, Switzerland) according to manufacturer's instructions. In brief, scaffolds were incubated at 37 °C at 10% CO_2 with WST-1 solution (diluted in 1:10 in cell culture medium). Color development in cell medium, corresponding to cellular metabolism, was measured at 450 nm.

4.7. LC-MS/MS Analysis

The extraction of proteins from decellularized and repopulated lung tissue scaffolds was modified after Rosmark et al. [13]. Instead of consecutive protein extraction we here performed one protein extraction procedure. The spanned tissue area of the scaffolds (decellularized or repopulated with heavy labeled cells) were lyophilized, diluted in extraction buffer with 100 mM ammonium bicarbonate with 8 M urea, and homogenized using a Bioruptor®Plus (Diagenode SA, Seraing, Belgium) at 4 °C for 20 cycles 15 s ON/OFF. Samples were reduced with 5 mM TCEP (tris-2-carboxyethyl phosphine) 30 min at 37 °C at 850 rpm, alkylated with 10 mM IAA (iodoacetamide) for 45 min at room temperature, followed by overnight trypsin digestion at 37 °C at 300 rpm. Decellularized scaffolds samples were desalted with C18 reversed-phase spin columns (Harvard Apparatus, Holliston, MA, USA) according to manufacturer's instructions, whereas repopulated scaffolds were desalted using SOLAµ™-SPE plates (Thermo Fisher Scientific) according to manufacturer's instructions.

After desalting, samples were resuspended in 2% acetonitrile, 0.1% formic acid and the peptide concentrations were measured using Pierce™ Quantitative Colorimetric Peptide Assay (Thermo Scientific, Rockford, IL, USA). For all samples we adjusted the volume to inject 1 µg peptides. Peptide separations and data acquisitions were performed as previously described [13]. Briefly samples were separated on a 25 cm EASY-spray column using an EASY-nLC 1000 LC-system (Thermo Fischer Scientific) using a gradient of 5%–30% buffer B over 60 min and 30%–95% buffer B for 5 min with a flow rate of 300 nL/min. Data were acquired with a Q Exactive Plus mass spectrometer (Thermo Fischer Scientific) using top-15 data dependent acquisition (DDA) where each full mass scan covered 400–1600 *m/z* at resolution 70,000 at 200 *m/z* for both MS and MS/MS scans. MS precursor values above 1.7×10^4 were required for triggering MS/MS scans. An automatic gain control (AGC) of 1×10^6 with ion accumulation time of 100 ms for MS scans and 60 ms for MS/MS was used.

Data Analysis

MaxQuant (version 1.5.3.30) was used for analysis of raw files. Searches were performed towards a reviewed UniProt human database with standard contaminants (downloaded 2015-11-17) in Andromeda. Enzyme specificity were set for trypsin with max two missed cleavages and a mass accuracy of 4.5 ppm for precursors and 20 ppm for fragment ions. Carbamidometylation was set as fixed modification and methionine oxidation as variable. For both proteins and peptides, a false discovery rate of 1% was used. The proteomics data was deposited to the ProteomeXchange Consortium via the PRIDE partner repository [51] with the dataset identifier (PXD012322). Adjusted intensity values were calculated by multiplying raw intensity with tissue density (μg/mm^3) specific for each patient to obtain intensity per mm^3. For repopulated scaffolds, the dry weight of cells is assumed to be negligible and adjusted with the same density as for the original scaffold.

4.8. Imaging

4.8.1. Scanning Electron Microscopy (SEM)

Scaffolds and native lung tissues were washed in Sorensen's phosphate buffer (0.1 M, pH 7.4) and fixed in 1.5% formaldehyde and 1.5% glutaraldehyde for 1 h. After washing with Sorensen's buffer, the samples were dehydrated with gradual increasing concentration of ethanol. Samples were critical point dried and sputtered with gold-palladium before being examined with electron microscopy Jeol JSM-7800F FEG-SEM at Lund University Bioimaging Center (LBIC).

4.8.2. Confocal Imaging

Cells were pre-stained with Cytopainter prior to cell seeding for 3D visualization of cell distribution. Cells were trypsinized, counted, and stained using CytoPainter Cell Proliferation Stain Deep Red (Abcam, ab176736) following manufacturer's protocol. Scaffolds were seeded as above and imaged after 1 day of culture using a Nikon Confocal A1 + microscope at LBIC. The scaffold was imaged by taking advantage of the autofluorescence, using 488 nm excitation.

4.8.3. Fixation, Paraffin Embedding, and Sectioning

At selected time points scaffolds were rinsed in PBS and fixated in 4% formaldehyde (VWR; Radnor, PA, USA) for 1 h, and subsequently dehydrated immediately (70% ethanol 1 h, 95% ethanol 1 h, 99.5% ethanol 30 min, 1:1 ethanol:xylene 15 min, xylene 30 min) or stored in PBS at 4 °C. Two changes of paraffin incubation at 60 °C (1 h and 30 min) were followed by embedding into paraffin blocks, from which 4 μm thick sections were produced. Repopulated scaffolds were processed in their scaffold holder to ensure stretched morphology, and the center was punched out with a biopsy punch prior to embedding.

4.8.4. Hematoxylin/Eosin Staining

After deparaffinization, hematoxylin/eosin staining was performed according to manufacturer's instructions (Mayer's hematoxylin, Histolab, Gothenburg, Sweden).

4.8.5. Immunohistochemistry (IHC), Immunofluorescence (IF)

After deparaffinization, heat-induced epitope retrieval was performed on a PT Tissue Link system (Histolab). IHC for collagen type IV, periostin, and decorin was performed using the EnVision Dual Link System (K4065, Dako, Glostrup, Denmark) according to manufacturer's instructions, including horse-radish peroxidase (HRP)-coupled secondary antibodies and counterstaining with Mayer's hematoxylin to visualize nuclei. IF for collagen type VI, biglycan, versican, vimentin, and vinculin was performed by incubation with primary antibodies for 1 h and with fluorochrome-coupled secondary antibodies (Thermo Fisher Scientific, 1:200) for 45 min. Sections were mounted with ProLong Gold Antifade Mountant with DAPI (Invitrogen) to visualize nuclei. Unspecific staining of the secondary antibodies was assessed by omitting the primary antibodies (negative control). For antigen retrieval and antibody-specifications see Table 2.

Table 2. Antibody specifications.

Antibody	Protein Group	Catalogue Number	Dilution	HIER	Method	Secondary Antibody
Collagen type IV ($\alpha 1/\alpha 2$)	Collagens	Abcam, ab6586	1:4000	low pH	IHC	HRP-coupled
Collagen type VI ($\alpha 1$)		Abcam, ab6588	1:1000	low pH	IF	A-21246
Decorin		Atlas Antibodies, HPA003315	1:1000	high pH	IHC	HRP-coupled
Biglycan	Proteoglycans	Atlas Antibodies, HPA003157	1:500	high pH	IF	A-21246
Versican		Atlas Antibodies, HPA004726	1:500	high pH	IF	A-21246
Periostin	Glycoprotein	Abcam, ab79946	1:1000	low pH	IHC	HRP-coupled
Vimentin	Cytoskeleton	R&D, AF2105	1:200	low pH	IF	A-21432
Vinculin	Focal adhesions	Sigma-Aldrich, HPA063777	1:100	low pH	IF	A-21246

HIER = heat induced epitope retrieval; HRP = horse-radish peroxidase; A = Alexa Fluor.

4.8.6. Image Acquisition

Images were obtained on a Zeiss fluorescence microscope (Nikon 4X NA 0.10 air, Nikon 10X NA 0.45 air) or with a VS120 virtual microscopy slide scanning system (Olympus, Tokyo, Japan, objectives Olympus 4X NA 0.16 air, Olympus 10X NA 0.4 air), either in brightfield mode (hematoxylin/eosin, IHC) or fluorescent mode (IF). From the scanned slides, representative images were acquired using the OlyVIA software 2.8 (Olympus). Exposure times, acquisition settings, and image brightness adjustments were done consistently for each respective staining including negative controls.

4.9. Statistics

Tissue stiffness and density were statistically analyzed with an unpaired *t*-test using software GraphPad Prism 7 (La Jolla, CA, USA). MS data were manually curated prior to statistical testing to remove single peptide hits, proteins with missing values for more than 25% per sample group for decellularized scaffolds, and proteins with 50% missing values for the repopulated samples groups.

RStudio version 1.1.442 (RStudio Team (2015). RStudio: Integrated Development for R. RStudio, Inc., Boston, MA, USA) was used for statistical analyses and for generation of heat maps, scatter plots, bar graphs, correlograms etc. Unsupervised hierarchical clustering was performed using the ward.D2 method and Euclidean distance for both row and column clusters. MS data were statistically analyzed with a Student's *t*-test and was followed by Benjamini–Hochberg correction for multiple testing of *p*-values. Statistical evaluation of single proteins was statistically analyzed with a Student's *t*-test treating each technical replicate as an individual data point.

5. Conclusions

We demonstrate how matrisome changes affect fibroblast activity using novel approaches to study temporal differences, where IPF scaffolds support a disorganized BM and upregulation of disease-associated proteins. These matrix-directed cellular responses emphasize the IPF matrisome and specifically the BM components as important factors for disease progression.

Supplementary Materials: Supplementary materials can be found at http://www.mdpi.com/1422-0067/20/16/4013/s1.

Author Contributions: L.E.R. and A.L. made substantial contributions to the study regarding design, acquisition, analysis, and interpretation of data, as well as composition of the written manuscript. E.A., C.M., G.W.-T. contributed to the design of the research study. E.A., C.M., B.M., conducted experiments. E.A., C.M., T.N., O.R., H.I., A.M., A.-K.L.-C., J.M. analyzed the data. All of the authors, including X.-H.Z., G.D., M.S., L.B., interpreted the data and revised the manuscript.

Funding: This research was funded by the Swedish Heart-Lung Foundation, grant number 20140293, the Swedish foundation for Strategic Research, grant number SBE13-0130, the Swedish research Council, grant number 2016-01190, the Royal Physiographic Society of Lund, the Olle Engkvist, the Crafoord Foundation, the Greta and John Kock Foundation, the Alfred Österlund Foundation, the Åke och Inger Bergkvist foundation, the Medical Faculty of Lund University and ALF.

Acknowledgments: We thank Oskar Hallgren (Lung medicine and Allergology, Lund University, Lund, Sweden) for his contribution to the collection and ethical approval for patient materials used in this study. We thank Sebastian Wasserström at LBIC Lund University Bioimaging center for his assistance at the SEM and confocal microscope and post-processing of images and Annika Nybom (Lung Biology) for her help with histology.

Conflicts of Interest: The authors have no conflicts of interest except for GD, who has research grants for two investigator initiated studies, one from Astellas A/S for the ScanCLAD study (ClinicalTrials.gov NCT02936505) and one from Abbott A/S for the SweVAD study (ClinicalTrials.gov, NCT02592499).

References

1. Richeldi, L.; Collard, H.R.; Jones, M.G. Idiopathic pulmonary fibrosis. *Lancet* **2017**, *389*, 1941–1952. [CrossRef]
2. Darby, I.A.; Laverdet, B.; Bonte, F.; Desmouliere, A. Fibroblasts and myofibroblasts in wound healing. *Clin. Cosmet. Investig. Dermatol.* **2014**, *7*, 301–311. [PubMed]
3. Mora, A.L.; Rojas, M.; Pardo, A.; Selman, M. Emerging therapies for idiopathic pulmonary fibrosis, a progressive age-related disease. *Nat. Rev. Drug Discov.* **2017**, *16*, 810. [CrossRef] [PubMed]
4. Andersson-Sjoland, A.; de Alba, C.G.; Nihlberg, K.; Becerril, C.; Ramirez, R.; Pardo, A.; Westergren-Thorsson, G.; Selman, M. Fibrocytes are a potential source of lung fibroblasts in idiopathic pulmonary fibrosis. *Int. J. Biochem. Cell Biol.* **2008**, *40*, 2129–2140. [CrossRef] [PubMed]
5. Liu, F.; Mih, J.D.; Shea, B.S.; Kho, A.T.; Sharif, A.S.; Tager, A.M.; Tschumperlin, D.J. Feedback amplification of fibrosis through matrix stiffening and COX-2 suppression. *J. Cell Biol.* **2010**, *190*, 693–706. [CrossRef] [PubMed]
6. Asano, S.; Ito, S.; Takahashi, K.; Furuya, K.; Kondo, M.; Sokabe, M.; Hasegawa, Y. Matrix stiffness regulates migration of human lung fibroblasts. *Physiol. Rep.* **2017**, *5*. [CrossRef] [PubMed]
7. Balestrini, J.L.; Niklason, L.E. Extracellular matrix as a driver for lung regeneration. *Ann. Biomed. Eng.* **2015**, *43*, 568–576. [CrossRef] [PubMed]

8. Jenkins, R.G.; Simpson, J.K.; Saini, G.; Bentley, J.H.; Russell, A.M.; Braybrooke, R.; Molyneaux, P.L.; McKeever, T.M.; Wells, A.U.; Flynn, A.; et al. Longitudinal change in collagen degradation biomarkers in idiopathic pulmonary fibrosis: An analysis from the prospective, multicentre PROFILE study. *Lancet Respir. Med.* **2015**, *3*, 462–472. [CrossRef]

9. Tian, Y.; Li, H.; Gao, Y.; Liu, C.; Qiu, T.; Wu, H.; Cao, M.; Zhang, Y.; Ding, H.; Chen, J.; et al. Quantitative proteomic characterization of lung tissue in idiopathic pulmonary fibrosis. *Clin. Proteom.* **2019**, *16*, 6. [CrossRef]

10. Ahrman, E.; Hallgren, O.; Malmstrom, L.; Hedstrom, U.; Malmstrom, A.; Bjermer, L.; Zhou, X.H.; Westergren-Thorsson, G.; Malmstrom, J. Quantitative proteomic characterization of the lung extracellular matrix in chronic obstructive pulmonary disease and idiopathic pulmonary fibrosis. *J. Proteomics* **2018**.

11. Spagnolo, P.; Tzouvelekis, A.; Bonella, F. The Management of Patients With Idiopathic Pulmonary Fibrosis. *Front. Med. (Lausanne)* **2018**, *5*, 148. [CrossRef] [PubMed]

12. Booth, A.J.; Hadley, R.; Cornett, A.M.; Dreffs, A.A.; Matthes, S.A.; Tsui, J.L.; Weiss, K.; Horowitz, J.C.; Fiore, V.F.; Barker, T.H.; et al. Acellular normal and fibrotic human lung matrices as a culture system for in vitro investigation. *Am. J. Respir. Crit. Care Med.* **2012**, *186*, 866–876. [CrossRef] [PubMed]

13. Rosmark, O.; Ahrman, E.; Muller, C.; Elowsson Rendin, L.; Eriksson, L.; Malmstrom, A.; Hallgren, O.; Larsson-Callerfelt, A.K.; Westergren-Thorsson, G.; Malmstrom, J. Quantifying extracellular matrix turnover in human lung scaffold cultures. *Sci. Rep.* **2018**, *8*, 5409. [CrossRef] [PubMed]

14. Naba, A.; Clauser, K.R.; Hoersch, S.; Liu, H.; Carr, S.A.; Hynes, R.O. The matrisome: In silico definition and in vivo characterization by proteomics of normal and tumor extracellular matrices. *Mol. Cell Proteomics* **2012**, *11*, M111.014647. [CrossRef]

15. LeBleu, V.S.; Macdonald, B.; Kalluri, R. Structure and function of basement membranes. *Exp. Biol. Med. (Maywood)* **2007**, *232*, 1121–1129. [CrossRef] [PubMed]

16. Santos, A.; Lagares, D. Matrix Stiffness: The Conductor of Organ Fibrosis. *Curr. Rheumatol. Rep.* **2018**, *20*, 2. [CrossRef]

17. Smithmyer, M.E.; Sawicki, L.A.; Kloxin, A.M. Hydrogel scaffolds as in vitro models to study fibroblast activation in wound healing and disease. *Biomater. Sci.* **2014**, *2*, 634–650. [CrossRef]

18. Jaffar, J.; Yang, S.H.; Kim, S.Y.; Kim, H.W.; Faiz, A.; Chrzanowski, W.; Burgess, J.K. Greater cellular stiffness in fibroblasts from patients with idiopathic pulmonary fibrosis. *Am. J. Physiol. Lung Cell Mol. Physiol.* **2018**, *315*, L59–L65. [CrossRef]

19. Hynes, R.O.; Naba, A. Overview of the matrisome–an inventory of extracellular matrix constituents and functions. *Cold Spring Harb. Perspect. Biol.* **2012**, *4*, a004903. [CrossRef] [PubMed]

20. Naba, A.; Clauser, K.R.; Ding, H.; Whittaker, C.A.; Carr, S.A.; Hynes, R.O. The extracellular matrix: Tools and insights for the "omics" era. *Matrix Biol.* **2016**, *49*, 10–24. [CrossRef]

21. Calle, E.A.; Hill, R.C.; Leiby, K.L.; Le, A.V.; Gard, A.L.; Madri, J.A.; Hansen, K.C.; Niklason, L.E. Targeted proteomics effectively quantifies differences between native lung and detergent-decellularized lung extracellular matrices. *Acta Biomater.* **2016**, *46*, 91–100. [CrossRef] [PubMed]

22. Katzenstein, A.L.; Mukhopadhyay, S.; Myers, J.L. Diagnosis of usual interstitial pneumonia and distinction from other fibrosing interstitial lung diseases. *Hum. Pathol.* **2008**, *39*, 1275–1294. [CrossRef] [PubMed]

23. Mendez, M.G.; Kojima, S.; Goldman, R.D. Vimentin induces changes in cell shape, motility, and adhesion during the epithelial to mesenchymal transition. *Faseb. J.* **2010**, *24*, 1838–1851. [CrossRef] [PubMed]

24. Cao, L.; Nicosia, J.; Larouche, J.; Zhang, Y.; Bachman, H.; Brown, A.C.; Holmgren, L.; Barker, T.H. Detection of an Integrin-Binding Mechanoswitch within Fibronectin during Tissue Formation and Fibrosis. *ACS Nano* **2017**, *11*, 7110–7117. [CrossRef] [PubMed]

25. Naik, P.K.; Bozyk, P.D.; Bentley, J.K.; Popova, A.P.; Birch, C.M.; Wilke, C.A.; Fry, C.D.; White, E.S.; Sisson, T.H.; Tayob, N.; et al. Periostin promotes fibrosis and predicts progression in patients with idiopathic pulmonary fibrosis. *Am. J. Physiol. Lung Cell Mol. Physiol.* **2012**, *303*, L1046–L1056. [PubMed]

26. Estany, S.; Vicens-Zygmunt, V.; Llatjo, R.; Montes, A.; Penin, R.; Escobar, I.; Xaubet, A.; Santos, S.; Manresa, F.; Dorca, J.; et al. Lung fibrotic tenascin-C upregulation is associated with other extracellular matrix proteins and induced by TGFbeta1. *BMC Pulm. Med.* **2014**, *14*, 120. [CrossRef] [PubMed]

27. Bhattacharyya, S.; Wang, W.; Morales-Nebreda, L.; Feng, G.; Wu, M.; Zhou, X.; Lafyatis, R.; Lee, J.; Hinchcliff, M.; Feghali-Bostwick, C.; et al. Tenascin-C drives persistence of organ fibrosis. *Nat. Commun.* **2016**, *7*, 11703. [CrossRef]

28. O'Dwyer, D.N.; Moore, B.B. The role of periostin in lung fibrosis and airway remodeling. *Cell Mol. Life. Sci.* **2017**, *74*, 4305–4314. [CrossRef]
29. Parker, M.W.; Rossi, D.; Peterson, M.; Smith, K.; Sikstrom, K.; White, E.S.; Connett, J.E.; Henke, C.A.; Larsson, O.; Bitterman, P.B. Fibrotic extracellular matrix activates a profibrotic positive feedback loop. *J. Clin. Investig.* **2014**, *124*, 1622–1635. [CrossRef]
30. Strieter, R.M. What differentiates normal lung repair and fibrosis? Inflammation, resolution of repair, and fibrosis. *Proc. Am. Thorac. Soc.* **2008**, *5*, 305–310. [CrossRef]
31. Petersen, T.H.; Calle, E.A.; Colehour, M.B.; Niklason, L.E. Matrix composition and mechanics of decellularized lung scaffolds. *Cells Tissues Organs* **2012**, *195*, 222–231. [CrossRef] [PubMed]
32. Nischt, R.; Schmidt, C.; Mirancea, N.; Baranowsky, A.; Mokkapati, S.; Smyth, N.; Woenne, E.C.; Stark, H.J.; Boukamp, P.; Breitkreutz, D. Lack of nidogen-1 and -2 prevents basement membrane assembly in skin-organotypic coculture. *J. Investig. Derm.* **2007**, *127*, 545–554. [CrossRef] [PubMed]
33. Morales-Nebreda, L.I.; Rogel, M.R.; Eisenberg, J.L.; Hamill, K.J.; Soberanes, S.; Nigdelioglu, R.; Chi, M.; Cho, T.; Radigan, K.A.; Ridge, K.M.; et al. Lung-specific loss of alpha3 laminin worsens bleomycin-induced pulmonary fibrosis. *Am. J. Respir. Cell Mol. Biol.* **2015**, *52*, 503–512. [CrossRef] [PubMed]
34. Hattori, N.; Carrino, D.A.; Lauer, M.E.; Vasanji, A.; Wylie, J.D.; Nelson, C.M.; Apte, S.S. Pericellular versican regulates the fibroblast-myofibroblast transition: A role for ADAMTS5 protease-mediated proteolysis. *J. Biol. Chem.* **2011**, *286*, 34298–34310. [CrossRef] [PubMed]
35. Kolb, M.; Margetts, P.J.; Sime, P.J.; Gauldie, J. Proteoglycans decorin and biglycan differentially modulate TGF-beta-mediated fibrotic responses in the lung. *Am. J. Physiol. Lung Cell Mol. Physiol.* **2001**, *280*, L1327–L1334. [CrossRef]
36. Bensadoun, E.S.; Burke, A.K.; Hogg, J.C.; Roberts, C.R. Proteoglycan deposition in pulmonary fibrosis. *Am. J. Respir. Crit. Care Med.* **1996**, *154*, 1819–1828. [CrossRef]
37. Westergren-Thorsson, G.; Hedstrom, U.; Nybom, A.; Tykesson, E.; Ahrman, E.; Hornfelt, M.; Maccarana, M.; van Kuppevelt, T.H.; Dellgren, G.; Wildt, M.; et al. Increased deposition of glycosaminoglycans and altered structure of heparan sulfate in idiopathic pulmonary fibrosis. *Intj. Biochem. Cell Biol.* **2017**, *83*, 27–38. [CrossRef]
38. Westergren-Thorsson, G.; Sime, P.; Jordana, M.; Gauldie, J.; Sarnstrand, B.; Malmstrom, A. Lung fibroblast clones from normal and fibrotic subjects differ in hyaluronan and decorin production and rate of proliferation. *Intj. Biochem. Cell Biol.* **2004**, *36*, 1573–1584. [CrossRef]
39. Vogel, V.; Sheetz, M. Local force and geometry sensing regulate cell functions. *Nat. Rev. Mol. Cell Biol.* **2006**, *7*, 265–275. [CrossRef]
40. Murray, M.E.; Mendez, M.G.; Janmey, P.A. Substrate stiffness regulates solubility of cellular vimentin. *Mol. Biol. Cell* **2014**, *25*, 87–94. [CrossRef]
41. Liu, F.; Lagares, D.; Choi, K.M.; Stopfer, L.; Marinkovic, A.; Vrbanac, V.; Probst, C.K.; Hiemer, S.E.; Sisson, T.H.; Horowitz, J.C.; et al. Mechanosignaling through YAP and TAZ drives fibroblast activation and fibrosis. *Am. J. Physiol. Lung Cell Mol. Physiol.* **2015**, *308*, L344–L357. [CrossRef]
42. Haak, A.J.; Tan, Q.; Tschumperlin, D.J. Matrix biomechanics and dynamics in pulmonary fibrosis. *Matrix Biol.* **2018**, *73*, 64–76. [CrossRef]
43. Melo, E.; Cardenes, N.; Garreta, E.; Luque, T.; Rojas, M.; Navajas, D.; Farre, R. Inhomogeneity of local stiffness in the extracellular matrix scaffold of fibrotic mouse lungs. *J. Mech. Behav. Biomed. Mater.* **2014**, *37*, 186–195. [CrossRef]
44. Li, Y.; Jiang, D.; Liang, J.; Meltzer, E.B.; Gray, A.; Miura, R.; Wogensen, L.; Yamaguchi, Y.; Noble, P.W. Severe lung fibrosis requires an invasive fibroblast phenotype regulated by hyaluronan and CD44. *J. Exp. Med.* **2011**, *208*, 1459–1471. [CrossRef]
45. McKeown, S.; Richter, A.G.; O'Kane, C.; McAuley, D.F.; Thickett, D.R. MMP expression and abnormal lung permeability are important determinants of outcome in IPF. *Eur. Respir. J.* **2009**, *33*, 77–84. [CrossRef]
46. Arpino, V.; Brock, M.; Gill, S.E. The role of TIMPs in regulation of extracellular matrix proteolysis. *Matrix Biol.* **2015**, *44–46*, 247–254. [CrossRef]
47. Pardo, A.; Cabrera, S.; Maldonado, M.; Selman, M. Role of matrix metalloproteinases in the pathogenesis of idiopathic pulmonary fibrosis. *Respir. Res.* **2016**, *17*, 23. [CrossRef]
48. Trebaul, A.; Chan, E.K.; Midwood, K.S. Regulation of fibroblast migration by tenascin-C. *Biochem. Soc. Trans.* **2007**, *35*, 695–697. [CrossRef]

49. Kii, I.; Nishiyama, T.; Li, M.; Matsumoto, K.; Saito, M.; Amizuka, N.; Kudo, A. Incorporation of tenascin-C into the extracellular matrix by periostin underlies an extracellular meshwork architecture. *J. Biol. Chem.* **2010**, *285*, 2028–2039. [CrossRef]

50. Hallgren, O.; Nihlberg, K.; Dahlback, M.; Bjermer, L.; Eriksson, L.T.; Erjefalt, J.S.; Lofdahl, C.G.; Westergren-Thorsson, G. Altered fibroblast proteoglycan production in COPD. *Respir. Res.* **2010**, *11*, 55. [CrossRef]

51. Vizcaino, J.A.; Deutsch, E.W.; Wang, R.; Csordas, A.; Reisinger, F.; Rios, D.; Dianes, J.A.; Sun, Z.; Farrah, T.; Bandeira, N.; et al. ProteomeXchange provides globally coordinated proteomics data submission and dissemination. *Nat. Biotechnol.* **2014**, *32*, 223–226. [CrossRef]

International Journal of
Molecular Sciences

Article

B-Cell Activating Factor Enhances Hepatocyte-Driven Angiogenesis via B-Cell CLL/Lymphoma 10/Nuclear Factor-KappaB Signaling during Liver Regeneration

Chia-Hung Chou [1], Cheng-Maw Ho [1], Shou-Lun Lai [1], Chiung-Nien Chen [1], Yao-Ming Wu [1], Chia-Tung Shun [2], Wen-Fen Wen [3] and Hong-Shiee Lai [1,4,*]

[1] Department of Surgery, National Taiwan University Hospital and National Taiwan University College of Medicine, Taipei 10002, Taiwan; ch640124@gmail.com (C.-H.C.); miningho@ntu.edu.tw (C.-M.H.); Sauron_lai@hotmail.com (S.-L.L.); cnchen@ntu.edu.tw (C.-N.C.); wyaoming@gmail.com (Y.-M.W.)
[2] Departments of Forensic Medicine and Pathology, College of Medicine, National Taiwan University, Taipei 10617, Taiwan; ctshun@ntu.edu.tw
[3] Departments of Pathology, College of Medicine, National Taiwan University, Taipei 10617, Taiwan; wenwenfen@gmail.com
[4] Department of Surgery, Hualien Tzu Chi Hospital, Buddhist Tzu Chi Medical Foundation, Hualien 97002, Taiwan
[*] Correspondence: hslai@ntu.edu.tw; Tel.: +886-2-2312-3456-9561 (ext. 65112); Fax: +886-2-2388-4277

Received: 13 August 2019; Accepted: 9 October 2019; Published: 10 October 2019

Abstract: B-cell activating factor (BAFF) is found to be associated with the histological severity of nonalcoholic steatohepatitis (NASH). BAFF was also found to have a protective role in hepatic steatosis via down regulating the expression of steatogenesis genes and enhancing steatosis in hepatocytes through BAFF-R. However, the roles of BAFF during liver regeneration are not well defined. In this study, C57/B6 mice with 70% partial hepatectomy were used as a liver regeneration model. BAFF expression was determined by enzyme immunoassay, and anti-BAFF-neutralizing antibodies were administered to confirm the effects of BAFF on liver regeneration. Western blotting, immunohistochemistry, and florescence staining determined the expression of B-cell CCL/lymphoma 10 (BCL10). The angiogenesis promoting capability was evaluated after the transfection of cells with siRNA targeting BCL10 expression, and the role of NF-κB was assessed. The results revealed that the BAFF and BCL10 levels were upregulated after partial hepatectomy. Treatment with anti-BAFF-neutralizing antibodies caused death in mice that were subjected to 70% partial hepatectomy within 72 h. In vitro, recombinant BAFF protein did not enhance hepatocyte proliferation; however, transfection with BCL10 siRNA arrested hepatocytes at the G2/M phase. Interestingly, conditioned medium from BAFF-treated hepatocytes enhanced angiogenesis and endothelial cell proliferation. Moreover, Matrix metalloproteinase-9 (MMP-9), Fibroblast growth factor 4 (FGF4), and Interleukin-8 (IL-8) proteins were upregulated by BAFF through BCL10/NF-κB signaling. In mice that were treated with anti-BAFF-neutralizing antibodies, the microvessel density (MVD) of the remaining liver tissues and liver regeneration were both reduced. Taken together, our study demonstrated that an increased expression of BAFF and activation of BCL10/NF-κB signaling were involved in hepatocyte-driven angiogenesis and survival during liver regeneration.

Keywords: B-cell activating factor (BAFF); B-cell CLL/lymphoma 10 (BCL10); angiogenesis; liver regeneration; 70% partial hepatectomy

---

1. Introduction

The liver is a unique organ with the ability to completely regenerate to the original size after massive loss. Seventy percent partial hepatectomy is the standard model for studying normal liver regeneration. [1] The orchestrated complex process involves a cytokine, growth factor, and metabolic network [2], among which the cytokine network is initiated through the binding of tumor necrosis factor (TNF) to TNF receptor 1 (TNFR1), which leads to the activation of nuclear factor (NF)-κB in nonparenchymal cells, the production of interleukin (IL)-6, and the activation of signal transducer and activator of transcription 3 (STAT3) in hepatocytes [2]. In fact, TNFR1$^{-/-}$ mice showed delayed regeneration attributed to inefficient activation of NF-κB [3].

Restoration of liver mass involves the proliferation of hepatocytes and nonparenchymal cells. Angiogenesis is essential for successful liver regeneration. [4–7] Mutual growth-regulatory signaling interactions between hepatocytes and endothelial cells during liver regeneration after 70% partial hepatectomy involve vascular endothelial growth factor (VEGF), IL-6, transforming growth factor (TGF) α, fibroblast growth factor (FGF) 1, and hepatocyte growth factor (HGF) [5]. Thus, interactions of multiple pathways during liver regeneration are evolutionarily preserved for host survival.

B-cell activating factor (BAFF) is a type II transmembrane glycoprotein that belongs to the TNF super family [8]. BAFF-mediated signaling involves B-cell CCL/lymphoma 10 (BCL10) nuclear translocation, changes in phospho-AKT levels, and NF-κB transactivity [9,10]. BCL10-related signaling controls the growth of cervical cancer cells via NF-κB-dependent cyclin D1 regulation [11]. Three BAFF receptors (BAFF-R, transmembrane activator and CAML interactor (TACI), and B-cell maturation antigen (BCMA)), which can specifically activate B lymphocytes and promote their proliferation, have been identified [12].

The clinical significance of BAFF is found with serum BAFF levels in patients with nonalcoholic steatohepatitis (NASH) patients had higher levels than patients with simple steatosis; meanwhile, the histological findings also demonstrated that higher BAFF levels were associated with the presence of hepatocyte ballooning and advanced fibrosis [13]. Furthermore, BAFF was also found to have a protective role in hepatic steatosis via down regulating the expression of steatogenesis genes and enhancing steatosis in hepatocytes through BAFF-R [14]. However, the role of BAFF in liver regeneration has not yet been fully elucidated.

Accordingly, we hypothesize that BAFF might play a role in liver regeneration after 70% partial hepatectomy. In this study, we investigated the role of BAFF in liver regeneration. Our findings provided important insights into the role of BAFF in angiogenesis and liver regeneration.

2. Results

2.1. Relationship between Increased Expression of BAFF and BCL10 and Survival during Liver Regeneration

BAFF levels in liver tissue were significantly increased at 6 h after partial hepatectomy and peaked at 16 h. However, these changes in BAFF levels were not detected in the serum (Figure 1A). As BCL10 is involved in BAFF-mediated signaling, we then evaluated the status of BCL10 in liver tissues. Western blotting (Figure 1B) and corresponding quantitative results revealed that BCL10 expression was significantly enhanced 24 h after partial hepatectomy in regenerative remnant liver tissues. Moreover, IHC confirmed these findings and showed that BCL10 expression was elevated in regenerative remnant liver tissues (Figure 1C).

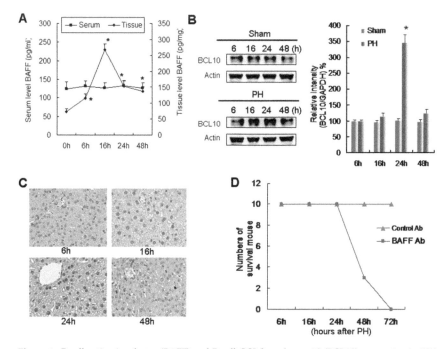

Figure 1. B-cell activating factor (BAFF) and B-cell CCL/lymphoma 10 (BCL10) expression in 70% partial hepatectomy-induced liver regeneration in mice. (**A**) Serum and tissue levels of BAFF were estimated by EIA at the indicated times after 70% partial hepatectomy. Data are presented as means ± SDs, and comparisons were made between each time and time zero. $n = 6$. * $p < 0.05$, by two-way ANOVA with Tukey's post hoc test. (**B**) Left panel, expression levels of BCL10 at different times in liver tissues from control or 70% partial hepatectomy (PH) groups were determined by western blotting; Acin was used as loading control. Right panel, the quantitative results of BCL10 western blotting. Data are presented as the relative intensity (BCL10/Actin) ± SD. Comparisons were made between the control and PH groups. $n = 6$. * $p < 0.05$, by Student's *t*-test. (**C**) Tissue BCL10 staining (brown color) of remnant liver tissues. Magnification, 400×. (**D**) Mice were intraperitoneally injected with 100 μg control IgG (Control Ab) or anti-mouse BAFF-neutralizing antibodies (BAFF Ab) at the time of 70% PH. The number of surviving mice was calculated at different times after 70% PH. $n = 10$ per group.

Mice were intraperitoneally injected with 100 μg anti-mouse BAFF-neutralizing antibodies after 70% partial hepatectomy to clarify the role of BAFF expression in liver regeneration. We found that treatment with anti-BAFF-neutralizing antibodies, but not control IgG, caused death in mice that were subjected to 70% partial hepatectomy within 72 h (Figure 1D). These results demonstrated that BAFF was essential for survival during liver regeneration.

2.2. BAFF/BCL10 Signaling Plays an Important Role in Hepatocyte Proliferation

The role of BAFF/BCL10 signaling in hepatocytes is not well defined. Therefore, we used the normal human embryonic liver cell line CL-48 cells [15] to evaluate the BAFF/BCL10 signaling pathway. We first determined the BAFF receptor expression in the CL-48 cells (Figure 2A) via comparing with PBMC, which was used as BAFF receptor positive expression control. The results demonstrated that the BAFF receptor is expressed in CL-48 hepatocytes. CL-48 cells were treated with recombinant BAFF, and BCL10 expression was determined by immunofluorescence staining. BCL10 was visibly upregulated and localized to the hepatocyte nuclei (Figure 2B). BCL10 siRNA was used to knockdown BCL10 to further clarify the role of BAFF/BCL10 signaling (Figure 2C). First, we determined the effects of BAFF and BCL10 on hepatocyte growth. The results demonstrated that BAFF did not enhance the growth of hepatocytes. However, transfection with BCL10 siRNA significantly inhibited the growth of hepatocytes (Figure 2D). Moreover, flow cytometric analysis showed that transfection with BCL10 siRNA caused a significant arrest of cells in the G_2/M phase of the cell cycles (Figure 2E).

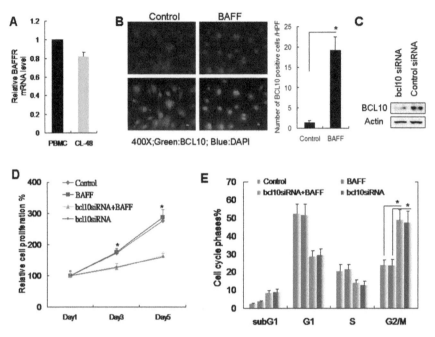

Figure 2. BAFF/BCL10 signaling in hepatocye cell proliferation. (**A**) The expression of BAFFR mRNA in human CL-48 hepatocytes was determined by q-Reverse Transcription Polymerase Chain Reaction (q-RT-PCR); commercialized human peripheral blood mononuclear cells (PBMC) cDNA was used as the positive control. (**B**) Left panel, human CL-48 hepatocytes were treated without (control) or with BAFF (1 ng/mL) for 1 h, and the expression of BCL10 was determined by immunofluorescence staining; BCL10 was identified as a green signal, and the nucleus was stained with DAPI (blue). Magnification, 400×. Right panel, the number of BCL10 positive cells was counted under high power field (HPF). $n = 6$. * $p < 0.05$, by Student's *t*-test. (**C**) CL-48 cells were treated with control or with BCL10 siRNA for 24 h; the expression of BCL10 was determined by western blotting. Actin was used as the loading control. (**D**) CL-48 cells were treated with control or BCL10 siRNA for 24 h prior treatment with BAFF (1 ng/mL). At different time points, relative cell proliferation was determined by the Trypan blue exclusion assay. The data are shown as mean ± SD of three independent experiments. Comparisons were made between the BAFF and bcl10siRNA + BAFF groups. * $p < 0.05$, by Student's *t*-test. (**E**) CL-48 cells were treated as indicated with BCL10 siRNA or BAFF, as described in (**D**). On day 3, the cell cycle phases were determined by propidium iodide staining and FACScan analysis. Populations of cells in the sub-G_1, G_1, S, and G_2/M phases were analyzed and quantified while using the Cell Quest software, and the data represent the means ±SDs of three independent experiments. Between-group comparisons were performed as indicated. * $p < 0.05$, by Student's *t*-test.

2.3. BAFF Promoted Hepatocyte-Mediated Angiogenesis

The liver is a vessel-rich organ; the capability of hepatocytes to undergo angiogenesis is critical for the maintenance of liver function. TNF-α, a potent inhibitor of endothelial cell growth in vitro, is angiogenic in vivo. Therefore, we next evaluated the role of BAFF in angiogenesis in hepatocytes while using in vitro angiogenesis assays with HUVECs. The results demonstrated that, when compared with the control group, CM from BAFF-stimulated hepatocytes induced gap formation and permeability changes (Figure 3A), migration (Figure 3B), tube formation on matrix gel (Figure 3C), and proliferation (Figure 3D) of endothelial cells. However, none of these effects were observed when CM from BCL10 siRNA-transfected hepatocytes (with or without BAFF treatment) was applied. These results demonstrated that BAFF stimulation might promote hepatocyte-driven angiogenesis.

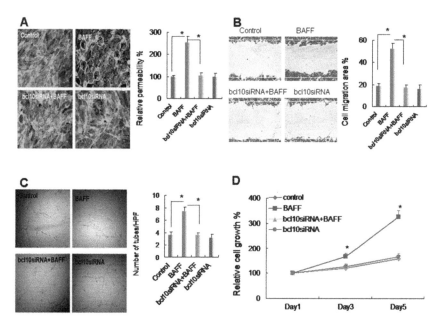

Figure 3. Effects of conditioned medium derived from BAFF-stimulated hepatocytes on angiogenesis. Conditioned medium from BAFF-stimulated CL-48 cells was used for angiogenic function assays. Four experimental conditions were used: control, the conditioned medium was collected from hepatocytes without any treatment; BAFF group, conditioned medium was from BAFF (1 ng/mL)-stimulated hepatocytes; BCL10siRNA+BAFF group, conditioned medium was from BCL10 siRNA-transfected hepatocytes following BAFF stimulation; and BCL10siRNA group, conditioned medium was from BCL10 siRNA-transfected hepatocytes. All conditioned medium was collected after 24 h culture. (**A**) **Left panel**, confluent and Human Umbilical Vein Endothelial Cell (HUVEC) monolayers were treated with conditioned medium for 1 h, and gap formation was determined by phalloidin staining. **Right panel**, conditioned medium from the indicated conditions was tested with HUVEC monolayers for 1 h using permeability assays. Data are shown as the relative permeability percentages, with the control conditioned medium in lane 1 defined as 100%. Comparisons are shown between the indicated groups. * $p < 0.05$. $n = 5$, by one-way ANOVA with Tukey's post hoc test. (**B**) Left panel, HUVECs were treated with conditioned medium for 6 h for migration assays, and representative images of migrated HUVECs in each group are shown. Right panel, quantitative results of migrated HUVECs was used to calculate the cell migration area. Comparisons are shown between the indicated groups. * $p < 0.05$. $n = 5$, by one-way ANOVA with Tukey's post hoc test. (**C**) **Left panel**, HUVECs were treated with conditioned medium for 6 h for capillary tube formation assays, and representative images of tube formation in each group are shown. **Right panel**, quantitative results of tube formation was calculated under high-power fields. Comparisons are shown between the indicated groups. * $p < 0.05$. $n = 5$, by one-way ANOVA with Tukey's post hoc test. (**D**) HUVECs were treated with conditioned medium for 1–5 days for cell growth determination by Trypan blue exclusion assays. Data are the relative cell growth percentages for the indicated conditions, with the control group in lane 1 defined as 100%. $n = 5$. Comparisons were made between the BAFF and bcl10siRNA+BAFF groups. * $p < 0.05$, by Student's *t*-test.

2.4. BAFF/BCL10/NF-κB Signaling in Hepatocytes Enhanced the Expression of Angiogenesis-Related Factors

Various factors promote angiogenesis. In this study, we used a commercial protein array to identify BAFF/BCL10-activated angiogenesis-related factors in CM from hepatocytes. The results of the array (Figure 4A,B) revealed that MMP-9, FGF4, and IL-8 were upregulated in CM from BAFF-stimulated hepatocytes when compared with those in the control cells and cells transfected with bcl10 siRNA following BAFF stimulation. Thus, BAFF/BCL10 activated the angiogenesis-related factors MMP-9, FGF4, and IL-8 in hepatocytes, resulting in increased levels in CM.

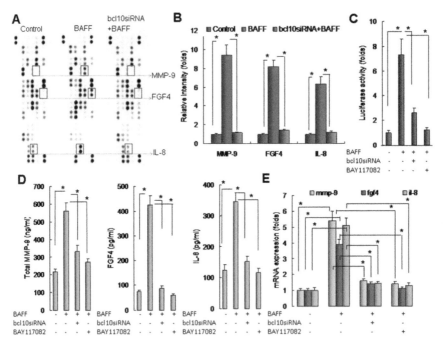

Figure 4. BAFF stimulated Matrix metalloproteinase-9 (MMP-9), Fibroblast growth factor 4 (FGF4), and Interleukin-8 (IL-8) expression in hepatocytes. (**A**) Conditioned medium from the three experimental conditions was applied to protein array analysis for identification of angiogenesis-related factors. Four experimental conditions were used: control, the conditioned medium was collected from hepatocytes without any treatment; BAFF group, conditioned medium was from BAFF (1 ng/mL)-stimulated hepatocytes; bcl10siRNA+BAFF group, conditioned medium was from bcl10 siRNA-transfected hepatocytes following BAFF stimulation; and bcl10 siRNA group, conditioned medium was from bcl10 siRNA-transfected hepatocytes. All conditioned medium was collected after 24 h of culture. Data shown are representative images of three independent experiments. Significantly altered protein spots are indicated. (**B**) Quantitative results for MMP-9, FGF4, and IL-8. Results are the relative intensity of spots from the angiogenesis protein arrays. $n = 3$. * $P < 0.05$, by Student's *t*-test. (**C**) CL-48 cells were transfected with an NF-κB binding site-driven luciferase plasmid and then transfected with bcl10 siRNA for 24 h or treated with BAY117082 (100 nM, for 1 h and then depleted the BAY117082 contained medium by twice wish with culture medium), following treatment with recombinant BAFF (1 ng/mL). After 4 h, NF-κB promoter activities were determined. Data are compared with that from lane 1. $n = 5$. * $P < 0.05$, by one-way ANOVA with Tukey's post hoc test. (**D**) CL-48 cells were transfected with BCL10 siRNA for 24 h or treated with BAY117082 (100 nM, for 1 h and then depleted the BAY117082 contained medium by

twice wish with culture medium), following treatment with recombinant BAFF (1 ng/mL). After 24 h, the protein levels of total MMP-9, FGF4 and IL-8 in the cell culture supernatants were determined by EIAs. Data are compared with that from lane 1. $n = 5$. * $P < 0.05$, by one-way ANOVA with Tukey's post hoc test. (**E**) CL-48 cells were transfected with BCL10 siRNA for 24 h or treated with BAY117082 (100 nM, for 1 h and then depleted the BAY117082 contained medium by twice wish with culture medium), following treatment with recombinant BAFF (1 ng/mL). After 8 h, mmp-9, fgf4 and il-8 mRNA levels were determined by qRT-PCR. Data are compared with that from lane 1. $n = 5$. * $P < 0.05$, by one-way ANOVA with Tukey's post hoc test.

BAFF/BCL10 signaling has been found to be involved in NF-κB activation, and MMP-9, FGF4, and IL-8 are regulated by NF-κB. Therefore, we further investigated the roles of BAFF/BCL10/NF-κB signaling in hepatocytes while using NF-κB binding site-driven luciferase assays; the results revealed that BAFF significantly increased NF-κB activity and that the induction of NF-κB was significantly reduced by transfection with bcl10 siRNA or the NF-κB chemical inhibitor BAY117082 (Figure 4C). The results demonstrated the importance of BAFF/BCL10/NF-κB signaling in hepatocytes.

Next, we determined the effects of BAFF on MMP-9, FGF4, and IL-8 induction and the role of BAFF/BCL10/NF-κB signaling in determining MMP-9, FGF4, and IL-8 protein (Figure 4D) and mRNA expression (Figure 4E) in hepatocytes. The results demonstrated that BAFF significantly enhanced MMP-9, FGF4, and IL-8 protein and mRNA expression, whereas transfection with bcl10 siRNA and treatment with BAY117082 significantly blocked these changes in MMP-9, FGF4, and IL-8 expression. Accordingly, we concluded that BAFF enhanced angiogenesis in hepatocytes by promoting the expression of angiogenesis-related factors through a pathway involving BCL10 and NF-κB signaling.

2.5. Downregulation of BAFF Reduced Angiogenesis and Hepatocyte Proliferation in a Liver Regeneration Model

Based on our in vitro study, we clarified the role of BAFF during liver regeneration by the administration of anti-BAFF-neutralizing antibodies to liver regeneration model mice that were subjected to 70% partial hepatectomy. After 48 h, the mice were sacrificed and the remaining liver tissues were dissected to identify the vessels positive for CD31 (Figure 5A; upper panel), an immunohistochemical marker of endothelial cells, and for Ki67 (Figure 5A; lower panel), a marker of cell proliferation. The quantitative result revealed that, when compared to the control group, mice that were treated with anti-BAFF-neutralizing antibodies showed reduced microvessel density (MVD), which corroborates the CD31-positive staining profiles (Figure 5B). Moreover, when compared to the control group, mice that were administered with anti-BAFF-neutralizing antibodies showed reduced Ki67 staining and liver regeneration (Figure 5C). Furthermore, as mentioned above, the level of MMP-9, an important angiogenic factor regulated by BAFF in the in vitro hepatocyte model, was determined in the remaining liver tissues. The results revealed that the administration of anti-BAFF-neutralizing antibodies significantly reduced the MMP-9 levels in liver tissue (Figure 5D). The results demonstrated that BAFF expression was involved in angiogenesis and hepatocyte proliferation in vivo. Please confirm that this is correct.

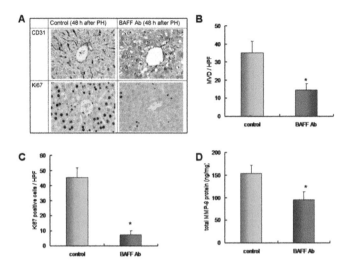

Figure 5. Microvessel density, cell proliferation, and MMP-9 expression in liver tissue of BAFF-neutralizing antibodies treated mice. (**A**) Mice were injected intraperitoneally with 100 µg control IgG or anti-mouse BAFF-neutralizing antibodies after 70% partial hepatectomy. After 48 h, mice were sacrificed, and the remaining liver tissues were dissected and stained for CD31 and Ki67. Magnification, 400×. (**B**) Quantitative results of microvessel density in remaining liver tissue, $n = 10$ per group. * $p < 0.05$, by Student's *t*-test. (**C**) Quantitative results of Ki67 positive staining cells in remaining liver tissue, $n = 10$ per group. * $p < 0.05$, by Student's *t*-test. (**D**) MMP-9 protein level in remaining liver tissue was determined by EIA, $n = 10$ per group. * $p < 0.05$, by Student's *t*-test.

In summary, our findings suggested that BAFF expression was involved in hepatocyte-driven angiogenesis in liver regeneration, as illustrated in Figure 6.

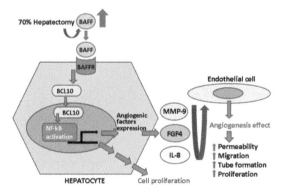

Figure 6. Summary of BAFF in liver regeneration. In this study, we found that BAFF was induced in the remaining liver tissue after 70% partial hepatectomy. Since BAFFR was found to be expressed in hepatocytes, we assumed the BAFF activated BCL10 nuclear translocation through BAFFR. BCL10 nuclear translocation subsequently activated NF-κB-dependent gene expression, including cell proliferation, as consistent with a previous study.[11] Interestingly, we found that BAFF may enhance the expression of factors that promote gap formation, permeability changes, migration, tube formation on matrix gel, and endothelial cell proliferation. Moreover, we found the BAFF/BCL10/NF-κB cascade activated the angiogenesis-related factors MMP-9, FGF4, and IL-8. The results demonstrated that BAFF expression was critically involved in hepatocyte-driven angiogenesis during liver regeneration.

Int. J. Mol. Sci. **2019**, *20*, 5022

3. Discussion

BAFF binds to the BAFF receptor to control B-cell differentiation into plasma cells and promote B-cell survival by activating the NF-κB and phosphoinositol 3-kinase/AKT pathways [16]. BAFF is induced by the nongenomic signaling of dioxin in the livers of C57BL/6 mice and HepG2 human hepatoma cells, and BAFF expression significantly contributes to early stress response reaction [17]. In this study, we observed that BAFF was upregulated in the remaining liver tissues after partial hepatectomy, which suggests that BAFF expression might be an important signal for liver regeneration. Although serum BAFF levels were not significantly increased, the local effects of BAFF in the liver tissue may be sufficient to affect regeneration signaling.

The survival of mature resting B cells in the periphery depends on signaling from the B-cell receptor and BAFF of the TNF receptor family. BCL10 promotes NF-κB activity, which contributes to B-cell survival through activation of the inhibitor of NF-κB kinase complex via Carma1 and mucosa-associated lymphoid tissue lymphoma translocation gene 1 and increases the expression of survival genes by directly modifying the chromatin of NF-κB target gene promoters. [18,19] Increased NF-κB activity and elevated cyclin D1 expression are critical for hepatocyte proliferation. [20] In this study, the CL-48 cells were treated with recombinant BAFF, and BAFF/BCL10 signaling was assessed by the detection of BCL10 nuclear translocation. However, there were no significant changes in CL-48 cell proliferation in response to BAFF treatment. In contrast, when CL-48 cells were transfected with BCL10 siRNA, cell growth retardation and cell cycle arrest at G_2/M phase were observed. Thus, BCL10 might trigger cell proliferation signaling without BAFF activation. Consistent with this, BCL10 controls the growth of cervical cancer cells via NF-κB-dependent cyclin D1 regulation in cervical cancer cells [11].

Serum BAFF levels have been shown to correlate with parameters of disease activity, such as bone marrow microvascular density and proliferating cell nuclear antigen expression, in patients with myeloma [21]. The inhibition of BAFF expression might have therapeutic applications because of its effects on angiogenesis in human multiple myeloma [22]. In MH7A synovial cells, TNF-α-induced BAFF expression controls VEGF-mediated angiogenesis by increasing the transcription and activity of VEGF [23]. In this study, we observed that CM from BAFF-stimulated CL-48 cells promoted angiogenesis, a process that is essential for liver regeneration. sFlt-1, which is a soluble receptor for VEGF, acts as a dominant-negative receptor and it has been shown to suppress sinusoidal endothelial cell growth and reduce remnant hepatic weight [24]. Immune cells also have important roles in liver regeneration. Indeed, in mice lacking the monocyte adhesion molecule CD11b, partial hepatectomy resulted in severe reduction in angiogenesis and the development of unstable, leaky vessels, eventually producing an aberrant hepatic vascular network and Küpffer cell distribution [25].

In this study, by using an angiogenesis-related protein array, we identified the BAFF-regulated angiogenesis factors MMP-9, FGF4, and IL-8. We also confirmed the transcriptional and translational regulation of MMP-9 and IL-8 through BAFF/BCL10/NF-kB signaling in hepatocytes. Importantly, the angiogenic role of MMP-9 was first identified in homozygous mice with a null mutation in the gene encoding MMP-9/gelatinase B, which revealed an abnormal pattern of skeletal growth plate vascularization and ossification. Additionally, growth plates from gelatinase B-null mice in culture showed a delayed release of angiogenic activators, demonstrating a role of MMP-9 in angiogenesis control [26]. A stress-induced increase in MMP-9 expression are critical for recruitment of human CD34+ progenitors with hematopoietic and/or hepatic-like potential to the livers of NOD/SCID mice [27]. In MMP-9-knockout mice, a delayed hepatic regenerative response after partial hepatectomy was observed [28], highlighting the importance of MMP-9 in liver regeneration. IL-8 is a cytokine that acts as a chemoattractant for lymphocytes and neutrophils. The role of IL-8 in angiogenesis was first demonstrated in a rabbit corneal pocket model, where IL-8 induced neovascularization [29]. The angiogenic role of IL-8 is also evident by its ability to induce proliferation and chemotaxis in HUVECs [30]. In humans, after liver surgery, IL-8 is produced in the remaining liver [31]. Notably, NF-κB regulates the expression of both MMP-9 and IL-8 [32,33]. Consistent with this, in the current study, we also confirmed the role of NF-κB in BAFF/BCL10 signaling by promoter assays and chemical inhibition.

The results demonstrated that the BAFF/BCL10/NF-κB signaling pathway was active in hepatocytes and it was involved in modulating the expression of angiogenesis-related factors. We also found that the inhibition of BAFF expression reduced angiogenesis and hepatocyte proliferation in a liver regeneration model. Thus, these results again confirmed the role of BAFF in liver regeneration and suggested that drugs targeting the BAFF/BCL10/NF-κB signaling pathway should be carefully used in patients with liver regeneration-related conditions.

Importantly, one limitation of this study was the lack of human tissue validation in regenerating liver based on the critical roles of BAFF/BCL10 in angiogenesis in animal models. Thus, further studies are required to investigate the potential interactions between BAFF/BCL10 and IL-6 signaling pathways, both of which involve activation of NF-κB.

In this study, although the HUVECs model demonstrated the role of BAFF in angiogenesis in hepatocytes, HUVECs are quite different than liver sinusoidal endothelial cells (LSECs). LSECs represent a permeable barrier which representing the interface between blood cells on the one side and hepatocytes and hepatic stellate cells on the other side are highly specialized endothelial cells. Furthermore, the absence of diaphragm and lack of basement membrane make LSECs the most permeable endothelial cells of the mammalian body [34]. It is worthy to investigate the BAFF promoted hepatocyte-driven angiogenesis in LSECs.

In conclusion, the increased expression of BAFF and activation of BCL10/NF-κB signaling were critically involved in hepatocyte-driven angiogenesis and survival during liver regeneration.

4. Materials and Methods

4.1. Animals and Grouping

Male C57/B6 mice weighing approximately 25 g were used in this study. The mice were sacrificed at 0, 6, 16, 24, and 48 h after hepatectomy. All animal use protocols were reviewed and approved by the Institutional Animal Care and Use Committee (IACUC) of National Taiwan University College of Medicine and College (IACUC Approval No: 20140146).

4.2. Surgical Procedures

All the mice were subjected to inhalational anesthesia by isoflurane (2-chloro-2-[difluoromethoxy] -1,1,1-trifluoroethane). A midline laparotomy was performed. Partial hepatectomy was then carried out while using aseptic extirpation of the median and left lateral lobes (around 70%). The removed liver sample was immediately weighed. Laparotomy with the manipulation of the liver was carried out in sham-operated mice.

4.3. Tissue Processing

The animals were anesthetized with isoflurane, blood samples were collected via cardiac puncture for serum isolation, and the remaining livers were immediately removed. Part of the liver was fixed in 10% neutral-buffered formalin, embedded in paraffin, and sectioned for immunohistochemistry (IHC). The other liver tissue was used fresh for total protein extraction for BAFF determination by enzyme-linked immunosorbent assays (ELISAs) or for BCL10 determination by western blot analysis. Proteins were extracted while using Cell Lysis (Total Protein Extraction) buffer (Thermo Fisher Scientific, Waltham, MA, USA).

4.4. Immunohistochemical Staining and Quantification

Slides were rehydrated in phosphate-buffered saline (PBS) for 15 min., and endogenous peroxidases were inhibited by treatment with 3% H_2O_2/methanol for 10 min. at room temperature (25 °C). For blocking, 5% nonfat milk/PBS was used for 30 min. at room temperature. Slides were incubated with anti-BCL10(sc-5273, dilution used 1:50; Santa Cruz Biotechnology, Dallas, TX, USA), Ki67(sc-7846, dilution used 1:200; Santa Cruz Biotechnology), and CD31 (sc-376764, dilution used 1:200; Santa Cruz Biotechnology) antibodies for 16 h at 4 °C and then with peroxidase-conjugated secondary antibodies for 1 h at room temperature. The slides were then developed by immersion in 0.06% 3,3′-diaminobenzidine tetrahydrochloride (DAB; DAKO, Glostrup, Denmark), followed by counterstaining with Gill's hematoxylin V.

IHC reactions for CD31 and Ki67 were imaged at low magnification (×40) and CD31 or Ki67-positive cells were counted in 10 representative high power fields (×400). Single immunoreactive endothelial cells, or endothelial cell clusters that were separate from other microvessels, were counted as individual microvessels. The mean visual microvessel density for CD31 was calculated. Ki67-positive cells were only counted in hepatocytes, which are with large cells with cuboidal morphology.

4.5. BAFF, Matrix Metalloproteinase (MMP)-9, Fibroblast Growth Factor 4 (FGF4), and Interleukin-8 (IL-8) Determination

Mouse BAFF levels in serum or tissue lysates, mouse matrix metalloproteinase-9 (MMP-9) levels in tissue lysates, and human MMP-9, FGF4, and IL-8 levels in conditioned medium were determined while using enzyme immunoassay (EIA) kits (R&D Systems, Minneapolis, MN, USA).

4.6. Culture of CL-48 Hepatocytes and Human Umbilical Vein Endothelial Cells (HUVECs)

Human normal CL-48 hepatocytes were obtained from (Manassas, VA, USA). The cells were maintained in Dulbecco's modified Eagle's medium (DMEM) supplemented with nonessential amino acids, L-glutamine, a 2× vitamin solution (Life Technologies Inc., Grand Island, NY, USA), sodium pyruvate, 10% fetal bovine serum, penicillin, and streptomycin (Flow Labs, Rockville, MD, USA). HUVECs were obtained from Cell Applications (San Diego, CA, USA) and then maintained in endothelial cell growth medium (Cell Applications). HUVECs were used at no more than passage 5. All of the cells were cultured at 37 °C in a humidified atmosphere of 5% CO_2 and 95% air.

4.7. BAFF Protein and Chemical Inhibitors

Recombinant human BAFF protein and anti-mouse BAFF neutralizing antibody were obtained from R&D Systems. BAY117082 was purchased from Sigma (St. Louis, MO, USA).

4.8. Preparation of Conditioned Medium (CM)

The CL-48 cells were washed with PBS twice and cultured in 5 mL serum-free DMEM for 24 h before stimulated with recombinant human BAFF protein for 1 h. The CL-48 cells were then washed with PBS twice and cultured in 5 mL serum-free M199 medium for 24 h. CM was then collected and clarified by centrifugation (4 °C, 1000× *g*, 5 min.) to remove cell debris. A solution of 25 mM HEPES buffer (pH 7.4), 1 mg/mL leupeptin, 1 mM phenylmethylsulfonyl fluoride, 1 mM ethylenediaminetetraacetic acid (EDTA), 0.02% NaN_3, and 0.1% bovine serum albumin (Sigma) was added to the CM. The CM was finally frozen and stored at −70 °C until use.

4.9. Cell Growth Determination

The CL-48 cells were plated in six-well cell culture plates at 20,000 cells/well in 2 mL culture medium containing fetal bovine serum. The cells were treated as indicated and harvested by suspension in 0.025% trypsin containing 0.02% EDTA. Cell counts were performed in triplicate while using a hemocytometer with trypan blue exclusion to identify the viable cells. Growth curves were generated.

Cell cycle analysis of CL-48 cells was carried out by quantifying the DNA content with propidium iodide staining and using a FACScan instrument with CellQuest software (Becton Dickinson).

4.10. Filamentous Actin (F-actin) Fluorescence Staining

HUVECs were cultured on cover slides and, after reaching confluence, the HUVECs were treated with CM. After 1 h, HUVECs were washed with serum-free M199 medium, fixed with 3.7% paraformaldehyde for 20 min, and permeabilized with 0.1% Triton-X-100. Fluorescence isothiocyanate-conjugated phalloidin (Invitrogen, Carlsbad, CA, USA), diluted in PBS (2 U/mL), was then applied to the specimens in the dark for 1 h. The specimens were mounted with 10% glycerol and images were acquired using a fluorescence microscope (Nikon, Tokyo, Japan).

4.11. HUVEC Monolayer Permeability Assays

HUVECs were cultured in Transwell chambers (0.4 μm pore polycarbonate filters; Costar, Cambridge, MA, USA). After reaching confluence, the medium was replaced with the CM (0.3 mL in the upper chamber and 1 mL in the lower chamber). Horseradish peroxidase molecule (Sigma-Aldrich, Saint Louis, MO, USA) was added to the upper compartment at a concentration of 0.2 μM. After incubation for 1 h, the medium in the lower compartment was assayed for enzymatic activity while using a photometric guaiacol substrate assay (Sigma-Aldrich).

4.12. HUVEC Migration Assays

Confluent HUVECs were grown in 24-well plates. To rule out the confounding influence of cell proliferation, the HUVECs were treated with 10 μg/mL mitomycin C (Sigma-Aldrich) for 2 h prior to the migration assay. A small linear scratch was created in the confluent monolayer by gently scraping with a sterile cell scrapper. The cells were extensively rinsed with M199 medium to remove cellular debris and then incubated with CM. Six hours later, images of the migrated cells were digitally photographed. The degree of wound closure was determined while using ImageJ® program to measure the percent closure of the wounded area within the captured images.

4.13. HUVEC Tube Formation Assays

HUVECs (2×10^4 cells/well in 96-well plates) were plated onto a thin coating of Matrigel (0.24 mg/cm^2) with CM. After 6 h, each well was digitally photographed through phase contrast microscopy. Tubes are defined that develop contain a lumen encircled by endothelial cells that are joined together via junctional complexes and the number of intact tubes was counted per high power field.

4.14. HUVEC Proliferation Tests

The cells were plated in six-well cell culture plates at 1×10^5 cells/well in 2 mL culture medium with CM. After 72 h of treatment at 37 °C, the cells were harvested by suspension in 0.025% trypsin with 0.02% EDTA. Cell counts were performed in triplicate while using a hemocytometer. Trypan blue exclusion assays were used to identify the viable cells. The cell number was determined and cell growth curves were generated.

4.15. Protein Array Analysis

A Proteome Profiler Human Angiogenesis Antibody Array (cat. #ARY007; R&D Systems) was used for the detection of angiogenesis-related factors according to the manufacturer's instructions. Briefly, CM was first mixed with the detection antibody cocktail at room temperature for 1 h prior to being added to the array membrane. The membrane was then incubated overnight at 2–8 °C on a shaker. After washing, horseradish peroxidase-conjugated streptavidin was added to the membrane, followed by incubation for 30 min. at room temperature on a shaker. After washing, X-ray film and a chemiluminescence imaging system were used to detect and quantify the array signals.

4.16. RNA Interference

Small interfering RNA (siRNA) duplexes were purchased from Santa Cruz Biotechnology (Santa Cruz, CA, USA; siRNA targeting BCL10, sc-29793; and control siRNA, sc-37007). The CL-48 cells were transfected with siRNA at a concentration of 25 nM in serum-free Opti-MEM using Oligofectamine (Invitrogen, Carlsbad, CA, USA).

4.17. Real-Time Quantitative Reverse Transcription Polymerase Chain Reaction (RT-PCR)

We quantified mRNA expression under various conditions while using a fluorescence quantitative real-time PCR detection system (Light Cycler DNA master SYBR Green I; Roche Molecular Biochemicals, Indianapolis, IN, USA). The primer pairs were as follows: human BAFF-R: 5′-AGACAAGGACGCCCCAGAGCCC-3′ and 5′-GTGGGGTGGTTCCTGGGTCTTC-3′; hMMP-9: 5′-CACTGTCCACCCCTCAGAGC-3′ and 5′-GCCACTTGTCGGCGATAAGG-3′; *IL-8*: 5′-TTTCTGCA GCTCTCTGTGAGG-3′ and 5′-CTGCTGTTGTTGTTGCTTCTC-3′; FGF4: 5′-GACTACCTGCTGGGCA TCAA-3′ and 5′-TGCACTCATCGGTGAAGAAG-3′; glyceraldehyde-3-phosphate dehydrogenase (*GAPDH*), 5′-GGGAAGGTGAAGGTCGG-3′ and 5′-TGGACTCCACGACGTACTCAG-3′. Amplification was followed by melting curve analysis to verify the authenticity of the amplicon. The amounts of BAFFR, MMP-9, FGF4, and IL-8 mRNAs were normalized to that of GAPDH mRNA and they are presented in arbitrary units, with 1 U corresponding to the value in cells that were treated with the vehicle control.

4.18. NF-κB Promoter Reporter Assays

Transfection with NF-κB binding site-driven luciferase plasmid (BD Bioscience) into CL-48 cells was performed while using Transfast transfection reagent (Promega, Madison, WI, USA). At 24 h after transfection, the cells were serum starved for 24 h and then treated as indicated.

4.19. Western Blotting

Protein concentrations in nuclear extracts from liver tissues or CL-48 cell lysates were quantified while using Bio-Rad protein assays (Hercules, CA, USA). Samples (10–50 μg protein) were separated by sodium dodecyl sulfate polyacrylamide gel electrophoresis, transferred onto polyvinylidene difluoride membranes, and immunoblotted with anti-BCL10 (sc-5273, dilution used 1:200; Santa Cruz Biotechnology) and anti-beta-Actin (sc-47778, dilution used 1:1000; Santa Cruz Biotechnology) antibodies. The entire western blots with marker were demonstrated in Supplementary Materials. The signals were detected by a Digital imaging system (Bio Pioneer Tech Co., New Taipei City, Taiwan). Meanwhile, the relative intensity of thesignals was analyzed with the ImageJ® program. Is the capitalization necessary? Additional examples will be highlighted below.

4.20. Statistical Analysis

Data are expressed as mean ± standard deviations (SDs), one- or two-way analysis of variance (ANOVA) with Turkey post hoc test was used to analyze the data in multiple groups. The Student's *t*-test was used to evaluate statistically significant differences between the groups. All statistical analyses were performed while using SPSS for Windows, version 18.0 (SPSS Inc., Chicago, IL, USA). A *p* value of less than 0.05 was considered to indicate statistical significance.

Supplementary Materials: Supplementary materials can be found at http://www.mdpi.com/1422-0067/20/20/5022/s1.

Author Contributions: Methodology, C.-T.S. and W.-F.W.; Project administration, H.-S.L.; Supervision, C.-N.C. and Y.-M.W.; Writing—original draft, C.-H.C. and C.-M.H.; Writing—review & editing, S.-L.L.

Funding: This study was supported by the Ministry of Science and Technology, Republic of China. (Grant Nos. MOST 105-2314-B-002-058 -MY2 and MOST 104-2320-B-002-043) and the National Taiwan University Hospital (Grant Nos. NTUH106-S3384 and NTUH105-S2973). The funders had no role in study design, data collection and analysis, decision to publish, or manuscript preparation of the manuscript.

Conflicts of Interest: The authors declare no conflict of interest.

References

1. Higgins, G.; Anderson, R.E.; Higgins, G.M.; Anderson, R.M. Experimental pathology of the liver: Restoration of the liver of the white rat following partial surgical removal. *Arch. Pathol.* **1931**, *12*, 186–202.
2. Fausto, N.; Campbell, J.S.; Riehle, K.J. Liver regeneration. *Hepatology* **2006**, *43*, S45–S53. [CrossRef]
3. Yamada, Y.; Kirillova, I.; Peschon, J.J.; Fausto, N. Initiation of liver growth by tumor necrosis factor: Deficient liver regeneration in mice lacking type I tumor necrosis factor receptor. *Proc. Natl. Acad. Sci. USA* **1997**, *94*, 1441–1446. [CrossRef] [PubMed]
4. Ding, B.S.; Nolan, D.J.; Butler, J.M.; James, D.; Babazadeh, A.O.; Rosenwaks, Z.; Mittal, V.; Kobayashi, H.; Shido, K.; Lyden, D.; et al. Inductive angiocrine signals from sinusoidal endothelium are required for liver regeneration. *Nature* **2010**, *468*, 310–315. [CrossRef] [PubMed]
5. Michalopoulos, G.K. Hepatostat: Liver regeneration and normal liver tissue maintenance. *Hepatology* **2017**, *65*, 1384–1392. [CrossRef] [PubMed]
6. Kron, P.; Linecker, M.; Limani, P.; Schlegel, A.; Kambakamba, P.; Lehn, J.M.; Nicolau, C.; Graf, R.; Humar, B.; Clavien, P.A. Hypoxia-driven Hif2a coordinates mouse liver regeneration by coupling parenchymal growth to vascular expansion. *Hepatology* **2016**, *64*, 2198–2209. [CrossRef] [PubMed]
7. Hu, J.; Srivastava, K.; Wieland, M.; Runge, A.; Mogler, C.; Besemfelder, E.; Terhardt, D.; Vogel, M.J.; Cao, L.; Korn, C.; et al. Endothelial cell-derived angiopoietin-2 controls liver regeneration as a spatiotemporal rheostat. *Science* **2014**, *343*, 416–419. [CrossRef] [PubMed]
8. Karpusas, M.; Cachero, T.G.; Qian, F.; Boriak-Sjodin, A.; Mullen, C.; Strauch, K.; Hsu, Y.M.; Kalled, S.L. Crystal structure of extracellular human BAFF, a TNF family member that stimulates B lymphocytes. *J. Mol. Biol.* **2002**, *315*, 1145–1154. [CrossRef] [PubMed]
9. Kuo, S.H.; Tsai, H.J.; Lin, C.W.; Yeh, K.H.; Lee, H.W.; Wei, M.F.; Shun, C.T.; Wu, M.S.; Hsu, P.N.; Chen, L.T.; et al. The B-cell-activating factor signalling pathway is associated with *Helicobacter pylori* independence in gastric mucosa-associated lymphoid tissue lymphoma without t(11;18)(q21;q21). *J. Pathol.* **2017**, *241*, 420–433. [CrossRef] [PubMed]
10. Kuo, S.H.; Yeh, P.Y.; Chen, L.T.; Wu, M.S.; Lin, C.W.; Yeh, K.H.; Tzeng, Y.S.; Chen, J.Y.; Hsu, P.N.; Lin, J.T.; et al. Overexpression of B cell-activating factor of TNF family (BAFF) is associated with *Helicobacter pylori*-independent growth of gastric diffuse large B-cell lymphoma with histologic evidence of MALT lymphoma. *Blood* **2008**, *112*, 2927–2934. [CrossRef]
11. Kuo, S.H.; Chou, C.H.; Cheng, A.L.; Wang, C.W.; Chen, Y.H.; Chen, R.J. Expression of BCL10 in cervical cancer has a role in the regulation of cell growth through the activation of NF-κB-dependent cyclin D1 signaling. *Gynecol. Onco.* **2012**, *126*, 245–251. [CrossRef] [PubMed]
12. Shen, X.; Wang, M.; Guo, Y.; Ju, S. The correlation between non-Hodgkin lymphoma and expression levels of B-cell activating factor and its receptors. *Adv. Clin. Exp. Med.* **2016**, *25*, 837–844. [CrossRef] [PubMed]
13. Puri, P.; Sanyal, A.J. The BAFFling problem of B cell-activating factor in nonalcoholic fatty liver disease. *Hepatol. Int.* **2013**, *7*, 309–312. [CrossRef] [PubMed]
14. Kawasaki, K.; Abe, M.; Tada, F.; Tokumoto, Y.; Chen, S.; Miyake, T.; Furukawa, S.; Matsuura, B.; Hiasa, Y.; Onji, M. Blockade of B-cell-activating factor signaling enhances hepatic steatosis induced by a high-fat diet and improves insulin sensitivity. *Lab. Invest.* **2013**, *93*, 311–321. [CrossRef] [PubMed]
15. Qiu, W.; David, D.; Zhou, B.; Chu, P.G.; Zhang, B.; Wu, M.; Xiao, J.; Han, T.; Zhu, Z.; Wang, T.; et al. Down-regulation of growth arrest DNA damage-inducible gene 45beta expression is associated with human hepatocellular carcinoma. *Am. J. Pathol.* **2003**, *162*, 1961–1974. [CrossRef]
16. Klein, B.; Tarte, K.; Jourdan, M.; Mathouk, K.; Moreaux, J.; Jourdan, E.; Legouffe, E.; de Vos, J.; Rossi, J.F. Survival and proliferation factors of normal and malignant plasma cells. *Int. J. Hematol.* **2003**, *78*, 106–113. [CrossRef] [PubMed]
17. Li, W.; Vogel, C.F.; Wu, D.; Matsumura, F. Non-genomic action of TCDD to induce inflammatory responses in HepG2 human hepatoma cells and in liver of C57BL/6J mice. *Biol. Chem.* **2010**, *391*, 1205–1219. [CrossRef]
18. Patke, A.; Mecklenbräuker, I.; Tarakhovsky, A. Survival signaling in resting B cells. *Curr. Opin. Immunol.* **2004**, *16*, 251–255. [CrossRef]

19. Yu, M.; Chen, Y.; He, Y.; Podd, A.; Fu, G.; Wright, J.A.; Kleiman, E.; Khan, W.N.; Wen, R.; Wang, D. Critical role of B cell lymphoma 10 in BAFF-regulated NF-κB activation and survival of anergic B cells. *J. Immunol.* **2012**, *189*, 5185–5193. [CrossRef]

20. Wang, W.; Du, Z.; Yan, J.; Ma, D.; Shi, M.; Zhang, M.; Peng, C.; Li, H. Mesenchymal stem cells promote liver regeneration and prolong survival in small-for-size liver grafts: Involvement of C-Jun N-terminal kinase, cyclin D1, and NF-κB. *PLoS ONE* **2014**, *9*, e112532.

21. Fragioudaki, M.; Tsirakis, G.; Pappa, C.A.; Aristeidou, I.; Tsioutis, C.; Alegakis, A.; Kyriakou, D.S.; Stathopoulos, E.N.; Alexandrakis, M.G. Serum BAFF levels are related to angiogenesis and prognosis in patients with multiple myeloma. *Leuk. Res.* **2012**, *36*, 1004–1008. [CrossRef] [PubMed]

22. Bolkun, L.; Lemancewicz, D.; Jablonska, E.; Kulczynska, A.; Bolkun-Skornicka, U.; Kloczko, J.; Dzieciol, J. BAFF and APRIL as TNF superfamily molecules and angiogenesis parallel progression of human multiple myeloma. *Ann. Hematol.* **2014**, *93*, 635–644. [CrossRef] [PubMed]

23. Lee, G.H.; Lee, J.; Lee, J.W.; Choi, W.S.; Moon, E.Y. B cell activating factor-dependent expression of vascular endothelial growth factor in MH7A human synoviocytes stimulated with tumor necrosis factor-α. *Int. Immunopharmacol.* **2013**, *17*, 142–147. [CrossRef] [PubMed]

24. Uda, Y.; Hirano, T.; Son, G.; Iimuro, Y.; Uyama, N.; Yamanaka, J.; Mori, A.; Arii, S.; Fujimoto, J. Angiogenesis is crucial for liver regeneration after partial hepatectomy. *Surgery* **2013**, *153*, 70–77. [CrossRef] [PubMed]

25. Melgar-Lesmes, P.; Edelman, E.R. Monocyte-endothelial cell interactions in the regulation of vascular sprouting and liver regeneration in mouse. *J. Hepatol.* **2015**, *63*, 917–925. [CrossRef]

26. Vu, T.H.; Shipley, J.M.; Bergers, G.; Berger, J.E.; Helms, J.A.; Hanahan, D.; Shapiro, S.D.; Senior, R.M.; Werb, Z. MMP-9/gelatinase B is a key regulator of growth plate angiogenesis and apoptosis of hypertrophic chondrocytes. *Cell* **1998**, *93*, 411–422. [CrossRef]

27. Kollet, O.; Shivtiel, S.; Chen, Y.Q.; Suriawinata, J.; Thung, S.N.; Dabeva, M.D.; Kahn, J.; Spiegel, A.; Dar, A.; Samira, S.; et al. HGF, SDF-1, and MMP-9 are involved in stress-induced human CD34+ stem cell recruitment to the liver. *J. Clin. Invest.* **2003**, *112*, 160–169. [CrossRef]

28. Zhou, B.; Fan, Y.; Rao, J.; Xu, Z.; Liu, Y.; Lu, L.; Li, G. Matrix metalloproteinases-9 deficiency impairs liver regeneration through epidermal growth factor receptor signaling in partial hepatectomy mice. *J. Surg. Res.* **2015**, *197*, 201–209. [CrossRef]

29. Strieter, R.M.; Kunkel, S.L.; Elner, V.M.; Martonyi, C.L.; Koch, A.E.; Polverini, P.J.; Elner, S.G. Interleukin-8. A corneal factor that induces neovascularization. *Am. J. Pathol.* **1992**, *141*, 1279–1284.

30. Koch, A.E.; Polverini, P.J.; Kunkel, S.L.; Harlow, L.A.; Di Pietro, L.A.; Elner, V.M.; Elner, S.G.; Strieter, R.M. Interleukin-8 as a macrophage-derived mediator of angiogenesis. *Science* **1992**, *258*, 1798–1801. [CrossRef]

31. Ueda, T.; Sakabe, T.; Oka, M.; Maeda, Y.; Nishida, M.; Murakami, F.; Maekawa, T. Levels of interleukin (IL)-6, IL-8, and IL-1 receptor antagonist in the hepatic vein following liver surgery. *Hepatogastroenterology* **2000**, *47*, 1048–1051. [PubMed]

32. Yokoo, T.; Kitamura, M. Dual regulation of IL-1 beta-mediated matrix metalloproteinase-9 expression in mesangial cells by NF-kappa B and AP-1. *Am. J. Physiol.* **1996**, *270*, F123–F130. [CrossRef] [PubMed]

33. Mukaida, N.; Mahe, Y.; Matsushima, K. Cooperative interaction of nuclear factor-kappa B- and cis-regulatory enhancer binding protein-like factor binding elements in activating the interleukin-8 gene by pro-inflammatory cytokines. *J. Biol. Chem.* **1990**, *265*, 21128–21133. [PubMed]

34. Poisson, J.; Lemoinne, S.; Boulanger, C.; Durand, F.; Moreau, R.; Valla, D.; Rautou, P.E. Liver sinusoidal endothelial cells: Physiology and role in liver diseases. *J. Hepatol.* **2017**, *66*, 212–227. [CrossRef] [PubMed]

International Journal of
Molecular Sciences

Article

Biological Features Implies Potential Use of Autologous Adipose-Derived Stem/Progenitor Cells in Wound Repair and Regenerations for the Patients with Lipodystrophy

Keiji Suzuki [1,*], Sadanori Akita [2,3], Hiroshi Yoshimoto [3], Akira Ohtsuru [4], Akiyoshi Hirano [3] and Shunichi Yamashita [1,5,6]

[1] Department of Radiation Medical Sciences, Atomic Bomb Disease Institute, Nagasaki University, 1-12-4 Sakamoto, Nagasaki 852-8523, Japan; shun@nagasaki-u.ac.jp
[2] Department of Plastic Surgery, Wound Repair and Regeneration, Fukuoka University, School of Medicine, 7-45-1 Nanakuma, Jonan-ku, Fukuoka 814-0180, Japan; akitas@hf.rim.or.jp
[3] Department of Plastic and Reconstructive Surgery, Nagasaki University, 1-12-4 Sakamoto, Nagasaki 852-8523, Japan; hy671117@nagasaki-u.ac.jp (H.Y.); akiyoshi@nagasaki-u.ac.jp (A.H.)
[4] Department of Radiation Health Management, Fukushima Medical University School of Medicine, 1 Hikariga-oka, Fukushima 960-1295, Japan; ohtsuru@fmu.ac.jp
[5] Fukushima Medical University School of Medicine, 1 Hikariga-oka, Fukushima 960-1295, Japan
[6] Center for Advanced Radiation Emergency Medicine at the National Institutes for Quantum and Radiological Science and Technology, 4-9-1 Anagawa, Inage-ku, Chiba 263-8555, Japan
[*] Correspondence: kzsuzuki@nagasaki-u.ac.jp; Tel.: +81-95-819-7116; Fax: +81-95-819-7117

Received: 27 September 2019; Accepted: 3 November 2019; Published: 5 November 2019

Abstract: A paradigm shift in plastic and reconstructive surgery is brought about the usage of cell-based therapies for wound healing and regeneration. Considering the imitations in the reconstructive surgeries in restoring tissue loss and deficiency, stem cell-based therapy, in particular, has been expected to pave the way for a new solution to the regenerative approaches. Limitations in the reconstructive surgeries in restoring tissue loss and deficiency have paved the way for new regenerative approaches. Among them, adipose-derived stem/progenitor cells (ADSCs)-based therapy could be the most promising clue, since ADSCs have pluripotent differentiation capabilities not only in adipocytes but also in a variety of cell types. Accumulating evidences have indicated that the unfavorable development of adipose-tissue damage, namely, lipodystrophy, is a systemic complication, which is closely related to metabolic abnormality. Considering ADSC-based regenerative medicine should be applied for the treatment of lipodystrophy, it is inevitable to ascertain whether the ADSCs obtained from the patients with lipodystrophy are capable of being used. It will be very promising and realistic if this concept is applied to lipoatrophy; one form of lipodystrophies that deteriorates the patients' quality of life because of excessive loss of soft tissue in the exposed areas such as face and extremities. Since lipodystrophy is frequently observed in the human immunodeficiency virus (HIV)-infected patients receiving highly active antiretroviral therapy (HAART), the present study aims to examine the biological potentials of ADSCs isolated from the HIV-infected patients with lipodystrophy associated with the HAART treatment. Growth properties, adipogenic differentiation, and mitochondrial reactive oxygen species (ROS) production were examined in ADSCs from HIV-infected and HIV-uninfected patients. Our results clearly demonstrated that ADSCs from both patients showed indistinguishable growth properties and potentials for adipocyte differentiation in vitro. Thus, although the number of cases were limited, ADSCs isolated from the patients with lipodystrophy retain sufficient physiological and biological activity for the reconstitution of adipose-tissue, suggesting that ADSCs from the patients with lipodystrophy could be used for autologous ADSC-based regenerative therapy.

Keywords: ADSC; lipodystrophy; HIV; HAART; adipogenesis

1. Introduction

Adult stem cells have been used as the promising source of stem cells, which can be applied for cell-based therapies [1–3]. Among the adult stem cells, adipose-derived stem/progenitor cells (ADSCs) are the most promising ones, since they can be easily obtained from liposuction aspirates or subcutaneous adipose tissue fragments and expanded in vitro and there are no ethical concerns like human embryonic stem cells [4–9]. Furthermore, accumulating evidences have indicated that ADSCs showed multi-lineage differentiation, including classical mesenchymal lineages as well as non-mesenchymal ectodermal and endodermal lineages [1,10–12]. Recently, we have applied ADSCs for autologous transplantation therapy for chronic radiation injury [13]. ADSCs were obtained by less invasive lipoaspiration in combination with automatic and aseptic isolation. As ADSCs could be the effective component of transplanted fat tissue, which has been applied to wound repair and regeneration, ADSCs transplantation is expected to show equivalent efficacy to fat tissue transplantation. Thus, ADSCs could be a critical and promising cell population in amending impaired subcutaneous adipose-tissue including lipodystrophy.

Lipodystrophy is characterized by either complete or partial loss of adipose tissue [14]. There are congenital and acquired lipodystrophy, and one representative acquired form occurs in human immunodeficiency virus (HIV)-infected individuals treated with highly active antiretroviral therapy (HAART), and up to 70% of patients receiving HAART are reported to have HIV-associated lipodystrophy. The HAART has been succeeded in inhibiting virus multiplication, and thus, it significantly improves the survival of HIV-infected patients [15–18]. However, as HIV-infected patients live longer, it became more evident that HAART induced multiple layers of adverse effects including adipose-tissue damage. Adipose-tissue damage manifests as abnormal distribution of adipose tissue, and clinical features of lipodystrophy include peripheral lipoatrophy and central lipohypertrophy [19–23].

It has been reported that lipodystrophy caused by nucleoside reverse transcriptase inhibitors (NRTIs) is related to its effect in mitochondria, which results in apoptosis induction in adipocytes [24–26]. Subsequently, NRTIs were substituted with protease inhibitors (PIs), and although PIs showed less effect on mitochondria than NRTIs, it becomes evident that PIs induce endoplasmic reticulum (ER) stress by accumulating unprocessed proteins in adipocytes, which are the inducer for unfolded protein response (UPR)-dependent apoptosis [27]. Thus, PIs have also brought about lipodystrophy in not a small number of the patients receiving HAART [28–31]. Previously, fat tissue transplantation was applied to lipodystrophy, particularly to facial lipodystrophy [32–34]. It efficiently improved facial disfigurement, which resulted in improvement in patient's quality of life, however, it needed surgical excision of fat tissue. Therefore, ADSCs-based therapy should be more beneficial to the patients with severe lipodystrophy in comparison with the fat tissue transplantation alone, since it is minimally invasive. However, because lipodystrophy is closely related to dysfunction of differentiated adipocytes, and ADSCs are those supply adipocytes in tissue, irreversible and detrimental effects of HARRT on ADSCs could be a possible cause resulting in lipodystrophy [22,23]. Thus, it is inevitable to ascertain whether the ADSCs obtained from the patients with lipodystrophy are capable of being used, which could be tested in vitro.

ADSCs in HIV-infected patients could be obtained from abdomen, thighs, and shoulders, where lipoatrophy was less severe but apparently induced; but, a study has claimed that adipose tissue may be damaged not only by HAART but also by HIV-infection itself through the possible impairment of mitochondrial function [35]. Thus, in order to achieve successful ADSCs-based therapy, the current study aimed at determining whether ADSCs isolated from HIV-infected patients receiving HAART retain sufficient biological and physiological activities for reconstitution of subcutaneous adipose tissue. Total eight ADSCs were established from the subcutaneous lipoaspirates obtained from the donor sites, such as lower abdomen, thighs, buttocks, and shoulders, from three HIV-infected patients and four uninfected patients [36]. Growth properties, adipogenic differentiation, and mitochondrial ROS production were examined in ADSCs from HIV-infected and HIV-unrelated patients ex vivo.

Our results clearly demonstrated that ADSCs from HIV-infected patients showed indistinguishable growth properties and potentials for adipocyte differentiation in vitro. Thus, although a number of cases was limited, ADSCs derived from the patients receiving HAART retain sufficient physiological and biological activity for the reconstitution of adipose-tissue, indicating that ADSCs from the patients with lipodystrophy could have sufficient biological potential so that they could be used for autologous ADSCs-based regenerative therapy.

2. Results

2.1. Isolation and Growth Properties of ADSCs

We have obtained lipoaspirates from three HIV-infected patients who are hemophilic and infected with HIV virus by unheated blood products, diagnosed as lipodystrophy after HAART (Table 1). Lipoaspirates from HIV-infected patients were obtained from the sites such as abdomen, thighs, and shoulders, where lipoatrophy was less severe. Lipoaspirates were also obtained from four patients, who are not related to HIV-infection (Table 1). Lipoaspirates obtained from one patient were mixed and used for ADSCs isolation.

Table 1. Origin of adipose tissue-derived cells.

Cell ID	Patients' Description	Origin
ADSC091809	HIV-infected patient #1	abdomen, back
ADSC020310	HIV-infected patient #2	thigh, abdomen, shoulder
ADSC060210	HIV-infected patient #3	thigh, abdomen, back
ADSC121710	HIV-infected patient #4	thigh, abdomen
ADSC121708	HIV-uninfected patient	abdomen, buttock
ADSC100709	HIV-uninfected patient	thigh, abdomen
ADSC110409	HIV-uninfected patient	thigh, abdomen
ADSC012710	HIV-uninfected patient	thigh, abdomen

Approximately 100 μL of processed lipoaspirates were plated onto type-I collagen-coated flasks and maintained in a serum-free medium. The cells, which clonally expanded were collected and stored as the primary ADSCs. We noticed that the number of colonies formed by the processed lipoaspirates obtained from the HIV-infected patients were about one-tenth of those observed in the lipoaspirates obtained from HIV-uninfected patients. ADSCs showed mesenchymal stem cell-like morphology (Figure 1).

ADSCs isolated from processed lipoaspirates were highly proliferative in serum-free medium, and a plenty of mitotic figures were discerned. We observed no detectable difference in cell morphologies and growth patterns between the ADSCs obtained from the HIV-infected patients and HIV-unrelated patients. We also extensively compared the growth kinetics of ADSCs by cell growth assay, and there was no detectable difference in the growth kinetics of both ADSCs (Table 2).

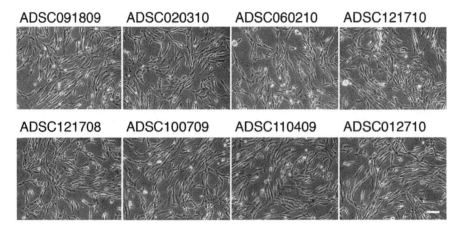

Figure 1. Morphology of adipose-derived stem/progenitor cells (ADSCs) cultures at passage 1 obtained from human immunodeficiency virus (HIV)-infected and HIV-unrelated patients. Exponentially growing ADSCs were cultured in serum free-medium in type I collage-coated flasks. Magnification ×100; the scale bar indicates 100 μm.

Table 2. Biological properties of ADSCs.

Cell ID	Saturation Density ($\times 10^6/cm^2$)	Cloning Efficiency (%)
ADSC091809	1.39 ± 0.21	34.2 ± 3.1
ADSC020310	1.46 ± 0.15	33.9 ± 3.3
ADSC060210	1.47 ± 0.19	35.1 ± 2.7
ADSC121710	1.41 ± 0.14	34.6 ± 2.9
ADSC121708	1.41 ± 0.19	32.1 ± 2.7
ADSC100709	1.39 ± 0.17	33.1 ± 2.9
ADSC110409	1.41 ± 0.23	37.3 ± 4.1
ADSC012710	1.38 ± 0.18	35.6 ± 3.4

2.2. Adipogenic Differentiation of ADSCs

Adipogenic differentiation was examined in confluent ADSCs by incubating them in a differentiation medium for 10 days. Multiple tiny lipid droplets became visible by day 5, and they gradually matured during 10 days' incubation. To quantify adipogenic differentiation, lipid droplets were stained with BODIPY 493/503, a highly sensitive lipophilic fluorescent dye. As shown in Figure 2, multiple lipid droplets were identified in the cytoplasm, whose morphology was similar to that observed in subcutaneous adipocytes. The frequency of differentiation-positive cells were approximately 97% or more in ADSCs from HIV-unrelated patients, and the same differentiation potential was confirmed in ADSCs derived from HIV-infected patients (Table 3). Average fluorescence per cell is compared in Table 3, and we detected significant difference between ADSCs derived from HIV-infected and HIV-unrelated patients.

Adipogenic differentiation was also confirmed by analyzing the expression of proteins associated with adipocytes. As shown in Figure 3, we identified significant induction of FABP4, adiponectin, and PPARγ in every ADSC differentiated into adipocytes, irrespective of HIV-infection. Average levels of protein expression also show any notable difference.

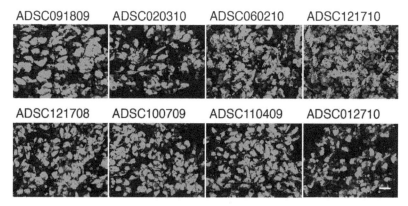

Figure 2. Adipogenic differentiation of ADSCs in culture. ADSCs were stained with 10 µg/mL BODIPY 493/503 and counterstained with 0.1 µg/mL of DAPI. Magnification ×100; the scale bar indicates 100 µm.

Table 3. Adipogenic differentiation of ADSCs.

Cell ID	BODIPY-Positive Cells (%)	Average FL/Cell
ADSC091809	96.9 ± 3.1	85.2 ± 6.7
ADSC020310	97.3 ± 2.7	80.1 ± 8.9
ADSC060210	98.4 ± 4.1	82.3 ± 7.7
ADSC121710	97.5 ± 3.9	84.6 ± 7.9
ADSC121708	97.3 ± 4.5	84.9 ± 5.1
ADSC100709	97.5 ± 3.7	81.0 ± 9.6
ADSC110409	97.4 ± 4.1	83.2 ± 7.5
ADSC012710	97.2 ± 3.9	86.7 ± 7.9

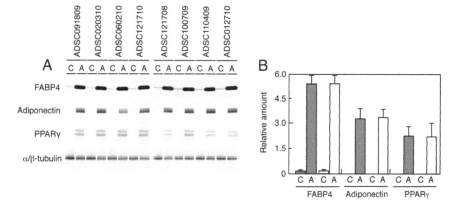

Figure 3. Western blot analysis of adipose-associated proteins. Samples (8 µg for tubulin and 16 µg for other proteins) were subjected to Western blot analysis probed with anti-FABP4, adiponectin, PPARγ, and α/β-tubulin antibodies (**A**). Relative levels of the bands to those of α/β-tubulin were calculated and summarized in (**B**). C—cells grown in the control medium; A—cells differentiated in adipogenic medium. Gray boxes indicate the mean amount observed in the cells from HIV-uninfected patients, while white boxes indicate that observed in the cells obtained from HIV-infected patients. Bars indicate S.D.

2.3. Mitochondrial ROS Production

Oxidative stress levels were evaluated by APF and MitoSox-Red in which the former represented intracellular oxidative stress and the latter measured the mitochondrial oxidative stress. As shown in Figure 4, we found no significant increase in ADSCs isolated from both HIV-infected and HIV-uninfected patients. ROS-induced DNA damage was also determined in ADSCs using 53BP1 foci, a surrogate marker for DNA double-strand breaks. While spontaneous DNA damage was detected in all ADSCs, there was no excess amount of DNA damage even in ADSCs obtained from HIV-infected patients.

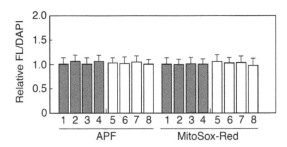

Figure 4. Oxidative stress levels in ADSCs. Intracellular oxidative stress level was measured by APF, and mitochondrial damage was quantified by MitoSox-Red. Gray boxes indicate the mean amount observed in the cells from HIV-uninfected patients, while white boxes indicate that observed in the cells obtained from HIV-infected patients. Bars indicate S.D.

3. Discussion

Several preadipocytes culture systems by which cells are able to be maintained for several passages have been established so far. For example, human preadipocytes were cultured in a medium 199 or DMEM/F-12 medium supplemented with 10% fetal bovine serum (FBS) [10]. ADSCs from lipoaspirates were generally cultured in a DMEM medium containing 10% FBS [8,37]. However, we have noticed that such ADSCs, cultured in a medium containing 10% FBS, rapidly lost their growth potential and exhibited senescence-like morphology. Since fetal bovine serum is well-known to contain some components showing growth inhibitory effects [38], we attempted to find a serum-free culture condition suitable for ADSCs. Our medium was originally prepared for primate embryonic stem cells [39], and it significantly improved the growth of ADSCs in culture, which enabled us to examine their biological and physiological activities.

In HIV-infected patients, subcutaneous adipose-tissue damage is quite obvious among those receiving HAART [19–22]. In the current study, ADSCs were isolated from the less affected parts of the body of HIV-infected patients. However, the recovery rates of ADSCs from the lipoaspirates obtained from the HIV-infected patients were about one-tenth of those observed in HIV-uninfected patients, indicating that ADSCs obtained from those parts of body were notably damaged. Therefore, it was expected that physiological activity of ADSCs in those parts of the body was compromised. However, our present study clearly demonstrated that there was no detectable difference in the growth kinetics, saturation density, and cloning efficiency between ADSCs obtained from HIV-infected and HIV-uninfected patients (Table 2). We are able to conclude that ADSCs from HIV-infected patients are biologically normal. We then compared the potential of adipogenic differentiation of ADSCs, and we found that the formation of lipid droplets was completely normal in ADSCs obtained from HIV-infected patients, indicating that adipogenic conversion was not compromised in those ADSCs (Figure 2 and Table 3). The conclusion was also confirmed by the protein analysis in Figure 3, in which no difference was detectable in the expression of several proteins involved in adipogenesis. Thus, it is quite obvious that ADSCs from HIV-infected patients retain normal physiological activity. Since previous study has claimed that HIV-infection alone causes lipodystrophy through abrogation of mitochondrial function [32], we have examined whether ADSCs from HIV-infected patients show increased oxidative stress levels or not. As shown in Figure 4, the results clearly showed no detectable change in oxidative stress level in all cases. While mitochondrial damage can occur in vivo, ADSCs isolated from the patients and expanded in culture might regain physiological mitochondrial function, suggesting that ADSCs used for therapy are better to allow time in culture to recover before transplantation.

Recent advances in plastic and reconstructive medicine have allowed autologous stem cell therapy [40–45]. As we recently reported [13], it is evident that autologous stem cell therapy is able to retrieve the abrogated function of skin. Furthermore, tissue regeneration using ADSCs involves indirect effects, which accelerate wound healing through secreting growth factors [46–52]. Thus, autologous ADSC therapy could be a promising solution for subcutaneous adipose-tissue damage, including lipodystrophy in the patients receiving HAART. So far, facial lipodystrophy has been recognized as a common side effect of HAART, and autologous fat grafting is an effective treatment modality. In this study, we proved that ADSCs derived from the patients receiving HAART retain sufficient physiological and biological activity for adipogenic differentiation. In this way, ADSCs from the HIV-infected patients are the ideal sources for autologous stem cell therapy for lipodystrophy. Although we should be cautious as a number of cases examined in this study was limited, ADSCs from the patients with lipodystrophy could have sufficient biological potentials, so that they could be used for autologous ADSCs-based regenerative therapy [53].

4. Materials and Methods

4.1. Characteristics of Patients

Lipoaspirates were obtained from three HIV-infected patients who are hemophilic and infected with HIV virus by unheated blood products and were diagnosed as lipodystrophy after HAART [36]. The patient #1 and #3, a 30 years-old man, diagnosed HIV positive when he was 15 years old, and the patient #2, a 46 years-of-old man, was notified HIV-positive when he was at the age of 22 years. The patient #4, a 36 years-old man, diagnosed HIV positive when he was 11 years old. Clinically all patients demonstrated the severe lipoatrophy in the naso-labial, melo-labial, temporal and parotid region of their faces. Patient #1 and #3 were severely lean in their torso, while the patient #2 was moderately built in the torso. The patient #4 was well-built in torso but lean in extremities. The body weights of the HIV-infected patients were 56.9 kg, 59.4 kg, and 70.3 kg, respectively and the body mass indexes (BMI) were 19.92, 21.96, and 21.94, respectively. Lipoaspirates from HIV-infected patients were obtained from abdomen, thighs, back, and shoulders where lipoatrophy was less severe. Lipoaspirates were also obtained from four patients, who are not related to HIV-infection. Their mean weight was 48.6 ± 3.93 kg with BMI 22.91 ± 3.303. The mean age of the HIV-infected patients was 35.5 ± 7.55, while it was 72.0 ± 16.1 in HIV-uninfected patients.

4.2. ADSCs and Culture

ADSCs were isolated from lipoaspirates as described previously [36]. Briefly, lipoaspirates, obtained from the donor sites, such as lower abdomen, thighs, buttocks, and shoulders, were processed using a Celution^{TM} system (Cytori Therapeutics, Inc, San Diego, CA, USA) based upon the method reported previously [36]. Mixed lipoaspirates isolated from different sites in one patient were used. Approximately 100 µL of processed lipoaspirates were plated onto type I-collagen-coated culture flasks. Since a medium containing 10% FBS promoted cellular senescence of ADSCs, the lipoaspirates were cultured in a serum-free medium originally developed for primate embryonic stem cells (Primate ES medium, ReproCELL, Tokyo, Japan). Clonally expanded cells were collected and stored in liquid nitrogen as the primary ADSCs (passage 0). Exponentially growing ADSCs were maintained by subculturing when they reached to 80% confluence. ADSCs were treated with trypsin/EDTA solution, trypsin-neutralizing solution, and collected by centrifugation for 5 min at 1200 rpm. The cells were resuspended in a fresh medium and 3×10^5 cells were replated onto the T25 flasks (25 cm^2), while rest of the cells were stored in liquid nitrogen at each passage.

ADSCs were obtained from three HIV-infected patients and four HIV-unrelated patients (Supplementary Table S1). The HIV-infected patient #1 and #3 are the same subject, and received treatments with indinavir, lamivudine (3TC), d4T, and lately, with atazanavir and Euzicom (3TC and abacavir combination) regimens for 15 years. The HIV-infected patient #2 received treatments with AZT, didanosine, 3TC, d4T, and lately, with atazanavir and Tenofovir/emtricitabine for 10 years. The patient #4 received treatments with AZT for 2 years, didaosine for 4 years, lamivudine (3TC) for 12 years, Nelfinavir for 3 years, d4T for 3 years, and Euzicom (3TC and abacavir combination) regimens for 10 years. All HIV-infected patients were diagnosed as HIV-negative by PCR-based assay at the time of isolating ADSCs. The study was approved by the Nagasaki University Hospital ethical committee (Internal Review Board approval No. 08070296, July 22, 2008, Nagasaki University Hospital), and all patients gave written informed consent.

4.3. Cell Growth

ADCSs were seeded onto 35 mm culture dishes at a density of 2×10^5 cells/dish. The medium was changed every 2 days, and they were cultured up to 7 days. Cells were collected every day and the numbers of cells were counted by a cell counter (CDA-500, Sysmex, Kobe, Japan). Saturation density was determined as the number of cells at confluence at day 7.

4.4. Cloning Efficiency

Exponentially growing ADSCs were collected, counted, and reseeded onto 100-mm culture dishes at a density of 100 cells/dish. The cells were cultured for 10 days without changing a medium before fixation with ethanol. The fix cells were then stained with 3% Giemsa's solution for 15 min. The numbers of colonies consist of 50 cells or more were counted. Cloning efficiency was determined by dividing the number of colonies by the number of cells plated. Data obtained from three independent experiments were compiled.

4.5. Adipocyte Differentiation

Exponentially growing ADSCs were collected, counted the number of cells, and 1×10^5 cells were replated onto 22 mm × 22 mm type I collagen-coated cover glass slips. They were cultured in a serum-free medium until they reached confluence. Then, the culture medium was changed to differentiation medium (DM-2, ZenBio, Inc., Research Triangle Park, NC, USA). They were cultured for another 10 days before fixation with 4% formalin. The fixed cells were stained with 10 μg/mL of BODIPY 493/503 (D-3922, Invitrogen, Carlsbad, CA, USA) for 20 min at room temperature and the nuclei were counterstained with 0.1 mg/mL of DAPI. Accumulation of lipid droplets was determined under a fluorescence microscope (F3000B, Leica, Tokyo, Japan). Digital images were captured and the images were analyzed by FW4000 software (Leica, Tokyo, Japan). Cells containing multiple lipid droplets in more than 50% of the cytoplasm were counted as differentiation positive cells. In order to quantify average fluorescence per cell, the same areas were marked, and the sum of the pixel intensity within the marked area was calculated by FW4000 software, and total green fluorescence was divided by total blue fluorescence obtained by DAPI staining.

4.6. Mitochondrial Oxidative Stress

Intracellular oxidative stress level was measured by 3'-(p-aminophenyl)-fluorescein (APF). Cells cultured in T25 flasks were washed with PBS and treated with 5 μM APF in PBS for 60 min at 37 °C in a 5% CO_2 incubator. After the treatment, cells were trypsinized, suspended in PBS at 4×10^4 cells/mL, and green fluorescent intensity was measured by a fluorometer (JASCO, Tokyo, Japan). The excitation and emission wavelengths were set up at 490 nm and 515 nm, respectively.

Mitochondrial damage was quantified by MitoSox-Red. Cells cultured in T25 flasks were washed with PBS and treated with 1 μM MitoSox-Red (Invitrogen) in PBS for 20 min at 37 °C in a 5% CO_2 incubator. After the treatment, cells were trypsinized, suspended in PBS at 4×10^4 cells/mL, and red fluorescent intensity was measured by a fluorometer (JASCO, Tokyo, Japan). The excitation and emission wavelengths were set up at 400 nm and 580 nm, respectively. The nuclei were counterstained with 0.1 mg/mL of DAPI. Relative fluorescence was calculated by dividing total green or red fluorescence by total blue fluorescence obtained by DAPI staining.

4.7. Immunofluorescence

Cells were collected by trypsinization and 5×10^4 cells were replated onto coverslips. The cells were fixed with cold methanol for 10 min on ice followed by washing with 1× PBS⁻. Then, the primary antibodies diluted in TBS-DT (20 mM Tris-HCl, pH 7.6, 137 mM NaCl, 0.1% Tween 20, 125 μg/mL ampicillin, 5% skim milk) were treated for 2 h at 37 °C, followed by the Alexa Fluor-labeled secondary antibodies for 1 h at 37 °C. Nuclei were counterstained with 1 μg/mL DAPI. The antibodies used was anti-53BP1 (A300-272A, BioLegend, San Diego, CA, USA), and Alexa Fluor 555-labed anti-rabbit IgG (A21428, Thermo Fisher Scientific, Waltham, MA, USA). Images were captured by fluorescence microscope (DM6000B, Leica, Tokyo, Japan) and analyzed by FW4000 (Leica, Tokyo, Japan).

4.8. Western Blotting

Exponentially growing cells were lysed in lysis buffer (50 mM Tris-HCl (pH 7.2), 150 mM NaCl, 1% NP-40, 1% sodium deoxycholate, and 0.1% SDS) containing 1 mM 4-(2-aminoethyl)-benzensulfonyl fluoride hydrochloride. The cell lysate was cleared by centrifugation at 15,000 rpm for 10 min at 4 °C, and then supernatant was used as the total cellular protein. Total protein concentration was determined by the BCA protein assay (Pierce, Rockford, IL). Protein samples (8 or 16 μg) were electrophoresed on SDS-polyacrylamide gel and were electrophoretically transferred to a polyvinyl difluoride membrane in a transfer buffer (100 mM Tris, 192 mM glycine). After overnight incubation with blocking solution (10% skim milk), the membrane was incubated with the primary antibodies, a biotinylated anti-mouse or anti-rabbit IgG antibodies, and streptavidine-alkaline phosphatase. The bands were visualized after addition of nitroblue tetrazolium/5-bromo-4-chloro-3-indolyl phosphate as a substrate. The primary antibodies used in this study are anti-adiponectin (clone 19F1, Abcam Co. Ltd., Tokyo, Japan), anti-FABP4 (Abcam Co. Ltd., Tokyo, Japan), anti-PPARγ (clone 81B8, Cell Signaling technology Japan, Tokyo, Japan), and anti-α/β-tubulin (Cell Signaling technology Japan).

4.9. Data Analysis

The data obtained from at least three independent experiments are expressed as mean ± SD. Wilcoxon rank test was used to evaluate the significant difference between the two groups. *P* values of less than 0.05 were considered significant difference.

Supplementary Materials: Supplementary materials can be found at http://www.mdpi.com/1422-0067/20/21/5505/s1.

Author Contributions: Conceptualization, K.S. and S.A.; methodology, H.Y. and A.O.; formal analysis, H.Y. and A.H.; resources, S.A. and H.Y.; data curation, K.S., H.Y. and S.A.; writing—original draft preparation, K.S.; writing—review and editing, S.A.; supervision, A.H.; project administration, K.S.; funding acquisition, S.Y.

Funding: This study was supported in part by the Nagasaki University Global Center of Excellence (GCOE) Program, Grant-in-Aid for Scientific Research (22390189) from the Ministry of Education, Culture, Sports, Science and Technology and Research on HIV/AIDS from Health Labor Science Research Grant in Japan.

Conflicts of Interest: The authors declare no conflict of interest.

Abbreviations

ADSC	adipose-derived stem/progenitor cells
HIV	human immunodeficiency virus
HAART	highly active antiretroviral therapy
NRTI	nucleoside reverse transcriptase inhibitor
PI	protease inhibitor
UPR	unfolded protein response
d4T	2',3'-didehydro-2'3'-dideoxythymidine

References

1. Zuk, P.A.; Zhu, M.; Mizuno, H.; Huang, J.; Futrell, J.W.; Katz, A.J.; Benhaim, P.; Lorenz, H.P.; Hedrick, M.H. Multilineage cells from human adipose tissue: Implications for cell-based therapies. *Tissue Eng.* **2001**, *7*, 211–228. [CrossRef] [PubMed]
2. Singh, V.K.; Kalsan, M.; Kumar, N.; Saini, A.; Chandra, R. Induced pluripotent stem cells: Applications in regenerative medicine, disease modeling, and drug discovery. *Front. Cell Dev. Biol.* **2015**, *3*, 1–18. [CrossRef] [PubMed]
3. De Luca, M.; Aiuti, A.; Cossu, G.; Parmar, M.; Pellegrini, G.; Robey, P.G. Advances in stem cell research and therapeutic development. *Nat. Cell Biol.* **2019**, *21*, 801–811. [CrossRef] [PubMed]
4. Zeve, D.; Tang, W.; Graff, J. Fighting fat with fat: The expanding field of adipose stem cells. *Cell Stem Cell* **2009**, *5*, 472–481. [CrossRef] [PubMed]
5. Zuk, P.A. The adipose-derived stem cell: Looking back and looking ahead. *Mol. Biol. Cell* **2010**, *21*, 1783–1787. [CrossRef] [PubMed]
6. Naderi, N.; Combellack, E.J.; Griffin, M.; Sedaghati, T.; Javed, M.; Findlay, M.W.; Wallace, C.G.; Mosahebi, A.; Butler, P.E.M.; Seifalian, A.M.; et al. The regenerative role of adipose-derived stem cells (ADSC) in plastic and reconstructive surgery. *Int. Wound J.* **2017**, *14*, 112–124. [CrossRef] [PubMed]
7. Tabatabaei, R.; Sheykhhasan, M. Adipose-derived stromal cell in regenerative medicine: A review. *World J. Stem Cells* **2017**, *9*, 107–117.
8. Palumbo, P.; Miconi, G.; Cinque, B.; La Torre, C.; Lombardi, F.; Zoccali, G.; Orsini, G.; Leocata, P.; Giuliani, M.; Cifone, M.G. In vitro evaluation of different methods of handling human liposuction aspirate and their effect on adipocytes and adipose derived stem cells. *J. Cell. Physiol.* **2015**, *230*, 1974–1981. [CrossRef]
9. Chu, D.T.; Nguyen Thi Phuong, T.; Tien, N.L.B.; Tran, D.T.; Minh, L.B.; Thanh, V.V.; Gia Anh, P.; Pham, V.H.; Thi Nga, V. Adipose tissue stem cells for therapy: An update on the progress of isolation, culture, storage, and clinical application. *J. Clin. Med.* **2019**, *8*, 917. [CrossRef]
10. Zuk, P.A.; Zhu, M.; Ashjian, P.; De Ugarte, D.A.; Huang, J.I.; Mizuno, H.; Alfonso, Z.C.; Fraser, J.K.; Benhaim, P.; Hedrick, M.H. Human adipose tissue is a source of multipotent stem cells. *Mol. Biol. Cell* **2002**, *13*, 4279–4295. [CrossRef]
11. Strem, B.M.; Hicok, K.C.; Zhu, M.; Wulur, I.; Alfonso, Z.; Schreiber, R.E.; Fraser, J.K.; Hedrick, M.H. Multipotential differentiation of adipose tissue-derived stem cells. *Keio J. Med.* **2005**, *54*, 132–141. [CrossRef] [PubMed]
12. Baer, P.C.; Geiger, H. Adipose-derived mesenchymal stromal/stem cells: Tissue localization, characterization, and heterogeniety. *Stem Cells Int.* **2012**, *2012*, 812693. [CrossRef] [PubMed]
13. Akita, S.; Akino, K.; Hirano, A.; Ohtsuru, A.; Yamashita, S. Mesenchymal stem cell therapy for cutaneous radiation syndrome. *Health Phys.* **2010**, *98*, 858–862. [CrossRef] [PubMed]
14. Fiorenza, C.G.; Chou, S.H.; Mantzoros, C.S. Lipodystrophy: Pathophysiology and advances in treatment. *Nat. Rev. Endocrinol.* **2011**, *7*, 137–150. [CrossRef] [PubMed]
15. Broder, S. The development of antiretroviral therapy and its impact on the HIV/AIDS pandemic. *Antivir. Res.* **2010**, *85*, 1–18. [CrossRef]
16. Esté, J.A.; Cihlar, T. Current status and challenges of antiretroviral research and therapy. *Antivir. Res.* **2010**, *85*, 25–33. [CrossRef]
17. Quinn, T.C. HIV epidemiology and the effects of antiviral therapy on long-term consequences. *AIDS* **2008**, *22*, S7–S12. [CrossRef]

18. Brown, T.T.; Glesby, M.J. Management of the metabolic effects of HIV and HIV drugs. *Nat. Rev. Endocrinol.* **2011**, *8*, 11–21. [CrossRef]
19. Mallon, P.W.; Cooper, D.A.; Carr, A. HIV-associated lipodystrophy. *HIV Med.* **2001**, *2*, 166–173. [CrossRef]
20. Mallon, P.W.G. Pathogenesis of lipodystrophy and lipid abnormalities in patients taking antiretroviral therapy. *AIDS Rev.* **2007**, *9*, 3–15.
21. da Cunha, J.; Maselli, L.M.; Stern, A.C.; Spada, C.; Bydlowski, S.P. Impact of antiretroviral therapy on lipid metabolism of human immunodeficiency virus-infected patients: Old and new drugs. *World J. Virol.* **2015**, *4*, 56–77. [CrossRef] [PubMed]
22. Kobayashi, N.; Nakahara, M.; Oka, M.; Saeki, K. Additional attention to combination antiretroviral therapy-related lipodystrophy. *World J. Virol.* **2017**, *6*, 49–52. [CrossRef] [PubMed]
23. Hussain, I.; Garg, A. Lipodystrophy syndromes. *Endocrinol. Metab. Clin. N. Am.* **2016**, *45*, 783–797. [CrossRef] [PubMed]
24. Brinkman, K.; Smeitink, J.A.; Romijin, J.A.; Reiss, P. Mitochondrial toxicity induced by nucleotide-analogue reverse-transcriptase inhibitors is a key factor in the pathogenesis of antiretroviral-therapy-related lipodystrophy. *Lancet* **1999**, *354*, 1112–1115. [CrossRef]
25. Caron-Debarle, M.; Lagathu, C.; Boccara, F.; Vigouroux, C.; Capeau, J. HIV-associated lipodystrophy: From fat injury to premature aging. *Trends Mol. Med.* **2010**, *16*, 218–229. [CrossRef]
26. Waters, L.; Nelson, M. Long-term complications of antiretroviral therapy: Lipoatrophy. *Int. J. Clin. Pract.* **2007**, *61*, 999–1014. [CrossRef]
27. Borsa, M.; Ferreira, P.L.; Petry, A.; Ferreira, L.G.; Camargo, M.M.; Bou-Habib, D.C.; Pinto, A.R. HIV infection and antiretroviral therapy lead to unfolded protein response activation. *Virol. J.* **2015**, *12*, 77. [CrossRef]
28. Carr, A.; Samaras, K.; Chisholm, D.J.; Cooper, D.A. Pathogenesis of HIV-1-protease inhibitor-associated peripheral lipodystrophy, hyperlipidaemia, and insulin resistance. *Lancet* **1998**, *351*, 1881–1883. [CrossRef]
29. Carr, A. HIV protease inhibitor-related lipodystrophy syndrome. *Clin. Infect. Dis.* **2000**, *30*, S135–S142. [CrossRef]
30. Paparizos, V.A.; Kyriakis, K.P.; Botsis, C.; Papastamopoulos, V.; Hadjivassiliou, M.; Stavrianeas, N.G. Protease inhibitor therapy-associated lipodystrophy, hypertriglyceridaemia and diabetes mellitus. *AIDS* **2000**, *14*, 903–905. [CrossRef]
31. Martinez, E.; Mocroft, A.; García-Viejo, M.A.; Pérez-Cuevas, J.B.; Blanco, J.L.; Mallolas, J.; Bianchi, L.; Conget, I.; Blanch, J.; Phillips, A.; et al. Risk of lipodystrophy in HIV-1-infected patients treated with protease inhibitors: A prospective cohort study. *Lancet* **2001**, *357*, 592–598. [CrossRef]
32. Burnouf, M.; Buffet, M.; Schwarzinger, M.; Roman, P.; Bui, P.; Prévot, M.; Deleuze, J.; Morini, J.P.; Franck, N.; Gorin, I.; et al. Evaluation of Coleman lipostructure for treatment of facial lipoatrophy in patients with human immunodeficiency virus and parameters associated with the efficiency of this technique. *Arch. Dermatol.* **2005**, *141*, 1220–1224. [CrossRef] [PubMed]
33. Dollfus, C.; Blanche, S.; Trocme, N.; Funck-Brentano, I.; Bonnet, F.; Levan, P. Correction of facial lipoatrophy using autologous fat transplants in HIV-infected adolescents. *HIV Med.* **2009**, *10*, 263–268. [CrossRef] [PubMed]
34. Guaraldi, G.; Fontdevila, J.; Christensen, L.H.; Orlando, G.; Stentarelli, C.; Carli, F.; Zona, S.; de Santis, G.; Pedone, A.; De Fazio, D.; et al. Surgical correction of HIV-associated facial lipoatrophy. *AIDS* **2011**, *25*, 1–12. [CrossRef]
35. Garrabou, G.; López, S.; Morén, C.; Martínez, E.; Fontdevila, J.; Cardellach, F.; Gatell, J.M.; Miró, O. Mitochondrial damage in adipose tissue of untreated HIV-infected patients. *AIDS* **2011**, *25*, 165–170. [CrossRef]
36. Akita, S.; Akino, K.; Hirano, A.; Ohtsuru, A.; Yamashita, S. Noncultured autologous adipose-derived stem cells therapy for chronic radiation injury. *Stem Cells Int.* **2010**, *2010*, 532704. [CrossRef]
37. Bunnell, B.A.; Flaat, M.; Gagliardi, C.; Patel, B.; Ripoll, C. Adipose-derived stem cells: Isolation, expansion, and differentiation. *Methods* **2008**, *45*, 115–120. [CrossRef]
38. Loo, D.T.; Fuguay, J.I.; Rawson, C.L.; Barnes, D.W. Extended culture of mouse embryo cells without senescence: Inhibition by serum. *Science* **1987**, *236*, 200–202. [CrossRef]
39. Takahashi, K.; Tanabe, K.; Ohnuki, M.; Narita, M.; Ichisaka, T.; Tomoda, K.; Yamanaka, S. Induction of pluripotent stem cells from adult human fibroblasts by defined factors. *Cell* **2007**, *131*, 861–872. [CrossRef]

40. Gentile, P. Autologous cellular method using micrografts of human adipose tissue derived follicle stem cells in androgenic alopecia. *Int. J. Mol. Sci.* **2019**, *20*, 3446. [CrossRef]

41. Gir, P.; Oni, G.; Brown, S.A.; Mojallal, A.; Rohrich, R.J. Human adipose stem cells: Current clinical applications. *Plast. Reconstr. Surg.* **2012**, *129*, 1277–1290. [CrossRef] [PubMed]

42. Karagoz, H.; Zor, F.; Goktas, E.; Gorantla, V.S. Adipogenesis for soft tissue reconstitution. *Curr. Opin. Organ Transplant.* **2019**, *24*, 598–603. [CrossRef] [PubMed]

43. Konno, M.; Hamabe, A.; Hasegawa, S.; Ogawa, H.; Fukusumi, T.; Nishikawa, S.; Ohta, K.; Kano, Y.; Ozaki, M.; Noguchi, Y.; et al. Adipose-derived mesenchymal stem cells and regenerative medicine. *Dev. Growth Differ.* **2013**, *55*, 309–318. [CrossRef] [PubMed]

44. Mazini, L.; Rochette, L.; Amine, M.; Malka, G. Regenerative capacity of adipose derived stem cells (SDSCs), comparison with mesenchymal stem cells (MSCs). *Int. J. Mol. Sci.* **2019**, *20*, 2523. [CrossRef]

45. Mizuno, H.; Tobita, M.; Uysal, A.C. Concise review: Adipose-derived stem cells as a novel tool for future regenerative medicine. *Stem Cells* **2012**, *30*, 804–810. [CrossRef]

46. Trivisonno, A.; Alexander, R.W.; Baldari, S.; Cohen, S.R.; Di Rocco, G.; Gentile, P.; Magalon, G.; Magalon, J.; Miller, R.B.; Womack, H.; et al. Concise review: Intraoperative strategies for minimal manipulation of autologous adipose tissue for cell- and tissue-based therapies. *Stem Cells Transl. Med.* **2019**. [CrossRef]

47. Pikula, M.; Marek-Trzonkowska, N.; Wardowska, A.; Renkielska, A.; Trzonkowski, P. Adipose tissue-derived stem cells in clinical applications. *Expert Opin. Biol. Ther.* **2013**, *13*, 1357–1370. [CrossRef]

48. Gimble, J.M.; Bunnell, B.A.; Guilak, F. Human adipose-derived cells: A update on the transition to clinical translation. *Regen. Med.* **2012**, *7*, 225–235. [CrossRef]

49. Skalnikova, K.H. Proteomic techniques for characterization of mesenchymal stem cell secretome. *Biochimie* **2013**, *95*, 2196–2211. [CrossRef]

50. Lee, E.Y.; Xia, Y.; Kim, W.S.; Kim, M.H.; Kim, T.H.; Kim, K.J.; Park, B.S.; Sung, J.H. Hypoxia-enhanced wound-healing function of adipose-derived stem cells: Increase in stem cell proliferation and up-regulation of VEGF and bFGF. *Wound Repair Regen.* **2009**, *17*, 540–547. [CrossRef]

51. Lombardi, F.; Palumbo, P.; Augello, F.R.; Cifone, M.G.; Cinque, B.; Giuliani, M. Secretome of adipose tissue-derived stem cells (ASCs) as a novel trend in chronic non-healing wounds: An overview of experimental in vitro and in vivo studies and methodological variables. *Int. J. Mol. Sci.* **2019**, *20*, 3721. [CrossRef] [PubMed]

52. Ren, S.; Chen, J.; Duscher, D.; Liu, Y.; Guo, G.; Kang, Y.; Xiong, H.; Zhan, P.; Wang, Y.; Wang, C.; et al. Microvesicles from human adipose stem cells promote wound healing by optimizing cellular functions via AKT and ERK signaling pathways. *Stem Cell Res. Ther.* **2019**, *10*, 47. [CrossRef] [PubMed]

53. Varghese, J.; Griffin, M.; Mosahebi, A.; Butler, P. Systematic review of patient factors affecting adipose stem cell viability and function: Implications for regenerative therapy. *Stem Cell Res. Ther.* **2017**, *8*, 45. [CrossRef] [PubMed]

Article

Cloning, Expression and Effects of *P. americana* Thymosin on Wound Healing

Jie Jing [1], Xiaohong Sun [1], Chuang Zhou [1], Yifan Zhang [1], Yongmei Shen [2], Xiaomao Zeng [3], Bisong Yue [1] and Xiuyue Zhang [4,*]

[1] Key Laboratory of Bio-Resources and Eco-Environment of Ministry of Education, College of Life Sciences, Sichuan University, Chengdu 610065, China; jingjie321@126.com (J.J.); xiaoyingsun007@163.com (X.S.); czhou_scu@163.com (C.Z.); 15527336358@163.com (Y.Z.); bsyue@scu.edu.cn (B.Y.)
[2] Sichuan Key Laboratory of Medicinal American Cockroach, Good doctor Pharmaceutical Group, Chengdu 610000, China; sym@hys.cn
[3] Department of Herpetology, Chengdu Institute of biology, Chinese Academy of Sciences, Chengdu 610041, China; zengxm@cib.ac.cn
[4] Sichuan Key Laboratory of Conservation Biology on Endangered Wildlife, College of Life Sciences, Sichuan University, Chengdu 610065, China
* Correspondence: zhangxiuyue@scu.edu.cn; Tel.: +86-28-85412057

Received: 25 August 2019; Accepted: 3 October 2019; Published: 5 October 2019

Abstract: The American cockroach (*Periplaneta americana*) is a medicinal insect. Its extract is used clinically to promote wound healing and tissue regeneration, but the effective medicinal components and mechanisms are not yet clear. It has been reported that human thymosin beta 4 (Tβ4) may accelerate skin wound healing, however, the role of *P. americana* thymosin (Pa-THYs) is still poorly understood. In the present study, we identify and analyze the DNA sequences of Pa-THYs by bioinformatics analysis. Then we clone, express, and purify the Pa-THYs proteins and evaluate the activity of recombinant Pa-THYs proteins by cell migration and proliferation assays in NIH/3T3 cells. To elucidate the role of Pa-THYs in wound healing, a mouse model is established, and we evaluate wound contraction, histopathological parameters, and the expressions of several key growth factors after Pa-THYs treatment. Our results showed that three THY variants were formed by skipping splicing of exons. Pa-THYs could promote fibroblast migration, but have no effect on fibroblast proliferation. In wound repair, Pa-THYs proteins could effectively promote wound healing through stimulating dermal tissue regeneration, angiogenesis, and collagen deposition. On the molecular mechanism, Pa-THYs also stimulated the expression of several key growth factors to promote wound healing. The data suggest that Pa-THYs could be a potential drug for promoting wound repair.

Keywords: *Periplaneta americana*; multimeric thymosin; prokaryotic expression; wound healing

---

1. Introduction

Skin is the largest external organ of the human body and is vulnerable to injuries. Particularly, in elderly or diabetic patients, wound healing tends to be delayed and the risk of wound infection is increased due to vascular aging and the weakness of tissue repair ability, which may eventually lead to chronic wounds. In addition, wound treatment brings serious economic burdens and psychological pressure to society, for example, in the United States, wound treatment costs more than $30 billion a year [1]. Therefore, wound repair is one of the hot topics in the field of dermal surgery. At present, few agents have been discovered to substantially promote wound repair in patients [2]. Current strategies mainly include small molecule compounds extracted from plants or growth factors (epidermal growth factor-like proteins (EGF), and human platelet-derived growth factor (PDGF-BB). However, small molecule compounds are unstable and less active, and growth factors are expensive, which restricts their clinical application [3,4]. Therefore, the development of new drugs for wound healing has become very important.

Thymosin β4 is a small (5 kDa) peptide, containing 43 amino acids and is found in many tissues and cell lines of vertebrates, and is also known to be rich in platelets [5]. Structurally, there is only one "THY" domain in human thymosin β4 (Tβ4), which usually contains a conserved motif "LKKTET" that can form a complex with G-actin in a 1:1 ratio and inhibits G-actin to polymerize into filaments [6]. Aside from the function in actin-sequestering of Tβ4, it participates in numerous biological activities, including wound healing [7], angiogenesis [8], cardiac repair [9], anti-inflammation [10,11], hair regrowth [12], and reproduction [13]. To date, β-thymosin has been well researched in vertebrates, but there are very limited studies on invertebrates, especially in insects. With the development of bioinformatics, more and more thymosin β4 homologues from invertebrates were identified. Compared with β-thymosin in vertebrates, β-thymosin from invertebrates has more than one "THY" domain which was categorized as a multimeric β-thymosin [14]. Although their homology is relatively high, some functions are different. For example, multimeric β-thymosin can promote actin polymerization, whereas β-thymosin is thought to be a sequester protein, which suggests that the function of these two kinds of thymosin behave differently [6]. In addition, owing to exon skip splicing, many varieties of thymosin in invertebrates have several isoforms, actually, they come from the same gene and the functions of different isoforms are different [15,16]. However, most researches about multimeric β-thymosin focused on its structural characterization, the style to connect with G-actin or the expression in mRNA level, and little information has been explored on its molecular function [16–18].

P. americana, is a traditional Chinese medicine. Its extract has a good effect on wound healing [19]. Yet the key effective medicinal composition is still unknown, which hinders the further clinical utilization and exploitation of *P. americana*. Considering that both vertebrate Tβ4 and the extract of *P. americana* have good effects on wound healing, it is surprising that there are no reports about *P. americana* thymosin. Therefore, the aim of this study is to get insights into the role of *P. americana* thymosin in wound healing using animal models. Herein, we obtained the DNA sequences of thymosin β4 homologue from *P. americana* genome and transcriptome by bioinformatics analysis. By in vitro and in vivo experiments, we evaluate the function of Pa-THYs in wound healing. The present study first demonstrates the role of multimeric β-thymosin protein for promoting wound healing in animal models and provides a potential drug for wound healing.

2. Results

2.1. Bioinformatics Analysis of P. americana Thymosin

Based on the genome and transcriptome databases of *P. americana* which were established by our laboratory, we identified the genome and transcript sequences of Pa-THYs by bioinformatics analysis. There are one genome sequence and three transcript sequences of Pa-THYs. The genome sequence, which contained six exons: exon 1 (139 bp), exon 2 (114 bp), exon 3 (114 bp), exon 4 (114 bp), exon 5 (114 bp), and exon 6 (26 bp) and five introns: intron 1 (4350 bp), intron 2 (7658 bp), intron 3 (6807 bp), intron 4 (2311 bp), and intron 5 (4419 bp) (Figure 1a).

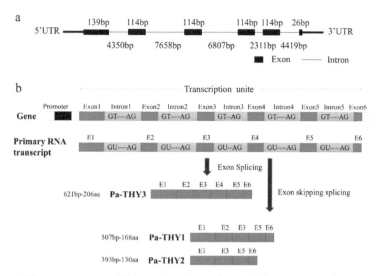

Figure 1. The gene structure of β-thymosin in *P. americana*. (**a**) The structure and composition of β-thymosin in *P. americana*. (**b**) The exon skipping splicing process of *P. americana* thymosin (Pa-THYs).

Due to skipping splicing of exons, three different transcripts were formed, which named as THY1, THY2 and THY3. THY3 contains all the exon sequences, while exon 4 is absent in THY1 and exon 2 and 4 are absent in THY2 (Figure 1b). These three transcript sequences were deposited in GenBank. They contain 507, 393, and 621 base pairs and encode 168, 130, and 206 amino acids respectively. The molecular weight of the THYs was 19 kDa, 14.6 kDa, and 23.4 kDa, and PI (isoelectric point) was 6.15, 5.70, and 5.95, respectively. The corresponding proteins were named as Pa-THY1, Pa-THY2, and Pa-THY3. No signal peptide was detected in Pa-THYs by the SignalP 3.0 software. These three proteins are hydrophilic non-transmembrane proteins. The secondary structure of the protein is mainly composed of an alpha helix and irregular curl. According to sequence BLAST (Basic Local Alignment Search Tool) results, the longest sequence of THY3 was wholly contained THY1 and THY2. By using motif scan software, we found that THY3 have five "THY" domains, THY1 and THY2 have four and three "THY" domains, respectively (Table 1).

Table 1. Results of bioinformatics analysis of Pa-THYs.

	Pa-THY1	Pa-THY2	Pa-THY3
Amino acid	168	130	206
Molecular weight (kDa)	19,039.55	14,582.52	23,435.50
Isoelectric point (PI)	6.15	5.70	5.95
Signal peptide	none	none	none
Transmembrane	no	no	no
Hydrophilic/Hydrophobic	Hydrophilic	Hydrophilic	Hydrophilic
Subcellular locations	plasma membrane and nucleus	plasma membrane and nucleus	plasma membrane and nucleus
Alpha helix (%)	52.38%	49.23%	51.%
Random coil (%)	45.24%	47.69%	42.72%
Beta turn (%)	2.38%	3.08%	3.40%
Extended strand (%)	0%	0%	2.43%
"THY" domains	4	3	5

2.2. Function Domain Analysis of P. americana Thymosin

According to the results of sequence alignment, Pa-THY isoforms 1, 2, and 3 resembled the "assembly-promoting form" like other multimeric thymosin, which can promote a free barbed-end filament elongation [6]. This is because they have a long N-terminal helix (green rectangle) and unstable C-terminal structure which was decided by two function residues (red rectangle) [20,21] (Figure 2). Additionally, multimeric thymosin contains more than two "THY" domains, which can bind at least two G-actins [17]. The "THY" domain has a highly conserved region. In vertebrates, the conserved motif sequence is LKKTET [13], while in *P. americana* and other invertebrates the motif sequences are LKH(R)TET, MKKAET, and MKPTQT (black rectangle), respectively (Figure 2). Pa-THY isoforms 1, 2, and 3 have 4, 3, and 5 domains, respectively, which means that they can combine more and different numbers of G-actin, hence their properties may be different from each other.

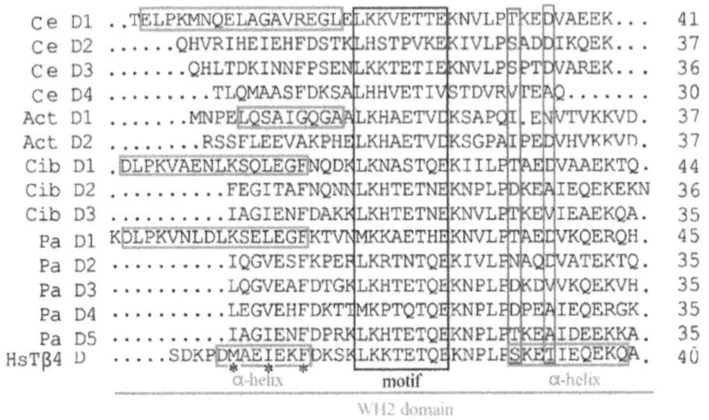

```
Ce  D1  ..TELPKMNQELAGAVREGLELKKVETTEKNVLPTKEDVAEEK...    41
Ce  D2  ......QHVRIHEIEHFDSTKLHSTPVKEKIVLPSADDIKQEK...    37
Ce  D3  .......QHLTDKINNFPSENLKKTETIEKNVLPSPTDVAREK...    36
Ce  D4  .........TLQMAASFDKSALHHVETIVSTDVRVTEAQ.......    30
Act D1  .......MNPELQSAIGQGAALKHAETVDKSAPQIL ENVTVKKVD.    37
Act D2  ........RSSFLEEVAKPHELKHAETVDKSGPAIPEDVHVKKVD.    37
Cib D1  .DLPKVAENLKSQLEGFNQDKLKNASTQEKIIILPTAEDVAAEKTQ.   44
Cib D2  ..........FEGITAFNQNNLKHTETNEKNPLPDKEAIEQEKEKN    36
Cib D3  ..........IAGIENFDAKKLKHTETNEKNVLPTKEVIEAEKQA.    35
Pa  D1  KDLPKVNLDLKSELEGFKTVNMKKAETHEKNVLPTAEDVKQERQH.    45
Pa  D2  ..........IQGVESFKPEFLKRTNTQEKIVLFNAQDVATEKTQ.    35
Pa  D3  ..........LQGVEAFDTGKLKHTETQEKNPLPDKDVVKQEKVH.    35
Pa  D4  .........LEGVEHFDKTTMKPTQTQEKNPLPDPEAIEQERGK.    35
Pa  D5  ..........IAGIENFDPRKLKHTETQEKNPLPTKEAIDEEKKA.    35
HsTβ4 D  .....SDKPDMAEIEKFDKSKLKHTETQEKNPLFSKETIEQEKQA.    40
                    α-helix        motif        α-helix
         ─────────────────────────────────────────
                          WH2 domain
```

Figure 2. Function domains analysis of thymosins. Alignment of five Pa-THYs domains with the other four thymosins from different species (Ciboulot (Cib D, three), Actobidin (Act D, two), tetra thymosinβ (Ce D, four), and human thymosin β4 (HsTβ4 D, one)). α-helix, motif sequences, and function residues were marked by green, black and red rectangle, respectively.

2.3. Expression and Purification of Recombinant Protein Pa-THYs

Recombinant plasmids (PET-THYs) were transformed into *E coli* BL21 (DE3) (Novagen, USA). The results were confirmed by bacterial PCR and Sanger sequencing (TSINGKE, Beijing). Then, the *E. coli* was induced to express the THYs protein and Ni-affinity chromatography was used to purify the proteins. As expected, after being analyzed by SDS-PAGE, recombinant protein Pa-THY1, Pa-THY2 and Pa-THY3 with a molecular mass of approximately 25 kDa, 20 kDa and 30 kDa were detected (Figure 3). All of the above proteins were soluble. In order to get higher concentration protein, the Millipore was used to concentrate these proteins. After that, the concentration of protein was about 3 µg/µL (Pa-THY1), 2 µg/µL (Pa-THY2), and 3 µg/µL (Pa-THY3), respectively.

2.4. Pa-THYs Promoted Cell Migration of Fibroblasts

To confirm the bioactivity and the ability for wound healing of purified proteins (Pa-THYs), the fibroblasts (NIH/3T3) were used to evaluate the ability of Pa-THYs on cell migration and proliferation. An in vitro cell scratch was performed to investigate the effect of Pa-THYs on the migration of fibroblasts. The results showed that Pa-THYs proteins promoted migration of fibroblasts with different concentrations. Based on the quantitative analysis of cell migration rates, Pa-THYs and Tβ4 obviously accelerated the migration of fibroblasts compared to PBS (phosphate buffer saline), and Pa-THY3 had a stronger effect than others during cell migration in a low concentration (0.1 µg/mL). For Tβ4, Pa-THY1 and Pa-THY2, the best concentration for cell migration was 1 µg/mL, while for Pa-THY3 was 0.1 µg/mL. Increasing protein concentration revealed a negative effect for cell migration in Tβ4 and all Pa-THYs proteins (Figure 4a,b).

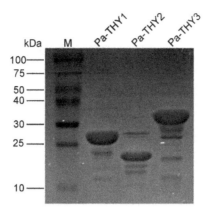

Figure 3. The purification of recombinant protein Pa-THYs: lane 1, marker (M) proteins and their corresponding molecular masses; lane 2, the concentrated Pa-THY1 protein; lane 3, the concentrated Pa-THY2 protein; lane 4, the concentrated Pa-THY3 protein.

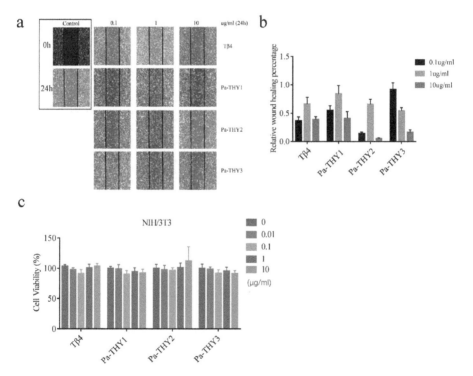

Figure 4. Effects of Pa-THYs on the migration and proliferation of fibroblasts. (**a**) Representative images of NIH/3T3 cells treated by Tβ4 and Pa-THYs proteins (0, 0.1 μg/mL, 1 μg/mL and 10 μg/mL). Magnification, ×200. (**b**) Quantification of wound-healing assays in NIH/3T3 cells treated with Tβ4 and Pa-THYs proteins. The wound healing percentage was compared with control group. (**c**) Cell viability of NIH/3T3 cells treated by Tβ4 and Pa-THYs proteins with different concentrations (0, 0.01 μg/mL, 0.1 μg/mL, 1 μg/mL, and 10 μg/mL).

MTT (3-(4,5-dimethyl-2-thiazolyl)-2,5-diphenyl-2-H-tetrazolium bromide, Thiazolyl Blue Tetrazolium Bromide) assays were employed to determine the effects of Pa-THYs on the proliferation of fibroblasts. Compared to the control group, all Pa-THYs and Tβ4 with different concentrations had no effect on the proliferation of fibroblasts (Figure 4c).

2.5. Recombinant Protein Pa-THYs Promoted Wound Healing

Previous data showed considerable migration effects of Pa-THYs on fibroblasts and initially proved that Pa-THYs were involved in wound healing. To observe the effect of Pa-THYs on wound healing, a full-thickness skin wound model was established on the dorsal region of mice. Mice were treated with Pa-THYs proteins every day (24 h interval), with PBS treatment as a negative control and Tβ4 treatment as a positive control. The body weight and area of wounds were measured every two days. The surface changes of dermal wounded skin and the images of the wound appearance were observed and obtained every two days after treatment. During the wound healing process, all wounds were dry and had a large scar at first, then the scar of Tβ4 and Pa-THYs groups became moist and granulation tissue appeared while those in the PBS group were about to fall off (Figure 5a). Compared to PBS and Tβ4 groups, Pa-THYs groups showed obvious wound contraction since day 3. Based on the statistical data, Pa-THYs groups significantly accelerated wound healing compared with the PBS group at day 3, Pa-THYs and Tβ4 treatment significantly accelerated wound healing compared with PBS group at day 9 and 11 (Figure 5b). The results also showed that the mice's body weight was not affected after treatment (Figure 5c). Obvious abnormal behavior or noticeable toxicity were not observed.

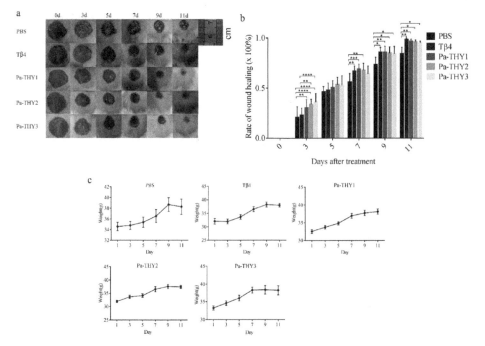

Figure 5. Effects of Pa-THYs proteins on wound healing in mouse models. (**a**) Representative images of skin wounds treated by Tβ4 and Pa-THYs proteins at indicated time points (0 d, 3 d, 5 d, 7 d, 9 d, and 11 d). (**b**) Quantification data of wound-healing closure in mice treated with Tβ4 and Pa-THYs proteins at indicated time points (0 d, 3 d, 5 d, 7 d, 9 d, and 11 d). * $p < 0.05$; ** $p < 0.01$; *** $p < 0.001$; **** $p < 0.0001$. (**c**) The body weight of mice treated with Tβ4 and Pa-THYs proteins at indicated time points (0 d, 3 d, 5 d, 7 d, 9 d, and 11 d).

2.6. Pa-THYs Promoted Wound Healing by Accelerating Dermal Regeneration

To examine the effect of Pa-THYs on dermal regeneration, we collected the dermal tissues of mice treated by Tβ4 and Pa-THYs proteins at indicated time points (3 d, 5 d, 7 d, and 10 d). We analyzed the formation of granulation tissue and the proliferation of fibroblasts and inflammatory cells by H&E (hematoxylin-eosin) staining. Compared with the PBS group, our results indicated that there were a large number of fibroblasts and monocytes that migrated to the bottom of the wound area in Tβ4 and Pa-THYs treated groups on day 3 and few granulations were formed. On day 5, compared with the PBS group, there were a large number of granulation tissues were formed in Pa-THYs and Tβ4 treated groups. On day 7, as expected, the results clearly demonstrated that a high level of inflammation reaction happened in the PBS group. By contrast, the inflammatory response was milder in Tβ4 and Pa-THYs treated groups, and granulation tissues almost filled the whole wound area. On day 10, except for the PBS group, inflammatory cells nearly disappeared in the other treated groups and the wound area displayed better epithelialization, forming a complete epithelial structure (stratum corneum, hyaline layer, granular layer, spinous cell layer, basal layer). There was no obvious difference between the treated groups (Figure 6).

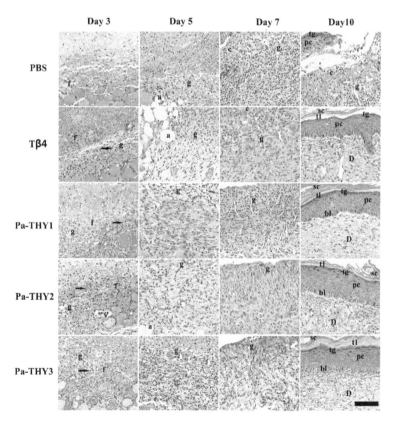

Figure 6. The H&E (hematoxylin-eosin) staining of dermal tissues treated with Tβ4 and Pa-THYs proteins. a: adipose tissue; c: connective tissue; f: fibroblasts; g: granulation tissue; sc: stratumcorneum; tl: transparent layer; tg: granular layer; pc: prickle cell layer; bl: basal layer; D: dermis; monocytes: marked by black arrowhead (Scale bar = 100 μm, ×200).

2.7. Pa-THYs Promoted Wound Healing Through Stimulating Angiogenesis

Angiogenesis is a critical process for wound healing in that newly formed blood vessels supply nutrients, amino acids, and oxygen to stimulate wound repair [22]. To evaluate the neovascularization during wound healing, the blood vessels were observed at indicated time points by CD31 (Platelet endothelial cell adhesion molecule-1) immunohistochemistry. Compared to the PBS group, Pa-THYs could significantly promote angiogenesis in the early stages of wound healing. As is seen, there were many newly formed blood vessels at the bottom of the wound area on days 3 and 5. Compared to the PBS group, the CD31$^+$ area in Tβ4 and Pa-THYs treated groups were significantly increased on day 3 and day 5. After that, the new blood vessels significantly increased on day 7 and day 10 in PBS group while the new blood vessels showed no obviously variation in Tβ4 and Pa-THYs treated groups, and a large number of stripe-like blood vessels remained in the PBS group on day 10 (Figure 7).

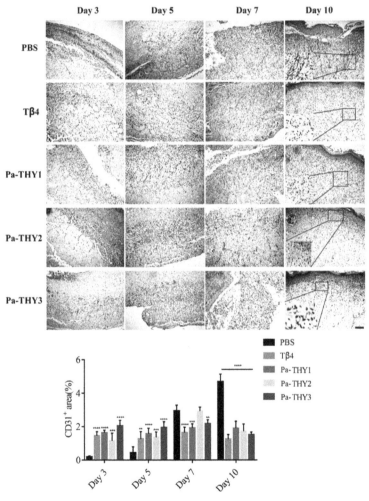

Figure 7. The CD31 staining of wound areas in dermal tissues treated with Tβ4 and Pa-THYs proteins (scale bar = 200 μm, ×100). All the groups compared to PBS group in certain time point, two-way ANOVA analysis,; ** $p < 0.01$; *** $p < 0.001$; **** $p < 0.0001$.

2.8. Pa-THYs Promoted Wound Healing Through Stimulating Collagen Deposition

Collagen is an important component for reconstructing dermis tissues at wound sites [23]. Masson's trichrome staining was applied to describe collagen deposition (the blue shaded area) in dermal tissues treated with Tβ4 and Pa-THYs proteins. As showed in Figure 8, compared with the PBS group, significant accumulation of the collagen fibers was observed in the bottom of wound tissues when treated with Tβ4 and Pa-THYs proteins on day 3 and day 5. From day 5 to day 10, collagen gradually filled up with the whole wound tissue in all groups. Statistical analysis found that collagen fibers were slowly formed on day 10 in Pa-THYs groups compared to PBS and Tβ4 treated groups. These data indicated that Pa-THYs could promote wound healing through stimulating collagen deposition in early stage.

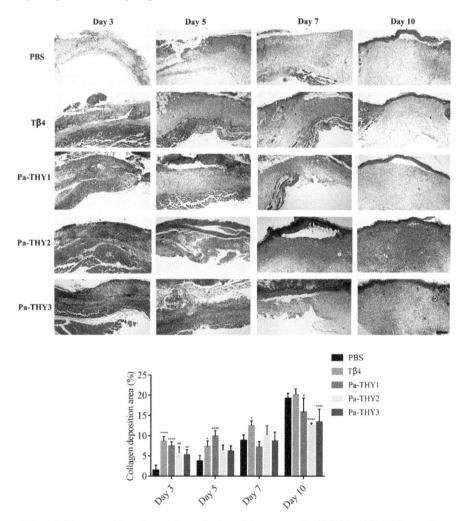

Figure 8. Masson staining of wound areas in dermal tissues treated with Tβ4 and Pa-THYs proteins (Scale bar = 500 μm, ×40). All the groups compared to PBS group in certain time point, two-way ANOVA analysis, * $p < 0.05$; ** $p < 0.01$; **** $p < 0.0001$.

2.9. Pa-THYs Stimulating the Expression of Cytokines and Growth Factors

To confirm the role of cytokines and growth factors to wound healing after Tβ4 and Pa-THYs proteins treatment, we examined the expression of relative factors (vascular endothelial growth factor (VEGF), fibroblast growth factor (b-FGF), transforming growth factor-β (TGF-β), matrix metallopeptidase 2 (MMP-2), and PDGF-BB at indicated time points (3 d, 5 d, 7 d, and 10 d). β-actin was used as a reference housekeeping gene to assess the different expression of factors between each group. As seen in Figure 9, our results show that all the factors participated in wound repair and that different Pa-THYs proteins may promote wound healing in different ways. Compared with the PBS group, Pa-THY1 mainly stimulated the expressions of b-FGF, MMP-2, TGF-β and PDGF-BB, but no factors significantly increased. Pa-THY2 mainly stimulated the expressions of MMP-2, TGF-β and PDGF-BB, and TGF-β significantly increased in day 5 and day 10. Pa-THY3 mainly stimulated the expressions of MMP-2 and PDGF-BB to accelerate wound healing, MMP-2 significantly increased in day 7 and PDGF-BB significantly increased in day 10.

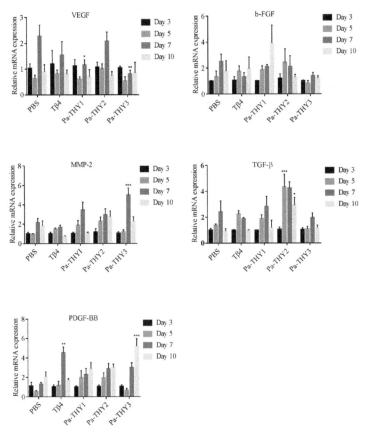

Figure 9. The expressions of vascular endothelial growth factor (VEGF), fibroblast growth factor (b-FGF), transforming growth factor-β (TGF-β), matrix metallopeptidase 2 (MMP-2), and platelet derived growth factor-BB (PDGF-BB) in mice treated with Tβ4 and Pa-THYs proteins were determined by qRT-PCR. All the factors were compared to PBS group in certain time point, Two-way ANOVA analysis, * $p < 0.05$; ** $p < 0.01$; *** $p < 0.001$.

3. Discussion

In vertebrates, β-thymosins usually have one conserved "THY" domain, while in invertebrates, the number of "THY" domains ranges from 2 (*Drosophila melanogaster*, NP_726909.1) to 27 (*Hydra vulgaris*, AAW82079.1) [16]. Different splicing methods could produce a variety of β-thymosin isoforms, and it can significantly increase the complexity of thymosin in invertebrates [15]. For example, there are two thymosin isoforms (HaTHY1 and HaTHY2) in *Helicoverpa armigera*, which are expressed differently in different organs and co-regulated growth and immune reaction [18]. In this study, due to exons alternative splicing, three *P. americana* thymosin isoforms were formed. The 4, 3, and 5 "THY" domains were identified in THY1, THY2 and THY3, respectively. A similar phenomenon was also found in other species such as the fruit fly [24], cotton bollworm [18], and termite [25]. Thus, the functions of these three isoforms may be different.

Multimeric thymosin could bind to more than one G-actin and enhance motility of filaments by promoting assembly in the barbed end (+). Its function was similar to profilin: G-actin complex was only occurring in multimeric thymosin [6,26]. The study found that the N-terminal a-helix amphipathic (M6, I9 and F12) and N-terminal a-helix length in β-thymosin/WH2 control the affinity of these peptides for actin, the elongation of N-terminal a-helix of β-thymosin may lead to the loss of actin sequester function [27,28]. Recent research confirmed that it is also relative to the stability of the C-terminal helix, which is mainly due to the two sites of Tβ4 (Ser31 and Thr34) were substitution [21,29]. Through sequence alignment, we found that thymosin from *P. americana* have a long N-terminal a-helix and unstable C-terminal helix. We observed that Pa-THYs not only combine more than one G-actin, but also promote G-actin assembly in the barbed end (+) of filament.

Cell migration involves dynamic change of the cytoskeleton. Multimeric β-thymosin could combine more than one G-actin to regulate assemble and disassemble of microfilaments. For example, Ciboulot (*Drosophila melanogaster*) have three "THY" domains and can bind two G-actin monomers; tetraThymosin (*Caenorhabditis elegans*) have four "THY" domains and can bind three G-actin monomers [17]. Pa-THYs could promote fibroblasts migration but have no effect on proliferation. It also demonstrated that the ability of Pa-THYs to stimulate fibroblasts migration was Pa-THY3 > Pa-THY1 > Pa-THY2. Therefore, we speculate that the different ability on cell migration may be related to the number of "THY" domains.

Wound healing is a complex physiological process of organisms, and is regulated by various cells and some intra- and intercellular signaling pathways derived from the epidermis and dermis [30]. It involves several interrelated phases, including hemostasis or coagulation (platelet aggregation and vasoconstriction), inflammation (release cytokines and remove debris), tissue regeneration (angiogenesis and granulation tissue formation) and tissue remolding (collagen deposition) [31]. Tβ4 could accelerate wound healing either directly applying to the surface of full-thickness dermal wound or giving intraperitoneal by stimulating angiogenesis, keratinocyte migration, collagen deposition and wound contraction [7,32–34]. It has also been found that Tβ4 have anti-inflammation properties in corneal wound healing [35], and cascade four Tβ4 (4xTβ4) was more efficient than standard Tβ4 in wound healing [36]. Researchers suggest that granulation tissue, which is mainly composed of fibroblasts, macrophages, and new blood capillaries, invades the wound space on the fourth day after injury [37]. Neovascularization occurs under hypoxic conditions, with the aim of transporting and utilizating adequate oxygen when tissue is destroyed [22]. In our research, at the early stage of wound healing, a large amount of fibroblasts, a few granulation tissues, and a few new blood vessels were observed in Pa-THYs and Tβ4 treatments. On day 7, granulation tissues were nearly filled in the whole wound, but there were still lots of inflammatory infiltrations in the PBS group. This may be one reason for delayed wound repair. Once the wound is filled up with new granulation tissue, the new blood vessels begin apoptosis [38]. On day 10, the wound in treatment groups had completely epithelialized, the inflammatory reactions and striate vessels disappeared compared with control group. Collagen is the major component for the improved strength of wound, and increasing collagen deposition can accelerate the epithelialization [39]. In this experiment, compared with the control group, the treatment groups present more collagen deposition at days 3 and 5. All of this confirmed that Pa-THYs could accelerate wound healing by promoting fibroblast migration, neovascularization, collagen deposition, and by inhibiting inflammation.

Researchers found that many growth factors are important in wound healing, such as VEGF, b-FGF, TGF-β, MMP-2, and PDGF-BB [40]. VEGF, b-FGF, and TGF-β are the most potent cytokines in promoting wound angiogenesis [41,42]. The expression of VEGF can be directly up-regulated by b-FGF, thus they have a synergistic effect [43]. MMPs were reported to be upregulated during wound healing when treated with Tβ4 [5]. PDGF-BB was approved for treatment of diabetic foot ulcers by the FDA [44], and it was reported that there is a more pronounced effect on myocardial angiogenesis when combined with PDGF-BB and b-FGF [45]. Previously, Tβ4 was reported to up-regulate the expression of VEGF and MMPs during dermal wound repair [46,47], which is in accordance with the results of our experiment. Most interestingly, researchers found that the new blood vessels were not formed after long time use Tβ4 to cure injured corneal [48]. This indicated that VEGF was not the major factor to promote angiogenesis. In this study, after treatment with protein Pa-THY1, Pa-THY2, and Pa-THY3, the expression changes of above factors were different. Pa-THY1 can obviously enhance the expression of b-FGF, MMP-2, TGF-β, and PDGF-BB. Pa-THY2 enhanced the expression of MMP-2, TGF-β, and PDGF-BB. Pa-THY3 up-regulated the expression of MMP-2 and PDGF-BB. Therefore, we suspect that different isoforms of thymosin from *P. americana* may regulate wound healing through different signal pathways. Further studies are required to evaluate the molecular mechanisms of Pa-THYs for accelerating wound healing.

4. Materials and Methods

4.1. Bioinformatics Analysis for DNA Sequences of P. americana Thymosin

We identified the gene and transcript sequences of *P. americana* thymosin from genomic and transcriptional databases which were built by our lab [49]. The introns and exons of the *P. americana* thymosin gene sequence were analyzed by the softberry program (http://linux1.softberry.com/all.htm). According to alternative splicing, there are three different transcript variants (THY1, THY2, and THY3) in *P. americana* thymosin. All complete thymosin cDNA sequences were deposited in GenBank (accession No. MK573540, MK573541, MK573542). The DNA sequences were analyzed by the online program at NCBI (https://blast.ncbi.nlm.nih.gov/Blast.cgi). Conserved motifs were determined using Motif Scan (http://myhits.isb-sib.ch/cgi-bin/motif_scan) and signal peptide was predicted using the SignalP Server (http://www.cbs.dtu.dk/services/SignalP/). The theoretical PI and molecular mass were estimated by ExPASy (http://www.expasy.ch/tools/peptide-mass.html).

4.2. Cloning, Expression, and Purification of Pa-THYs

The sequences of THYs were cloned into a PET-28(a) vector, the proteins Pa-THYs were expressed in *E. coli* cells and purified by His Trap TMFF crude. Briefly, the sequences of THYs were amplified from the total cDNA of *P. americana* with specific primers, as follows: PET-Pa-F (*EcoR* I): 5'-CGCGAATTCATGTCGGCCCCAGTC-3'; PET-Pa-R (*Xho* I): 5'-CCGCTCGAGTTATGCTTTCTT CTCTTCATCG-3 and then cloned into PET-28(a) vector at EcoR I and Xho I recognition sites. The plasmids of PET-THY1, PET-THY2, and PET-THY3 were transformed into *E. coli* BL21 (DE3) competent cells for the final expression. The proteins (Pa-THY1, Pa-THY2, and Pa-THY3) were induced by isopropyl β-D-thiogalactoside (IPTG) at 37 °C for 6 h. The cells were harvested by centrifuging at 8000 rpm for 10 min and suspending in a 1× PBS phosphate buffer. The *E. coli* was shattered using ultrasonication, then centrifuged at 12,000× g for 10 min at 4 °C to remove the precipitate. The recombined proteins were purified by His Trap TMFF crude (1 mL) according to the manufacturer's instructions and analyzed with SDS-PAGE. To get the high concentration of these proteins, they were concentrated by an ultrafiltration centrifuge tube (Millipore, Massachussettes, USA), and the total protein concentration was measured by BCA (bicinchoninic acid) protein assay kit (Biosharp, Hefei, Anhui, China) according to the manufacturer's instructions.

4.3. Cell Culture

The NIH/3T3 cell line was provided by the Core Facility of West China Hospital. The NIH/3T3 cell was cultured with DMEM (HyClone, Boston, MA, USA) supplemented with 10% fetal bovine serum (FBS) at 37 °C in a humidified atmosphere of 5% CO_2.

4.4. Cell Migration and Proliferation Assays

Effects of Pa-THYs on NIH/3T3 cell migration were determined by wound healing assay. Briefly, wound healing assay was carried out in six-well plates (3×105 cells/well), wounds were created using a pipette tip. The cells were then rinsed with PBS to remove any free-floating cells and debris. After washing, the medium was replaced by a control medium with different concentrations (0, 0.1, 1 and 10 μg/mL) Pa-THYs, and the cells were incubated at 37 °C. The area of wound healing was observed at 0, and 24 h, and representative images for each concentration were photographed. NIH/Image J software (https://imagej.net/NIH_Image) was used for quantification of the scratch wound area based on an edge-detection and thresholding technique. We calculated the migrated area by calculating the blank area of the scratch in different time point after Pa-THYs protein treatment.

Effects of Pa-THYs on NIH/3T3 cell proliferation were determined by MTS (3-(4,5-dimethylthiazol-2-yl)-5-(3-carboxymethoxyphenyl)-2-(4-sulfophenyl)-2H-tetrazolium) (72 h) assays. Briefly, MTS assays were carried out in 96-well plates (2000 cells/well, five replicates), and the treatments of proteins were initiated at 24 h post-seeding, cells were cultured for 72 h. Then 20 μL MTS (Promega, Madison, WI, USA) was added to each well (100 μL medium) and incubated for 1–2 h at 37 °C. OD490 was measured by a Gen5 Microplate Reader (BioTek, Winooski, Vermont, USA) according to the manufacturer's instructions. IC50 values were calculated by GraphPad Prism 5 (San Diego, CA, USA).

4.5. Animal Model

The *P. americana* were raised in our lab in an appropriate environment (T: 25–30 °C; humidity: 70–80%). Synthetic Tβ4 was purchased from Shanghai Zhengyan Chemical Technology Co., Ltd. (Shanghai, China). A total of 75 free of viruses, bacteria and parasites KUNMING mice (7 weeks old, male) were purchased from Da Shuo (Cheng Du, China). The mice were raised in a standard laboratory pellet diet and water ad libitum about a week to adapt the environment under controlled temperature (22–25 °C) and humidity (about 60%) with a 12 h light/ dark cycle. All animals testing used in this study were performed in accordance with guidelines of the Animal Care Committee of Sichuan University (Chengdu, China).(20190412001, 12, April 2019).

Before the mouse model was established, all mice were anesthetized by intraperitoneal injection of 10% chloral hydrate. Under sterile conditions, the dorsal hair of the mice was shaved and completely removed with hair removal cream (Veet, Tokyo, Japan), then the skin was sterilized with 75% EtOH and a circular full-thickness excisional wound on dorsal of each mouse was made, 1.2 cm in diameter, which was created by a surgical scissor. The mice were divided into five groups of fifteen animals, each including: control group with wound and PBS treatment, positive group with wound and Tβ4 (5 μg) treatment, test group I with wound and Pa-THY1 (5 μg) treatment, test group II with wound and Pa-THY2 (5 μg) treatment, test group III with wound and Pa-THY3 (5 μg) treatment. After 24 h of surgery, they were applied to the wound by pipetting the liquid (50 μL) directly into the wound area until 11 days later. The wounds were left open with no dressing.

4.6. Macroscopic Evaluation

Appetite and general health conditions were monitored daily, and body weight was measured every other day. For wound area study, the wound beds were photographed with a digital camera and a ruler at the specific time points (0 d, 3 d, 5 d, 7 d, 9 d, and 11 d). Wound images were used to calculate the wound area by the NIH/Image J software. The following equation was used to measure the rate of wound closure,

$$y(n) = \frac{A_0 - X_n}{A_0} \cdot 100\% \tag{1}$$

where y (n): the rate of wound closure (%); A_0: wound area at day 0; X_n: wound area at day (n). Wound healing curves were constructed by Graph Pad Prism 5.

4.7. Sample Collection and Histological Analysis

To examine re-epithelialization, granulation tissue, vessel counts, and collagen content of the wounds, three mice from each group were euthanized at 3, 5, 7, and 10 days after treatment. The entire wound and adjacent wound were harvested down to the fascia, and then bisected through the center of the lesion to get the largest diameter of the wound, one-part tissue was stored in liquid nitrogen to detect the expression of relative factors and another part was fixed in formalin solution (4%) for histological evaluation of wound healing. The fixed tissue samples were routinely processed and embedded in paraffin, 4 μm sections of middle wound bed were stained with hematoxylin and eosin (HE), CD31 antibody and Masson Trichrome. The positive area of CD31 and collagen deposition were measured by NIH/Image J software (https://imagej.net/NIH_Image).

4.8. RNA Extraction and qRT-PCR

Total RNA was extracted frozen tissues of wound healing models by using Trizol reagent (Takara, Japan) according to the manufacturer's instructions. The purity and concentration of total RNA were determined by UV Spectrophotometer (Eppendorf, Hamburg, Germany) and 1% agarose gel electrophoresis. The first-stand cDNA was synthesized by the HiScript®II 1st Strand cDNA Synthesis Kit (Vazyme, Nanjing, China) following the manufacturer's instructions. The primers of the quantitative real-time PCR (qRT-PCR) was designed by Prim5 software (Table 2). The qRT-PCR was used to detect relative expression of b-FGF, PDGF-BB, TGF-β, VEGF, and MMP-2 by an ABI 7500 real-time PCR detection system (ABI, Carlsbad, CA, USA), and the relative expression of these genes were normalized by an internal control (β-actin). The qRT-PCR final reaction volume was 20 μL which was added according to the instructions, and under the following conditions: 2 min of pre-denaturation at 95 °C, followed by the 30 cycles for 15 s, 59–60 °C for 15 s, and 72 °C for 30 s, and each reaction was performed in triplicate. Relative expression of genes was calculated using the $2^{-\Delta\Delta CT}$ method.

Table 2. Oligonucleotide primers used in the experiments.

Primer Name	Sequence F (5′–3′)	Sequence R (5′–3′)
VEGF	F:CTACTGCCGTCCGATTGA	R:TCTCCGCTCTGAACAAGG
TGF-β	F:AATACGTCAGACATTCGGGAAGCA	R:GTCAATGTACAGCTGCCGTACACA
b-FGF	F:TGCTTCCACCTCGTCTGTCT	R:GAGGCAAAGTGAAAGGGACC
MMP-2	F:GAACTTGCGATTATGCCATGATGAC	R:TCTGAGGGATGCCATCAAAGAC
PDGF-BB	F:CCAGGACGGTCATTTACG	R:TGGTCTGGGTTCAGGTTG
β-actin	F:CATCCGTAAAGATCTATGCCAAC	R:ATGGAGCCACCGATCCACA

4.9. Statistical Analysis

Data was shown as mean ± SD. The data were performed using a student's t-test (for two groups), one-way ANOVA followed by Tukey's test (for more than two groups) and two-way ANOVA followed by multiple comparisons were performed using Graph Pad Prism 5 (San Diego, CA, USA). The p-value < 0.05 was considered to be significant, the p-value < 0.01 was considered to be extremely significant.

Author Contributions: Conceptualization, J.J. and X.Z. (Xiuyue Zhang); software, C.Z. and Y.Z.; formal analysis, J.J. and X.S.; writing—original draft preparation, J.J. and C.Z.; writing—review and editing, X.Z. (Xiaomao Zeng), X.Z. (Xiuyue Zhang) and B.Y.; funding acquisition, Y.S. and X.Z. (Xiuyue Zhang).

Funding: The research was funded by the Science and Technology Project of Sichuan Province (2017SZ0019).

Conflicts of Interest: The authors declare no conflict of interest.

Abbreviations

IPTG	isopropyl β-D-thiogalactoside
Tβ4	human thymosin β4
THY	*P. americana* thymosin
VEGF	vascular endothelial growth factor
TGF-β	transforming growth factor-β
b-FGF	fibroblast growth factor
MMP-2	matrix metallopeptidase 2
PDGF-BB	platelet derived growth factor-BB

References

1.   Sosne, G.; Qiu, P.; Goldstein, A.L.; Wheater, M. Biological activities of thymosin beta4 defined by active sites in short peptide sequences. *FASEB J.* **2010**, *24*, 2144–2151. [CrossRef] [PubMed]

2.   Li, X.; Wang, Y.; Zou, Z.; Yang, M.; Wu, C.; Su, Y.; Tang, J.; Yang, X. OM-LV20, a novel peptide from odorous frog skin, accelerates wound healing in vitro and in vivo. *Chem. Biol. Drug Design* **2018**, *91*, 126–136. [CrossRef] [PubMed]

3.   Hardwicke, J.; Schmaljohann, D.; Boyce, D.; Thomas, D. Epidermal growth factor therapy and wound healing—Past, present and future perspectives. *Surgeon* **2008**, *6*, 172–177. [CrossRef]

4.   Yong, L.; Weichang, L.; Yanpeng, J.; Rui, G.; Yi, Z.; Wei, X.; Yuanming, Z. Therapeutic efficacy of antibiotic-loaded gelatin microsphere/silk fibroin scaffolds in infected full-thickness burns. *Acta Biomater.* **2014**, *10*, 3167–3176.

5.   Huff, T.; Otto, A.M.; Müller, C.S.; Meier, M.; Hannappel, E. Thymosin beta4 is released from human blood platelets and attached by factor XIIIa (transglutaminase) to fibrin and collagen. *FASEB J.* **2002**, *16*, 691. [CrossRef]

6.   Hertzog, M.; van Heijenoort, C.; Didry, D.; Gaudier, M.; Coutant, J.; Gigant, B.; Didelot, G.; Preat, T.; Knossow, M.; Guittet, E.; et al. The beta-thymosin/WH2 domain: Structural basis for the switch from inhibition to promotion of actin assembly. *Cell* **2004**, *117*, 611–623. [CrossRef]

7.   Malinda, K.M.; Sidhu, G.S.; Mani, H.; Banaudha, K.; Maheshwari, R.K.; Goldstein, A.L.; Kleinman, H.K. Thymosin beta 4 accelerates wound healing. *J. Investig. Dermatol.* **1999**, *113*, 364–368. [CrossRef]

8.   Philp, D.; Goldstein, A.L.; Kleinman, H.K. Thymosin β 4 promotes angiogenesis, wound healing, and hair follicle development. *Mech. Ageing Dev.* **2004**, *125*, 113–115. [CrossRef]

9.   Marks, E.D.; Kumar, A. Thymosin β4: Roles in Development, Repair, and Engineering of the Cardiovascular System. *Vitam. Horm.* **2016**, *102*, 227.

10.   Kim, C.E.; Kleinman, H.K.; Sosne, G.; Ousler, G.W.; Kim, K.; Kang, S.; Yang, J. RGN-259 (thymosin β4) improves clinically important dry eye efficacies in comparison with prescription dr μgs in a dry eye model. *Sci. Rep.* **2018**, *8*, 10500. [CrossRef]

11.   Sosne, G.; Szliter, E.A.; Barrett, R.; Kernacki, K.A.; Kleinman, H.; Hazlett, L.D. Thymosin Beta 4 Promotes Corneal Wound Healing and Decreases Inflammation in Vivo Following Alkali Injury. *Exp. Eye Res.* **2002**, *74*, 293–299. [CrossRef] [PubMed]

12.   Hee-Jae, C.; Deborah, P.; Soo-Hyun, L.; Hye-Sung, M.; Kleinman, H.K.; Takashi, N. Over-expression of thymosin beta 4 promotes abnormal tooth development and stimulation of hair growth. *Int. J. Dev. Biol.* **2010**, *54*, 135–140.

13.   Mohamad, S.; Pascal, P.; Christine, P.; Catherine, G.J.; Joelle, D.; Pascal, M.; Svetlana, U. Thymosins β-4 and β-10 are expressed in bovine ovarian follicles and upregulated in cumulus cells during meiotic maturation. *Reprod. Fertil. Dev.* **2010**, *22*, 1206.

14.   Troys, M.V.; Dhaese, S.; Vandekerckhove, J.; Ampe, C. *Multirepeat β-Thymosins*; Lappalainen, P., Ed.; Springer: New York, NY, USA, 2007; pp. 71–81.

15. Ma, S.; Kang, Z.; Peng, L.; Yang, Y.; Yao, Q.; Xia, H.; Chen, K. Molecular and Physiological Characterization of Two Novel Multirepeat β-Thymosins from Silkworm, Bombyx mori. *PLoS ONE* **2015**, *10*, e0140182. [CrossRef] [PubMed]

16. Gai, Y.; Zhao, J.; Song, L.; Wang, L.; Qiu, L.; Ning, X.; Zheng, X.; Zhang, Y.; Mu, C.; Zhang, Y.; et al. Two thymosin-repeated molecules with structural and functional diversity coexist in Chinese mitten crab Eriocheir sinensis. *Dev. Comp. Immunol.* **2009**, *33*, 867–876. [CrossRef] [PubMed]

17. Aguda, A.H.; Xue, B.; Irobi, E.; Préat, T.; Robinson, R.C. The Structural Basis of Actin Interaction with Multiple WH2/β-Thymosin Motif-Containing Proteins. *Structure* **2006**, *14*, 469–476. [CrossRef]

18. Zhang, F.X.; Shao, H.L.; Wang, J.X.; Zhao, X.F. beta-thymosin is upregulated by the steroid hormone 20-hydroxyecdysone and microorganisms. *Insect Mol. Biol.* **2011**, *20*, 519–527. [CrossRef] [PubMed]

19. Song, Q.; Gou, Q.; Xie, Y.; Zhang, Z.; Fu, C. Periplaneta americana Extracts Promote Skin Wound Healing via Nuclear Factor Kappa B Canonical Pathway and Extracellular Signal-Regulated Kinase Signaling. *Evid. -Based Complement. Altern. Med.* **2017**, *2017*, 5821706. [CrossRef]

20. Bo, X.; Cedric, L.; Grimes, J.M.; Robinson, R.C. Structural basis of thymosin-β4/profilin exchange leading to actin filament polymerization. *Proc. Natl. Acad. Sci. USA* **2014**, *111*, 4596–4605.

21. Xue, B.; Robinson, R.C. Chapter Three–Actin-Induced Structure in the Beta-Thymosin Family of Intrinsically Disordered Proteins. *Vitam. Horm.* **2016**, *102*, 55.

22. Knighton, D.R.; Silver, I.; Hunt, T.K. Regulation of wound-healing angiogenesis—Effect of oxygen gradients and inspired oxygen concentration. *Surgery* **1981**, *90*, 262–270. [PubMed]

23. Lei, C.; Qi, X.; Qiyi, Z.; Mitchell, T.; Fei, Z.; Lili, C.; Yingbin, X.; Shaohai, Q.; Feng, Z. Pre-vascularization Enhances Therapeutic Effects of Human Mesenchymal Stem Cell Sheets in Full Thickness Skin Wound Repair. *Theranostics* **2017**, *7*, 117–131.

24. Boquet, I.; Boujemaa, R.; Carlier, M.F.; Préat, T. Ciboulot Regulates Actin Assembly during Drosophila Brain Metamorphosis. *Cell* **2000**, *102*, 797–808. [CrossRef]

25. Shigeyuki, K.; Richard, C.; Tadao, M.; Toru, M. The homolog of Ciboulot in the termite (Hodotermopsis sjostedti): A multimeric β-thymosin involved in soldier-specific morphogenesis. *BMC Dev. Biol.* **2010**, *10*, 63.

26. Tompa, P. Intrinsically unstructured proteins evolve by repeat expansion. *Bioessays* **2003**, *25*, 847–855. [CrossRef] [PubMed]

27. Troys, M.; Van Dewitte, D.; Goethals, M.; Carlier, M.F.; Vandekerckhove, J.; Ampe, C. The actin binding site of thymosin beta 4 mapped by mutational analysis. *EMBO J.* **1996**, *15*, 201–210. [CrossRef] [PubMed]

28. Simenel, C.; Van Troys, M.; Vandekerckhove, J.; Ampe, C.; Delepierre, M. Structural requirements for thymosin β4 in its contact with actin. *FEBS J.* **2000**, *267*, 3530–3538. [CrossRef] [PubMed]

29. Didry, D.; Cantrelle, F.X.; Husson, C.; Roblin, P.; Moorthy, A.M.E.; Perez, J.; Clainche, C.L.; Hertzog, M.; Guittet, E.; Carlier, M.F. How a single residue in individual β-thymosin/WH2 domains controls their functions in actin assembly. *EMBO J.* **2014**, *31*, 1000–1013. [CrossRef]

30. Guo, S.; Dipietro, L.A. Factors Affecting Wound Healing. *Otolaryngol. Clin. North Am.* **1984**, *17*, 243. [CrossRef]

31. Arul, V.; Kartha, R.; Jayakumar, R. A therapeutic approach for diabetic wound healing using biotinylated GHK incorporated collagen matrices. *Life Sci.* **2007**, *80*, 275–284. [CrossRef]

32. Blain, E.J.; Mason, D.J.; Duance, V.C. The effect of thymosin beta4 on articular cartilage chondrocyte matrix metalloproteinase expression. *Biochem. Soc. Trans* **2002**, *30*, 879–882. [CrossRef]

33. Philp, D.; Badamchian, M.; Scheremeta, B.; Nguyen, M.; Goldstein, A.L.; Kleinman, H.K. Thymosin beta(4) and a synthetic peptide containing its actin-binding domain promote dermal wound repair in db/db diabetic mice and in aged mice. *Wound Repair Regen.* **2003**, *11*, 19–24. [CrossRef] [PubMed]

34. Li, X.; Zheng, L.; Peng, F.; Qi, C.; Zhang, X.; Zhou, A.; Liu, Z.; Wu, S. Recombinant thymosin beta 4 can promote full-thickness cutaneous wound healing. *Protein Expr. Purif.* **2007**, *56*, 229–236. [CrossRef] [PubMed]

35. Sosne, G.; Dunn, S.; Crockford, D.; Kim, C.; Dixon, E. Thymosin Beta 4 Eye Drops Significantly Improve Signs and Symptoms of Severe Dry Eye in a Physician-Sponsored Phase 2 Clinical Trial. *Investig. Ophthalmol. Vis. Sci.* **2013**, *54*, 6033.

36. Janarthini, R.; Wang, X.; Chen, L.; Lei, G.; Zhao, L. A Tobacco-Derived Thymosinβ4 Concatemer Promotes Cell Proliferation and Wound Healing in Mice. *Biomed. Res. Int.* **2016**, *2016*, 1–8. [CrossRef]

37. Singer, A.J.; Clark, R.A. Cutaneous wound healing. *N. Engl. J. Med.* **2007**, *341*, 738–746. [CrossRef] [PubMed]

38. Ilan, N.; Mahooti, S.; Madri, J.A. Distinct signal transduction pathways are utilized during the tube formation and survival phases of in vitro angiogenesis. *J. Cell Sci.* **1998**, *111*, 3621–3631.

39. Long, K.B.; Burgwin, C.M.; Huneke, R.; Artlett, C.M.; Blankenhorn, E.P. Tight Skin 2 Mice Exhibit Delayed Wound Healing Caused by Increased Elastic Fibers in Fibrotic Skin. *Adv. Wound Care* **2014**, *3*, 573–581. [CrossRef]

40. Barrientos, S.; Stojadinovic, O.; Golinko, M.S.; Brem, H.; Tomic-Canic, M. PERSPECTIVE ARTICLE: Growth factors and cytokines in wound healing. *Wound Repair Regen.* **2008**, *16*, 585–601. [CrossRef]

41. Peters, K.G.; De Vries, C.; Williams, L.T. Vascular endothelial growth factor receptor expression during embryogenesis and tissue repair s uggests a role in endothelial differentiation and blood vessel growth. *Proc. Natl. Acad. Sci. USA* **1993**, *90*, 8915–8919. [CrossRef]

42. Nissen, N. Vascular endothelial growth factor mediates angiogenic activity during the proliferative phase of wound healing. *Am. J. Pathol.* **1998**, *152*, 1445. [PubMed]

43. Heike, H. Modified fibrin hydrogel matrices: Both, 3D-scaffolds and local and controlled release systems to stimulate angiogenesis. *Curr. Pharm. Des.* **2007**, *13*, 3597–3607.

44. Smiell, J.M. Clinical safety of becaplermin (rhPDGF-BB) gel. *Am. J. Surg.* **1998**, *176*, 68S–73S. [CrossRef]

45. Hao, X.; Månsson-Broberg, A.; Gustafsson, T.; Grinnemo, K.H.; Blomberg, P.; Siddiqui, A.J.; Wärdell, E.; Sylvén, C. Angiogenic effects of dual gene transfer of bFGF and PDGF-BB after myocardial infarction. *Biochem. Biophys. Res. Commun.* **2004**, *315*, 1058. [CrossRef] [PubMed]

46. Philp, D.; Scheremeta, B.; Sibliss, K.; Zhou, M.I.N.; Fine, E.L.; Nguyen, M.; Wahl, L.; Hoffman, M.P.; Kleinman, H.K. Thymosin b 4 Promotes Matrix Metalloproteinase Expression During Wound Repair. *J. Cell. Physiol.* **2010**, *208*, 195–200. [CrossRef] [PubMed]

47. Yu, H.; Ma, R.J.; Zhang, S.Y. Thymosin beta 4 regulates the expression of VEGF and laminin-5 in accelerating skin wound healing in diabetic rat. *Chin. J. Diabetes* **2011**, *19*, 60–63.

48. Gabriel, S.; Christopherson, P.L.; Barrett, R.P.; Rafael, F. Thymosin-beta4 modulates corneal matrix metalloproteinase levels and polymorphonuclear cell infiltration after alkali injury. *Investig. Ophthalmol. Vis. Sci.* **2005**, *46*, 2388–2395.

49. Jin, J.; Wujiao, L.I.; Mou, B.; Shen, Y.; Geng, F.; Yue, B.; Fan, Z. Whole Genome Sequencing and Analysis of Medicinal Periplaneta americana. *Sichuan J. Zool.* **2018**, *37*, 121–126.

International Journal of
Molecular Sciences

Review

The Role of Maresins in Inflammatory Pain: Function of Macrophages in Wound Regeneration

Sung-Min Hwang [1], Gehoon Chung [2,3], Yong Ho Kim [1,*] and Chul-Kyu Park [1,*]

[1] Gachon Pain Center and Department of Physiology, College of Medicine, Gachon University, Incheon 21999, Korea; unclehwang76@gmail.com
[2] Department of Oral Physiology and Program in Neurobiology, School of Dentistry, Seoul National University, Seoul 08826, Korea; gehoon@snu.ac.kr
[3] Dental Research Institute, Seoul National University, Seoul 03080, Korea
* Correspondence: euro16@gachon.ac.kr (Y.H.K.); pck0708@gachon.ac.kr (C.-K.P.); Tel.: +82-32-899-6691 (Y.H.K.); +82-32-899-6692 (C.-K.P.)

Received: 30 September 2019; Accepted: 19 November 2019; Published: 21 November 2019

Abstract: Although acute inflammatory responses are host-protective and generally self-limited, unresolved and delayed resolution of acute inflammation can lead to further tissue damage and chronic inflammation. The mechanism of pain induction under inflammatory conditions has been studied extensively; however, the mechanism of pain resolution is not fully understood. The resolution of inflammation is a biosynthetically active process, involving specialized pro-resolving mediators (SPMs). In particular, maresins (MaRs) are synthesized from docosahexaenoic acid (DHA) by macrophages and have anti-inflammatory and pro-resolving capacities as well as tissue regenerating and pain-relieving properties. A new class of macrophage-derived molecules—MaR conjugates in tissue regeneration (MCTRs)—has been reported to regulate phagocytosis and the repair and regeneration of damaged tissue. Macrophages not only participate in the biosynthesis of SPMs, but also play an important role in phagocytosis. They exhibit different phenotypes categorized as proinflammatory M1-like phenotypes and anti-inflammatory M2 phenotypes that mediate both harmful and protective functions, respectively. However, the signaling mechanisms underlying macrophage functions and phenotypic changes have not yet been fully established. Recent studies report that MaRs help resolve inflammatory pain by enhancing macrophage phagocytosis and shifting cytokine release to the anti-inflammatory M2 phenotypes. Consequently, this review elucidated the characteristics of MaRs and macrophages, focusing on the potent action of MaRs to enhance the M2 macrophage phenotype profiles that possess the ability to alleviate inflammatory pain.

Keywords: inflammation; macrophage; specialized pro-resolving mediators; maresin; pain

---

1. Introduction

Inflammation is an immune response to harmful stimuli, including pathogens, damaged cells, toxic compounds, surgery, or irradiation [1]. Inflammation is characterized by swelling, heat, pain, redness, and loss of tissue function, which is caused by local immune, vascular, and inflammatory cell responses to infection or injury [2]. Inflammatory processes that include changes in vascular permeability, recruitment and accumulation of leukocytes, and release of inflammatory mediators, are important in the regeneration of injured tissues [3]. Therefore, inflammation is an essential defense mechanism for preserving health. A weak inflammatory response can lead to tissue destruction by harmful stimuli, while chronic unresolved inflammation may culminate in various pathological conditions, including cancer, fibrosis, and pain [4]. Wound regeneration promotes resolution of inflammation by restoring barrier function [5]. Neutrophils are the first circulating inflammatory cells to be recruited to the wound site [6]. Clinical observations demonstrating that leukocyte recruitment disorders and reduced neutrophil infiltration are associated with delayed wound healing indicate the importance of neutrophils for efficient wound repair [7]. Recent studies have shown that macrophages exhibit different functions during the immune response, with proinflammatory signaling occurring during the early stages of inflammation and, once inflammation is resolved, promotion of tissue regeneration at late stages [8,9].

Inflammatory pain indicates increased mechanical and thermal sensitivity due to inflammatory reactions [10]. These mechanisms have been extensively investigated over the past two decades [11,12]. The earliest factors causing inflammatory pain are lipid mediators (leukotrienes (LTs) and prostaglandins (PGs)) and proinflammatory cytokines (Tumor necrosis factor (TNF)-α and interleukin (IL)-1β) [13]. They sensitize nociceptors of the primary sensory neurons (peripheral sensitization) through modulation of ion channels including TRP channels [14–16]. However, our understanding of the resolution processes and mechanisms that causes inflammatory pain is limited. The acute inflammatory response is protective, evolved to repair damaged tissues and eliminate invading organisms [17,18]. This is ideally a self-limited inflammatory response that leads to a complete resolution of leukocyte infiltrates and removal of cellular debris, allowing for the return to normal homeostasis [18]. However, uncontrolled or unresolved acute inflammatory conditions can lead to chronic inflammation, causing greater tissue damage, tissue remodeling disorders, and poor tissue healing [19,20]. These conditions are known to induce the transition to chronic and maladaptive inflammatory pain [21,22] and may lead to vascular disease, metabolic syndromes, and neurological diseases [19].

In general, the resolution of acute inflammation is an active rather than a passive process that requires the biosynthesis of SPMs including lipoxins (LXs), resolvins (Rvs), protectins (PDs), and maresins (MaRs), derived from the omega-6 fatty acid arachidonic acid (AA) and the omega-3 polyunsaturated fatty acids docosahexaenoic acid (DHA) and eicosapentaenoic acid (EPA) [23]. SPMs turn off the inflammatory response by acting on distinct G-protein-coupled receptors expressed in immune cells that activate dual anti-inflammatory and pro-resolution activity in various animal models of inflammation [24–26]. In response to injury or infection, an acute inflammatory response involves early tissue edema and neutrophil infiltration, some of which transits to mature macrophages [27,28]. Macrophages are major repair mediators in peripheral nerve and spinal cord injuries [29] that exist in two polarization states [30]. These states are not fixed but instead change rapidly in response to the microenvironment [31–33]. M1 (classically activated) macrophages produce proinflammatory cytokines and promote nociceptor sensitization that can be converted into inflammatory pain, whereas M2 (alternatively activated) macrophages produce anti-inflammatory cytokines and promote wound healing [34]. Based on these functional roles, macrophages regulate the enhancement or alleviation of pain sensitivity under various conditions [32,35]. For example, M1 infiltration has been identified in pain-associated synovial tissue in models of muscle, joint, and paw inflammation [35,36]. In contrast, M1 deficiency has been reported to reduce increased proinflammatory cytokines and prevent local inflammatory pain in response to proinflammatory agents or chemotherapy-induced peripheral neuropathy [37]. The transition from M1 to M2 phenotypes—or the balance thereof—appears to be crucial for resolution associated with acute inflammatory response [13,38]. Spinal cord injury (SCI), a condition frequently associated with prolonged inflammatory pain, increases the abundance of M1 phenotype cells in the spinal cord [13]. Thus, the balance of M1/M2 macrophages plays an important role in the resolution of inflammation and inflammatory pain relief.

MaRs are believed to act as potent protective mediators of macrophage function [39,40] and promote the resolution of acute inflammation and tissue regeneration [23,41,42]. Recent studies report that MaRs promote inflammatory activity in macrophages; furthermore, the incubation of human macrophages with MaRs improves resolution by increasing phagocytosis and efferocytosis. These effects are likely due to various substances released by MaRs that alter macrophage function and possibly contribute to the resolution of inflammation. For example, biosynthesized MaRs downregulate proinflammatory cytokines, such as IL-1β, IL-6, and TNF-α, to induce inflammation resolution and tissue regeneration [43,44]. However, defective or delayed resolution causes chronic inflammation that can eventually lead to chronic inflammatory pain [20]. It has been reported that inflammatory resolution is reduced due to the following functional problems of the lipid mediator family and macrophages: (a) M1/M2 macrophage imbalance [45,46]; (b) reduced MaR or other SPM formation [27,42,47–49]; (c) impaired synthesis of DHA [50]; and (d) aging [2,51,52]. Therefore, MaRs may act directly or indirectly to reverse the inflammation relief deficiencies caused by these functional problems, thereby restoring normal inflammation relief function. Moreover, a new series of bioactive peptide-lipid conjugated mediators—MCTRs—are produced in the later stages of self-resolved infection [23,41] that regulate inflammation and resolution mechanisms as well as tissue regeneration [23,41]. Consequently, this review described the functional mechanisms of MaRs based on their potential ability to control macrophage activation and inflammatory resolution.

2. Tissue Inflammation and Regeneration

2.1. Tissue Inflammation

The inflammatory response after tissue damage is an important biological process that is essential for the survival of living organisms [1]. When tissues are damaged by infection, exposure to toxins, or mechanical damage, an inflammatory response is induced by damage-associated molecular patterns (DAMPs) and pathogen-associated molecular patterns (PRR) released by dead cells and invading organisms [53]. These molecules provoke a complex inflammatory response characterized by the recruitment, proliferation, and activation of various hematopoietic and non-hematopoietic cells, including neutrophils, macrophages, innate lymphoid cells, natural killer cells, B cells, T cells, fibroblasts, epithelial cells, endothelial cells, and stem cells, which together constitute the cellular response that orchestrates tissue repair [54–56].

2.2. Tissue Regeneration

When the wound healing reaction is well organized and controlled, the inflammatory response is quickly resolved and normal tissue structure is restored [57]. However, if the wound healing response is chronic or becomes dysregulated, it can lead to the development of pathological fibrosis or scars, which impair normal tissue function and may ultimately lead to organ failure and death [56]. Therefore, the wound-healing reaction must be strictly regulated. Biological processes involved in cutaneous wound healing include infiltration of inflammatory cells, fibroblast repopulation and new vessel formation, keratinocyte migration, and proliferation [54,58,59]. Although many cells are involved in tissue repair, macrophages exhibit significant regulatory activity at all repair and fibrosis stages and are critically involved in normal tissue homeostasis [60]. It is clear that monocytes and macrophages play more complex roles in tissue repair and in contributing to fibrosis and tissue regeneration [8]. Macrophages are an important source of chemokines, matrix metalloproteinases (MMPs), and other inflammatory mediators that induce early cellular response after injury [61]. Indeed, when macrophages are depleted soon after injury, the inflammatory response is often greatly reduced [8]. However, their removal can also reduce wound debris and cause less efficient repair and regeneration [56]. After the initial inflammatory phase subsides, the main macrophage population develops a wound healing phenotype characterized by the production of numerous growth factors, such as transforming growth factor beta 1 (TGF-β1), platelet-derived growth factor (PDGF), vascular endothelial growth factor alpha (VEGF-α), and insulin-like growth factor 1 (IGF-1) [5].

3. Specialized Pro-Resolving Mediators (SPMs)

3.1. Biosynthesis of SPMs

SPMs are bioactive autacoids enzymatically produced from the omega-6 fatty acids arachidonic acid (AA), eicosapentaenoic acid (EPA), and docosahexaenoic acid (DHA); they include lipoxins (LXs), resolvins (Rvs), protectins (PDs), and maresins (MaRs) generated via the action of lipoxygenases (LOXs) and cytochrome p450 (CYP450) and cyclooxygenase-2 (COX-2) enzymes usually found in different cell types residing in inflammatory environments [62,63]. Although many cell types can produce SPMs, immune cells, such as neutrophils, monocytes, and macrophages, are reported to be primarily responsible for the synthesis of these SPMs [24,64,65] (Figure 1) [66].

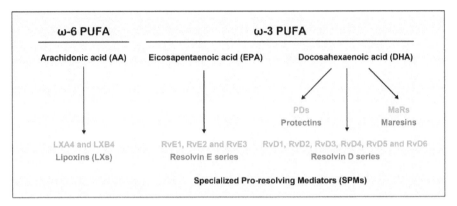

Figure 1. Biosynthesis of specialized pro-resolving mediators (SPMs) derived from omega-3 and omega-6 polyunsaturated fatty acids (PUFAs).

3.2. SPMs: Resolution Function

The mechanisms involved in acute inflammatory conditions are critical for the restoration of tissue homeostasis [19,20]. The acute inflammatory response can be divided into two general phases: initiation of acute inflammation and resolution [23]. Initiation is marked by tissue edema, resulting from increased blood flow and vessel dilation that allows for the migration of leukocytes from the post-capillary lumen to the interstitial space [17,18]. This process is mediated by proinflammatory lipid mediators—namely, leukotrienes (LTs) and prostaglandins (PGs)—derived from the omega-6 fatty acid AA [28,67]. The initial recruitment of neutrophils (polymorphonuclear leukocytes (PMNs)) is followed by the recruitment of monocytes/macrophages from the blood and into the affected tissue [67,68]. In contained inflammatory exudates, coordinated lipid mediator class switching occurs in the course of acute inflammation and resolution (Figure 2) [23,69,70]. AA-derived LXA4 is the first PUFA-derived mediator found to have anti-inflammatory and pro-resolving activities [71,72]. Platelet-leukocyte interaction leads to the formation of LXA4 and LXB4, which stimulates the lipid signaling class switch by blocking the further recruitment of polymorphonuclear cells from post-capillary venules [73]. Once the noxious materials are removed via phagocytosis, the inflammatory reaction must be resolved to maintain homeostasis [70,74]. The resolution of acute inflammation is an active process that is controlled by SPMs [39,75]. These SPMs lead to the recovery of homeostasis by blocking leukocyte trafficking to the inflamed site, reversing vasodilation and vascular permeability, and promoting the clearance of inflammatory cells, exudates, and tissue debris [76,77]. In the lipid class-switch process, SPMs share similar biological functions, limiting neutrophil infiltration, shifting cytokine profiles from pro- to anti-inflammatory, and promoting macrophage phagocytosis [78].

Acute inflammation   Inflammation resolution

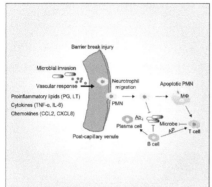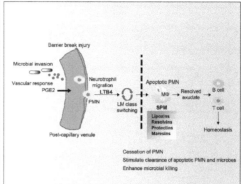

Figure 2. The outcome of acute inflammation and resolution. Under stimulation of injury or infection, release of proinflammatory lipids (prostaglandin (PG), leukotriene (LT)), chemokines (C-C motif chemokine ligand 2 (CCL2), C-X-C motif ligand 8 (CXCL8)), and cytokines (tumor necrosis factor-α (TNF-α), interleukin (IL)-6) induce the recruitment of neutrophils. Other immune cells (macrophages, B cells, and T cells) also participate in the process. Macrophages directly phagocytize organisms and apoptotic neutrophils, while B cells are converted into plasma cells to kill organisms through secreted antibodies, referred to as antibody-dependent cell-mediated cytotoxicity. Macrophages and B cells activate T cells via antigen cross presentation (AP). PGE2 leads to vasodilation and LTB4 stimulates PMN influx into the inflammatory locus. Subsequently, lipid mediator (LM) class switching converts proinflammatory signals into pro-resolving signals and triggers resolution. SPMs restrict excessive PMN influx to the injury site, enhance efferocytosis, and stimulate pro-resolving signals.

4. MaRs

4.1. Biosynthesis of MaRs

MaRs (from macrophage mediator in resolving inflammation) are a fourth family of DHA-derived SPMs [79]. In macrophages, MaR-1 biosynthesis is initiated by 12-LOX from DHA, producing 14S-hydroperoxydocosa-4Z,7Z,10Z,12E,16Z,19Z-hexaenoic acid—the hydroperoxy intermediate—which undergoes further conversion via enzymatic 13(14)-epoxidation. This epoxide intermediate is hydrolyzed enzymatically via an acid-catalyzed nucleophilic attack by water at carbon 7, resulting in the introduction of a hydroxyl group at that position and a double bond rearrangement to form the stereochemistry of bioactive MaR1, which has potent pro-resolution properties. The 13S, 14S-epoxy-MaR intermediate is also the precursor of MaR-2 (13R, 14S-dihydroxy-4Z,7Z,9E,11Z,16Z,19Z-DHA). This product of DHA biosynthesis by 12-LOX produces the 14S-hydroperoxide that is converted to the 13S, 14S-epoxy-MaR and finally converted by a soluble epoxide hydrolase into MaR-2 (Figure 3A) [49].

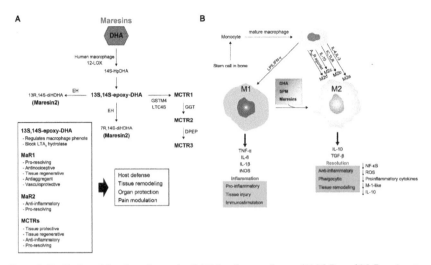

Figure 3. Synthesis and function of maresins (MaRs) and macrophages. (**A**) MaRs and MaR conjugates in tissue regeneration (MCTRs) biosynthesis. Human macrophage 12-LOX converts DHA to the 13S,14S-epoxy-maresin intermediate and hydrolase or soluble epoxide hydrolase is converted to MaR1 and MaR2, respectively. The MCTR biosynthetic pathway is initiated by lipoxygenation of 14S-HpDHA, converted by lipoxygenase activity to the 13S,14S-epoxy-maresin intermediate. MCTR1 is catalyzed by glutathione s-transferase mu4 (GSTM4) and/or leukotriene C4 synthase (LTC4S). MCTR1 is converted by gamma-glutamyl transferase (GGT) to MCTR2, which then acts as a substrate for conversion by dipeptidase (DPEP) to MCTR3. (**B**) M1 and M2 polarization of macrophages. Bone marrow-derived macrophages differentiate into mononuclear cells and gradually become mature macrophages that can be released into circulation. IFN-γ, TNF-α, and LPS stimulate macrophages into M1, IL-4 and IL-13 into M2a, IC and TLR into M2b, and IL-10 into M2c; A2AR agonist stimulates them into M2d. M1 macrophages induce a proinflammatory response, whereas M2 macrophages induce an anti-inflammatory response. M1 macrophages can also differentiate into M2 macrophages through local cues. The M1 phenotype is proinflammatory, phagocytic, and bactericidal, while the M2 macrophages act to switch off inflammation. IFN-γ: interferon gamma; TNF-α: tumor necrosis factor alpha; LPS: lipopolysaccharides; IC: immune complexes; TLR: toll-like receptor; A2AR: adenosine A2A receptor; IL: interleukin; IL-1R: IL-1 receptor.

4.2. Biosynthesis of MaR Conjugates in Tissue Regeneration (MCTRs)

Macrophages also produce a family of bioactive peptide-conjugated mediators called MCTRs [80]. MCTR compounds are produced from the 13(S), 14S-epoxide MaR intermediate during MaR biosynthesis. This epoxide intermediate is enzymatically converted to an MCTR. DHA is converted by 12-LOX into 13,14-epoxy-maresin (an intermediate of MaR-1 and MaR-2) that can be directly conjugated at C13 to glutathione by LTC4 synthase, yielding MaR conjugated in tissue regeneration 1(MCTR 1). MCTR 1 (13R-glutathionyl, 14S-hydroxy-4Z,7Z,9E,11E,13R,14S,16Z,19Z-DHA)—the first cysteinyl-SPM to be identified—is synthesized in the presence of leukotriene C4 (LTC4) synthase and γ-glutamyltransferase-μ4 in human macrophages. γ-Glutamyl transferase is involved in the conversion of MCTR-1 to MCTR2 (13R-cysteinylglycinyl, 14S-hydroxy-4Z,7Z,9E,11E,13R,14S,16Z,19Z-DHA) and MCTR-3 (13R-cysteinyl,14S-hydroxy-4Z,7Z,9E,11E,13R,14S,16Z,19Z-DHA) (Figure 3A) [34,39].

4.3. Function of MaRs and MCTRs

13S, 14S-epoxy-DHA(eMaR) stimulates the conversion of the M1 macrophage phenotype to M2 and blocks LTA4 hydrolase [81]. MaR1 possesses potent pro-resolving, antinociceptive, tissue regenerative, antiaggregant, and vasculoprotective functions. Recently, MaR-2 was reported to have powerful bioregulatory effects. Similarly, MCTRs act as tissue protective and regenerative agents, with anti-inflammatory and pro-resolving properties [25]. Thus, MaRs and MCTRs are regulated during acute self-limited infectious-inflammation and possess many attributes that contribute to host defense, tissue regeneration, organ protection, and pain modulation [25,34,39,49,72].

5. Macrophages

5.1. Macrophage Origin, Polarization, and Function

Naïve macrophages are widely distributed in all tissues via circulation through the bloodstream [82]. These cells remove apoptotic cells and foreign material via phagocytosis and participate in various processes, such as wound healing and tissue repair [83]. Macrophages are derived from bone marrow hematopoietic stem cells [84]. When stimulated by cytokines, bone marrow-derived macrophages develop into monocytes that then differentiate into pre-macrophages [35,85]. Finally, they become mature macrophages that can be released into the bloodstream [35,86]. Macrophages respond to current conditions to form a heterogeneous cell population [87]. Under the influence of various stimuli, they usually differentiate into one of two phenotypes (polarization) [88]: proinflammatory type (M1) and anti-inflammatory or reparative type (M2) [89]. M1 macrophages are proinflammatory and secrete cytokines, while M2 macrophages are anti-inflammatory and promote tissue repair to resolve inflammation [87]. M2 macrophages can be further sub-classified as M2a, M2b, M2c, and M2d based on transcriptional changes that result from exposure to different stimuli [90]. Lipopolysaccharides (LPS), TNF-α, and interferon gamma (IFN)-γ are used to convert macrophages to M1, IL-4 and IL-13 to M2a, immune complexes (IC) and toll-like receptors (TLR) to M2b, IL-10 to M2c, and adenosine A2A receptor (A2AR) agonist to M2d (Figure 3B) [29]. Therefore, stimulus-dependent polarization controls the specific functions and phenotypes of macrophages.

5.2. Relationships between Macrophages and MaRs

Macrophages participate in the biosynthesis of SPMs with both anti-inflammatory and pro-resolving properties [34]. SPMs are enzymatically biosynthesized from essential fatty acids with different stereochemistry [74,80,91]. MaRs—a new family of macrophage-derived mediators—are synthesized from DHA by macrophages and are potent in the resolution of inflammation [33]. Most importantly, MaR1 directly enhances neutrophil activation and the switch from macrophage M1 to M2 phenotype [92], both of which promotes anti-inflammatory and pro-resolving actions, inhibiting neutrophil infiltration and stimulating macrophage phagocytosis and efferocytosis to enhance the clearance of inflammation without affecting the innate response [27,49].

6. Role of MaRs in Inflammation Resolution

The level of this potent leukocyte agonist decreases in the later stages of the self-limited inflammatory response [93]. It is possible that other signals regulate leukocyte responses to promote tissue repair and regeneration. Given the pivotal roles of chemical signals in infections, it has been revealed that new mediators, within self-resolving infections, can regulate tissue repair and regeneration without immune suppression [34]. MaR-1 exhibits potent pro-resolving and tissue regenerative activity and is involved in self-limited infections that regulate tissue regeneration [34,94]. New pathways and mediators in planaria promote recovery and regeneration during infection [27]. The recruitment of leukocytes into the lesioned spinal cord is regulated by various proinflammatory mediators [95,96]. Cytokines mediate inflammation by acting on specific receptors that activate different intracellular inflammatory cascades [97]. Additionally, MaR-1 downregulates cytokine expression in mouse models of colitis and acute respiratory distress syndrome [41,49,92]. However, little is known about the intracellular cascades regulated by MaR-1.

Although IL-10 has anti-inflammatory properties, its contribution to the healing process is not fully established. In a recent report, MaR1 increased the levels of IL-10 postoperatively for 14 days [98].

Notably, MaR-1 has been reported to interact with stem cells to reduce chronic inflammation and improve wound healing following SCI [77,99]. Interestingly, macrophages incubated with MaR-1 are polarized toward an anti-inflammatory phenotype and increase MRC1 mRNA expression (an M2 macrophage phenotype marker), implying a possible role of MaR-1 in M2 macrophage polarization [42]. TNF-α is one of the earliest cytokines to appear following tissue damage and is associated with the production of many cytokines, including IL-1β and IL-6. MaR-1 attenuates the release of proinflammatory cytokines and TNF-α in macrophages [49,100]. In addition, intracellular adhesion molecule 1 (ICAM-1) is an epithelial PMN ligand that promotes neutrophil migration through epithelial cells during inflammation [92]. MaR-1 inhibits the 10-fold upregulation of ICAM-1, suggesting that it contributes to the resolution of inflammation by affecting neutrophil clearance and efferocytosis. Another possible avenue for treatment with MaRs is motor neuron disease, a fatal neurodegenerative disease that causes loss of motor neuron function and progressive degeneration [101]. However, the molecular mechanisms of motor neuron degeneration in amyotrophic lateral sclerosis (ALS) are not yet full known. Many pathogenic changes occur in the affected motor neurons, including mitochondrial dysfunction, hyper excitability, glutamate excitotoxicity, and nitroxidative stress [101]. Superoxide dismutase 1 (SOD1) G93A and transactivation response DNA-binding protein (TDP)-43A315T cause oxidative stress, endoplasmic reticulum (ER) stress, and inflammation. MaR-1 possesses neuroprotective effects against stress-induced cell death induced by various factors, such as SOD1 G93AA315T and TDP-43A315T, inhibiting NF-κB activation [102]. Therefore, MaR-1 may also contribute to treatment options for motor neuron diseases, such as ALS and SMA (spinal muscular atrophy).

7. Role of MaRs and Macrophages in Inflammation Resolution

Macrophages are involved in the processes of homeostasis, tissue repair, and regeneration [29]. They are recruited to damaged nerve sites through the activation of M1 and M2 subtypes [29]: M1 macrophages exhibit a proinflammatory profile and mediate cytotoxic actions; and M2 macrophages have anti-inflammatory effects and promote tissue healing and recovery [31,32]. The balance of M1 and M2 macrophages regulates early events in local inflammation [103]. In this process, cytokine contributes to the recruitment of M1 macrophages [104]. It releases other proinflammatory cytokines, such as TNF-α, IL-1α, and IL-β, to promote further tissue damage [105]. To control this process, activated M2 macrophages release anti-inflammatory cytokines, IL-10 and TGF-β, which mediate tissue regeneration and inhibition of the proinflammatory function [106]. Also, an increased ratio of M2 macrophages significantly enhances nerve regeneration and wound healing [107]. DHA plays important roles in peripheral organs, as well as in the central nervous system, and is the precursor of various molecules that regulate the resolution of inflammation [50,108]. Macrophages derived from mice deficient of Elov12 (Elovl2-/-)—the main enzyme for DHA synthesis—demonstrate an increased expression of M1-like markers (iNOS and CD86), whereas M2 macrophages downregulate M2-like markers such as CD206 [50]. Similarly, the impairment of systemic DHA synthesis in activated macrophages results in an alteration of M1/M2 macrophages, supporting the important role played by DHA in regulating the balance between pro- and anti-inflammatory processes. Inflammation resolution is an active and highly regulated inflammatory process that is necessary to prevent the transition into chronic inflammation with the spread of tissue injury or exacerbated scarring [13]. However, differential leukocyte subpopulations reduce or otherwise impair the ability to resolve inflammation at the lesion site after acute experimental spinal cord injury (SCI) [95,103]. For example, after SCI, M2 macrophage function is shown to be defective in resolving inflammation, impairing tissue remodeling and healing [77]. Macrophages in SCI are not defined within the M1-M2 dichotomy. MaR1 is effective in enhancing several stages of inflammation resolution after SCI through the downregulation of cytokines, reduction of neutrophils and macrophages, shift in macrophage phenotype, and stimulation of macrophage phagocytosis [77]. Treatment with MaR1 after SCI reportedly enhances neutrophil clearance and reduces macrophage accumulation in the lesioned tissue [77]. Inappropriate biosynthesis of SPMs after SCI interferes with the resolution of inflammation and contributes to the pathophysiology of SCI. Abnormal production of

SPMs is also reported in the cerebrospinal fluid (CSF) of patients with Alzheimer's disease and multiple sclerosis [68,75]. Thus, the potential function of MaRs can be confirmed by their immunoresolvent effects on the phagocytosis of macrophages and their inhibitory functions on cytokine levels and inflammatory signaling pathways [77]. Chronic inflammation is the basis of the common pathology of age-related diseases, such as cardiovascular disease, diabetes, and Alzheimer's disease [2], involving alterations to the immune system that promote chronic inflammation. Macrophages are important in these age-associated changes that cause chronic inflammatory diseases [72]. Recent studies have shown that aging impairs macrophage phagocytosis, resulting in a failure to resolve damage-associated molecular patterns in aged animals [2,45,51].

8. Role of MaRs in Resolution of Inflammatory Pain

MaR1 not only regulates the resolution of inflammation, but also plays a powerful role in preventing hyperalgesia sensitivity in inflammatory- and chemotherapy-induced chronic inflammatory pain [23,27]. MaR1 dramatically reduces vincristine-initiated neuropathic pain in a cancer chemotherapy model [27] and in temporomandibular joint pain [26]. In addition, MaR1 has played an important role in the prevention of postoperative pain in orthopedic surgery models [24]. Postoperative pain management with MaR1 may help control the onset of neuroinflammation. Acute perioperative treatment with MaR1 delayed the development of mechanical and cold allodynia. Moreover, MaR1 has been shown to induce analgesia by regulating transient receptor potential vanilloid 1 (TRPV1) currents in neurons. [27]. Intrathecal treatment with MaR1 reduces inflammatory pain with a long-lasting analgesic profile through the inhibition of astrocytic and microglial activation [109].

In the periphery, various cytokines contribute to neutrophil recruitment into the tissue and, consequently, an increase in inflammatory processes and pain [28,110]. Intrathecal MaR1 treatment reduces recruitment and leukocyte count [94,100]. In addition, MaR1 reduces CFA-induced mRNA expression of Nav1.8 and Trpv1 channels [26]. MaR1 likely controls TRPV1 expression in DRG neurons during inflammation. Thus, targeting these channels is effective for reducing inflammatory pain [111,112]. Under noxious stimuli, nociceptor neurons release neuropeptides, such as CGRP and substance P, which control the recruitment of immune cells to the inflamed tissue [113,114]. MaR1 reduced the release of CGRP from DRG neurons, indicating a possible mechanism by which MaR1 reduces inflammatory pain through reduced recruitment of neutrophils and macrophages. In the spinal cord, TNF-α and IL-1β contribute to spinal cord plasticity and, hence, central sensitization [97]. Cytokines improve the amplitude of AMPA- and glutamate-induced excitatory currents [97]. Indeed, the CFA model induces central sensitization with stronger activation of astrocytes when compared to microglia [111,115,116]. Central sensitization has been recognized as the main cause of pathological pain, resulting in plastic changes in the CNS [117]. Intrathecal treatment with MaR1 reduced CFA-induced astrocyte and microglial activation and decreased activation by TNF-α, IL-1β, and NF-κB [26]. In addition, the interaction between glial cells and nociceptor neurons has been linked to these plastic changes in the spinal cord [26]. MaR1 reduces glial cell activation and blocks capsaicin-induced TRPV1 calcium influx as well as spontaneous EPSC frequency [26]. Thus, MaR1 can reduce spinal cord plastic changes and inhibit central sensitization via presynaptic and postsynaptic mechanisms [26]. MCTRs also rescue *Escherichia coli* infection-mediated delays in tissue regeneration of planaria, in addition to protecting mice from second-organ reflow injury and promoting repair by limiting neutrophil infiltration [41]. Furthermore, each MCTR promotes the resolution of *E. coli* infections by increasing bacterial phagocytosis and limiting neutrophil infiltration [25]. Phagocytosis is a main means by which macrophages resolve inflammation [2]. Increasing evidence suggests that MaRs produce potent anti-inflammatory and pro-resolution profiles, partially by enhancing macrophage activity [17,93]. However, it remains unclear how MaRs regulate macrophage phagocytosis.

9. Conclusions

MaRs belong to the most recently uncovered family of anti-inflammatory lipid mediators with pro-resolving activity in the amelioration of inflammation. The activation of MaRs in macrophages enhances phagocytosis and helps to reverse inflammatory pain by shifting cytokine release to an anti-inflammatory state. However, M1/M2 macrophage imbalance, reduced SPM formation, impaired synthesis of DHA, and aging reduce and generally impair the resolution of inflammation under pathological conditions. MaRs have been shown to alleviate this deficiency by reversing and improving the function of macrophages (Figure 4). However, the specific receptors and signaling mechanisms involved in the ability of MaRs to resolve inflammation must be investigated in order to fully establish their important role in the treatment of inflammation in various diseases.

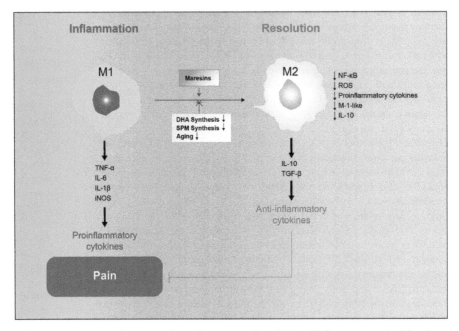

Figure 4. Maresins regulate macrophage phenotype and resolution of inflammatory pain. Maresins (MaRs) improve M2 macrophage function, shifting cytokine release to an anti-inflammatory profile and thereby facilitating the resolution of inflammatory pain.

Acknowledgments: This work was supported by the National Research Foundation of Korea (NRF) grant (NRF-2017M3C7A1025600, NRF-2017M3A9E4057929, and NRF-2014S1A2A2028387) funded by the Korean government (MSIP). All authors approved the final manuscript.

Conflicts of Interest: The authors declare no conflict of interest.

References

1. Chen, L.; Deng, H.; Cui, H.; Fang, J.; Zuo, Z.; Deng, J.; Li, Y.; Wang, X.; Zhao, L. Inflammatory responses and inflammation-associated diseases in organs. *Oncotarget* **2018**, *9*, 7204–7218. [CrossRef]
2. Oishi, Y.; Manabe, I. Macrophages in age-related chronic inflammatory diseases. *NPJ Aging Mech. Dis.* **2016**, *2*, 16018. [CrossRef]
3. Sansbury, B.E.; Spite, M. Resolution of acute inflammation and the role of resolvins in immunity, thrombosis, and vascular biology. *Circ. Res.* **2016**, *119*, 113–130. [CrossRef]

4. Karin, M.; Clevers, H. Reparative inflammation takes charge of tissue regeneration. *Nature* **2016**, *529*, 307–315. [CrossRef]

5. Landen, N.X.; Li, D.; Stahle, M. Transition from inflammation to proliferation: A critical step during wound healing. *Cell Mol. Life Sci.* **2016**, *73*, 3861–3885. [CrossRef] [PubMed]

6. Wang, J. Neutrophils in tissue injury and repair. *Cell Tissue Res.* **2018**, *371*, 531–539. [CrossRef] [PubMed]

7. Wilgus, T.A.; Roy, S.; McDaniel, J.C. Neutrophils and wound repair: Positive actions and negative reactions. *Adv. Wound Care* **2013**, *2*, 379–388. [CrossRef] [PubMed]

8. Oishi, Y.; Manabe, I. Macrophages in inflammation, repair and regeneration. *Int. Immunol.* **2018**, *30*, 511–528. [CrossRef] [PubMed]

9. Mescher, A.L. Macrophages and fibroblasts during inflammation and tissue repair in models of organ regeneration. *Regeneration* **2017**, *4*, 39–53. [CrossRef] [PubMed]

10. Kidd, B.L.; Urban, L.A. Mechanisms of inflammatory pain. *Br. J. Anaesth.* **2001**, *87*, 3–11. [CrossRef]

11. Rifbjerg-Madsen, S.; Christensen, A.W.; Christensen, R.; Hetland, M.L.; Bliddal, H.; Kristensen, L.E.; Danneskiold-Samsoe, B.; Amris, K. Pain and pain mechanisms in patients with inflammatory arthritis: A Danish nationwide cross-sectional DANBIO registry survey. *PLoS ONE* **2017**, *12*, e0180014. [CrossRef] [PubMed]

12. Mackey, S. Mechanisms of inflammatory pain: Therapeutic implications. *J. Clin. Rheumatol.* **2004**, *10*, S5–S11. [CrossRef] [PubMed]

13. Pruss, H.; Kopp, M.A.; Brommer, B.; Gatzemeier, N.; Laginha, I.; Dirnagl, U.; Schwab, J.M. Non-Resolving aspects of acute inflammation after spinal cord injury (SCI): Indices and resolution plateau. *Brain Pathol.* **2011**, *21*, 652–660. [CrossRef] [PubMed]

14. Ji, R.R.; Berta, T.; Nedergaard, M. Glia and pain: Is chronic pain a gliopathy? *Pain* **2013**, *154*, S10–S28. [CrossRef]

15. Baral, P.; Udit, S.; Chiu, I.M. Pain and immunity: Implications for host defence. *Nat. Rev. Immunol.* **2019**, *19*, 433–447. [CrossRef]

16. Chen, G.; Zhang, Y.Q.; Qadri, Y.J.; Serhan, C.N.; Ji, R.R. Microglia in pain: Detrimental and protective roles in pathogenesis and resolution of pain. *Neuron* **2018**, *100*, 1292–1311. [CrossRef]

17. Serhan, C.N.; Chiang, N.; Van Dyke, T.E. Resolving inflammation: Dual anti-inflammatory and pro-resolution lipid mediators. *Nat. Rev. Immunol.* **2008**, *8*, 349–361. [CrossRef]

18. Serhan, C.N.; Brain, S.D.; Buckley, C.D.; Gilroy, D.W.; Haslett, C.; O'Neill, L.A.; Perretti, M.; Rossi, A.G.; Wallace, J.L. Resolution of inflammation: State of the art, definitions and terms. *FASEB J.* **2007**, *21*, 325–332. [CrossRef]

19. Greaves, D.R.; Channon, K.M. Inflammation and immune responses in atherosclerosis. *Trends Immunol.* **2002**, *23*, 535–541. [CrossRef]

20. Van Dyke, T.E.; Serhan, C.N. Resolution of inflammation: A new paradigm for the pathogenesis of periodontal diseases. *J. Dent. Res.* **2003**, *82*, 82–90. [CrossRef]

21. Ji, R.R.; Xu, Z.Z.; Strichartz, G.; Serhan, C.N. Emerging roles of resolvins in the resolution of inflammation and pain. *Trends Neurosci.* **2011**, *34*, 599–609. [CrossRef] [PubMed]

22. Willemen, H.L.; Eijkelkamp, N.; Garza Carbajal, A.; Wang, H.; Mack, M.; Zijlstra, J.; Heijnen, C.J.; Kavelaars, A. Monocytes/Macrophages control resolution of transient inflammatory pain. *J. Pain* **2014**, *15*, 496–506. [CrossRef] [PubMed]

23. Serhan, C.N. Pro-Resolving lipid mediators are leads for resolution physiology. *Nature* **2014**, *510*, 92–101. [CrossRef] [PubMed]

24. Zhang, L.; Terrando, N.; Xu, Z.Z.; Bang, S.; Jordt, S.E.; Maixner, W.; Serhan, C.N.; Ji, R.R. Distinct analgesic actions of DHA and DHA-derived specialized pro-resolving mediators on post-operative pain after bone fracture in mice. *Front. Pharmacol.* **2018**, *9*, 412. [CrossRef]

25. Serhan, C.N.; Chiang, N.; Dalli, J. New pro-resolving n-3 mediators bridge resolution of infectious inflammation to tissue regeneration. *Mol. Aspects Med.* **2018**, *64*, 1–17. [CrossRef]

26. Park, C.K. Maresin 1 Inhibits TRPV1 in temporomandibular joint-related trigeminal nociceptive neurons and tmj inflammation-induced synaptic plasticity in the trigeminal nucleus. *Mediat. Inflamm.* **2015**, *2015*, 275126. [CrossRef]

27. Serhan, C.N.; Dalli, J.; Karamnov, S.; Choi, A.; Park, C.K.; Xu, Z.Z.; Ji, R.R.; Zhu, M.; Petasis, N.A. Macrophage proresolving mediator maresin 1 stimulates tissue regeneration and controls pain. *FASEB J.* **2012**, *26*, 1755–1765. [CrossRef]

28. Kolaczkowska, E.; Kubes, P. Neutrophil recruitment and function in health and inflammation. *Nat. Rev. Immunol.* **2013**, *13*, 159–175. [CrossRef]

29. Liu, P.; Peng, J.; Han, G.H.; Ding, X.; Wei, S.; Gao, G.; Huang, K.; Chang, F.; Wang, Y. Role of macrophages in peripheral nerve injury and repair. *Neural Regen. Res.* **2019**, *14*, 1335–1342.

30. Di Benedetto, P.; Ruscitti, P.; Vadasz, Z.; Toubi, E.; Giacomelli, R. Macrophages with regulatory functions, a possible new therapeutic perspective in autoimmune diseases. *Autoimmun. Rev.* **2019**, *18*, 102369. [CrossRef]

31. Murray, P.J.; Allen, J.E.; Biswas, S.K.; Fisher, E.A.; Gilroy, D.W.; Goerdt, S.; Gordon, S.; Hamilton, J.A.; Ivashkiv, L.B.; Lawrence, T.; et al. Macrophage activation and polarization: Nomenclature and experimental guidelines. *Immunity* **2014**, *41*, 14–20. [CrossRef] [PubMed]

32. David, S.; Greenhalgh, A.D.; Kroner, A. Macrophage and microglial plasticity in the injured spinal cord. *Neuroscience* **2015**, *307*, 311–318. [CrossRef] [PubMed]

33. Dalli, J.; Serhan, C. Macrophage proresolving mediators-the when and where. *Microbiol. Spectr.* **2016**, *4*, 3.

34. Tang, S.; Wan, M.; Huang, W.; Stanton, R.C.; Xu, Y. Maresins: Specialized proresolving lipid mediators and their potential role in inflammatory-related diseases. *Mediat. Inflamm.* **2018**, *2018*, 2380319. [CrossRef]

35. Chen, P.; Piao, X.; Bonaldo, P. Role of macrophages in Wallerian degeneration and axonal regeneration after peripheral nerve injury. *Acta Neuropathol.* **2015**, *130*, 605–618. [CrossRef] [PubMed]

36. Sakurai, Y.; Fujita, M.; Kawasaki, S.; Sanaki, T.; Yoshioka, T.; Higashino, K.; Tofukuji, S.; Yoneda, S.; Takahashi, T.; Koda, K.; et al. Contribution of synovial macrophages to rat advanced osteoarthritis pain resistant to cyclooxygenase inhibitors. *Pain* **2019**, *160*, 895–907. [CrossRef]

37. Gong, W.Y.; Abdelhamid, R.E.; Carvalho, C.S.; Sluka, K.A. Resident macrophages in muscle contribute to development of hyperalgesia in a mouse model of noninflammatory muscle pain. *J. Pain* **2016**, *17*, 1081–1094. [CrossRef]

38. Sekiguchi, F.; Domoto, R.; Nakashima, K.; Yamasoba, D.; Yamanishi, H.; Tsubota, M.; Wake, H.; Nishibori, M.; Kawabata, A. Paclitaxel-Induced HMGB1 release from macrophages and its implication for peripheral neuropathy in mice: Evidence for a neuroimmune crosstalk. *Neuropharmacology* **2018**, *141*, 201–213. [CrossRef]

39. Dalli, J.; Vlasakov, I.; Riley, I.R.; Rodriguez, A.R.; Spur, B.W.; Petasis, N.A.; Chiang, N.; Serhan, C.N. Maresin conjugates in tissue regeneration biosynthesis enzymes in human macrophages. *Proc. Natl. Acad. Sci. USA* **2016**, *113*, 12232–12237. [CrossRef]

40. Wang, C.W.; Colas, R.A.; Dalli, J.; Arnardottir, H.H.; Nguyen, D.; Hasturk, H.; Chiang, N.; Van Dyke, T.E.; Serhan, C.N. Maresin 1 biosynthesis and proresolving anti-infective functions with human-localized aggressive periodontitis leukocytes. *Infect. Immun.* **2015**, *84*, 658–665. [CrossRef]

41. Dalli, J.; Chiang, N.; Serhan, C.N. Identification of 14-series sulfido-conjugated mediators that promote resolution of infection and organ protection. *Proc. Natl. Acad. Sci. USA* **2014**, *111*, E4753–E4761. [CrossRef] [PubMed]

42. Dalli, J.; Zhu, M.; Vlasenko, N.A.; Deng, B.; Haeggstrom, J.Z.; Petasis, N.A.; Serhan, C.N. The novel 13S,14S-epoxy-maresin is converted by human macrophages to maresin 1 (MaR1), inhibits leukotriene A4 hydrolase (LTA4H), and shifts macrophage phenotype. *FASEB J.* **2013**, *27*, 2573–2583. [CrossRef] [PubMed]

43. Serhan, C.N. Treating inflammation and infection in the 21st century: New hints from decoding resolution mediators and mechanisms. *FASEB J.* **2017**, *31*, 1273–1288. [CrossRef] [PubMed]

44. Spite, M.; Claria, J.; Serhan, C.N. Resolvins, specialized proresolving lipid mediators, and their potential roles in metabolic diseases. *Cell Metab.* **2014**, *19*, 21–36. [CrossRef]

45. Li, S.; Sun, Y.; Liang, C.P.; Thorp, E.B.; Han, S.; Jehle, A.W.; Saraswathi, V.; Pridgen, B.; Kanter, J.E.; Li, R.; et al. Defective phagocytosis of apoptotic cells by macrophages in atherosclerotic lesions of ob/ob mice and reversal by a fish oil diet. *Circ. Res.* **2009**, *105*, 1072–1082. [CrossRef]

46. Liu, B.; Zhang, M.; Zhao, J.; Zheng, M.; Yang, H. Imbalance of M1/M2 macrophages is linked to severity level of knee osteoarthritis. *Exp. Ther. Med.* **2018**, *16*, 5009–5014. [CrossRef]

47. Quiros, M.; Nusrat, A. Saving problematic mucosae: SPMs in intestinal mucosal inflammation and repair. *Trends Mol. Med.* **2019**, *25*, 124–135. [CrossRef]

48. Recchiuti, A.; Serhan, C.N. Pro-Resolving lipid mediators (SPMs) and their actions in regulating miRNA in novel resolution circuits in inflammation. *Front. Immunol.* **2012**, *3*, 298. [CrossRef]

49. Serhan, C.N.; Yang, R.; Martinod, K.; Kasuga, K.; Pillai, P.S.; Porter, T.F.; Oh, S.F.; Spite, M. Maresins: Novel macrophage mediators with potent antiinflammatory and proresolving actions. *J. Exp. Med.* **2009**, *206*, 15–23. [CrossRef]

50. Talamonti, E.; Pauter, A.M.; Asadi, A.; Fischer, A.W.; Chiurchiu, V.; Jacobsson, A. Impairment of systemic DHA synthesis affects macrophage plasticity and polarization: Implications for DHA supplementation during inflammation. *Cell Mol. Life Sci.* **2017**, *74*, 2815–2826. [CrossRef]

51. Bliederhaeuser, C.; Grozdanov, V.; Speidel, A.; Zondler, L.; Ruf, W.P.; Bayer, H.; Kiechle, M.; Feiler, M.S.; Freischmidt, A.; Brenner, D.; et al. Age-Dependent defects of alpha-synuclein oligomer uptake in microglia and monocytes. *Acta Neuropathol.* **2016**, *131*, 379–391. [CrossRef] [PubMed]

52. Rea, I.M.; Gibson, D.S.; McGilligan, V.; McNerlan, S.E.; Alexander, H.D.; Ross, O.A. Age and age-related diseases: Role of inflammation triggers and cytokines. *Front. Immunol.* **2018**, *9*, 586. [CrossRef] [PubMed]

53. Hou, S.; Liu, Z.; Shen, H.; Wu, D. Damage-Associated molecular pattern-triggered immunity in plants. *Front. Plant. Sci.* **2019**, *10*, 646. [CrossRef] [PubMed]

54. Nicoletti, G.; Saler, M.; Villani, L.; Rumolo, A.; Tresoldi, M.M.; Faga, A. Platelet rich plasma enhancement of skin regeneration in an ex-vivo human experimental model. *Front. Bioeng. Biotechnol.* **2019**, *7*, 2. [CrossRef] [PubMed]

55. Tsepkolenko, A.; Tsepkolenko, V.; Dash, S.; Mishra, A.; Bader, A.; Melerzanov, A.; Giri, S. The regenerative potential of skin and the immune system. *Clin. Cosmet. Investig. Dermatol.* **2019**, *12*, 519–532. [CrossRef]

56. Wynn, T.A.; Vannella, K.M. Macrophages in tissue repair, regeneration, and fibrosis. *Immunity* **2016**, *44*, 450–462. [CrossRef]

57. Larouche, J.; Sheoran, S.; Maruyama, K.; Martino, M.M. Immune regulation of skin wound healing: Mechanisms and novel therapeutic targets. *Adv. Wound Care* **2018**, *7*, 209–231. [CrossRef]

58. Serra, M.B.; Barroso, W.A.; da Silva, N.N.; Silva, S.D.N.; Borges, A.C.R.; Abreu, I.C.; Borges, M. From inflammation to current and alternative therapies involved in wound healing. *Int. J. Inflam.* **2017**, *2017*, 3406215. [CrossRef]

59. Ridiandries, A.; Tan, J.T.M.; Bursill, C.A. The role of chemokines in wound healing. *Int. J. Mol. Sci.* **2018**, *19*, 3217. [CrossRef]

60. Boniakowski, A.E.; Kimball, A.S.; Jacobs, B.N.; Kunkel, S.L.; Gallagher, K.A. Macrophage-Mediated inflammation in normal and diabetic wound healing. *J. Immunol.* **2017**, *199*, 17–24. [CrossRef]

61. Minutti, C.M.; Knipper, J.A.; Allen, J.E.; Zaiss, D.M. Tissue-Specific contribution of macrophages to wound healing. *Semin. Cell Dev. Biol.* **2017**, *61*, 3–11. [CrossRef] [PubMed]

62. Gilroy, D.W.; Bishop-Bailey, D. Lipid mediators in immune regulation and resolution. *Br. J. Pharmacol.* **2019**, *176*, 1009–1023. [CrossRef] [PubMed]

63. Giannakis, N.; Sansbury, B.E.; Patsalos, A.; Hays, T.T.; Riley, C.O.; Han, X.; Spite, M.; Nagy, L. Dynamic changes to lipid mediators support transitions among macrophage subtypes during muscle regeneration. *Nat. Immunol.* **2019**, *20*, 626–636. [CrossRef] [PubMed]

64. Zhang, L.Y.; Jia, M.R.; Sun, T. The roles of special proresolving mediators in pain relief. *Rev. Neurosci.* **2018**, *29*, 645–660. [CrossRef] [PubMed]

65. Wang, Q.; Yan, S.F.; Hao, Y.; Jin, S.W. Specialized pro-resolving mediators regulate alveolar fluid clearance during acute respiratory distress syndrome. *Chin. Med. J.* **2018**, *131*, 982–989. [CrossRef]

66. Leuti, A.; Maccarrone, M.; Chiurchiu, V. Proresolving lipid mediators: Endogenous modulators of oxidative stress. *Oxid. Med. Cell. Longev.* **2019**, *2019*, 8107265. [CrossRef] [PubMed]

67. Li, Y.; Dalli, J.; Chiang, N.; Baron, R.M.; Quintana, C.; Serhan, C.N. Plasticity of leukocytic exudates in resolving acute inflammation is regulated by MicroRNA and proresolving mediators. *Immunity* **2013**, *39*, 885–898. [CrossRef]

68. Pruss, H.; Rosche, B.; Sullivan, A.B.; Brommer, B.; Wengert, O.; Gronert, K.; Schwab, J.M. Proresolution lipid mediators in multiple sclerosis—Differential, disease severity-dependent synthesis—A clinical pilot trial. *PLoS ONE* **2013**, *8*, e55859. [CrossRef]

69. Serhan, C.N.; Chiang, N.; Dalli, J.; Levy, B.D. Lipid mediators in the resolution of inflammation. *Cold Spring Harb. Perspect. Biol.* **2014**, *7*, a016311. [CrossRef]

70. Serhan, C.N.; Chiang, N.; Dalli, J. The resolution code of acute inflammation: Novel pro-resolving lipid mediators in resolution. *Semin. Immunol.* **2015**, *27*, 200–215. [CrossRef]

71. Hansen, T.V.; Vik, A.; Serhan, C.N. The protectin family of specialized pro-resolving mediators: Potent immunoresolvents enabling innovative approaches to target obesity and diabetes. *Front. Pharmacol.* **2018**, *9*, 1582. [CrossRef] [PubMed]

72. Jadapalli, J.K.; Halade, G.V. Unified nexus of macrophages and maresins in cardiac reparative mechanisms. *FASEB J.* **2018**, *32*, 5227–5237. [CrossRef] [PubMed]

73. Serhan, C.N.; Savill, J. Resolution of inflammation: The beginning programs the end. *Nat. Immunol.* **2005**, *6*, 1191–1197. [CrossRef] [PubMed]

74. Basil, M.C.; Levy, B.D. Specialized pro-resolving mediators: Endogenous regulators of infection and inflammation. *Nat. Rev. Immunol.* **2016**, *16*, 51–67. [CrossRef] [PubMed]

75. Zhu, M.; Wang, X.; Hjorth, E.; Colas, R.A.; Schroeder, L.; Granholm, A.C.; Serhan, C.N.; Schultzberg, M. Pro-Resolving Lipid Mediators Improve Neuronal Survival and Increase Abeta42 Phagocytosis. *Mol. Neurobiol.* **2016**, *53*, 2733–2749. [CrossRef] [PubMed]

76. Eming, S.A.; Wynn, T.A.; Martin, P. Inflammation and metabolism in tissue repair and regeneration. *Science* **2017**, *356*, 1026–1030. [CrossRef]

77. Francos-Quijorna, I.; Santos-Nogueira, E.; Gronert, K.; Sullivan, A.B.; Kopp, M.A.; Brommer, B.; David, S.; Schwab, J.M.; Lopez-Vales, R. Maresin 1 promotes inflammatory resolution, neuroprotection, and functional neurological recovery after spinal cord injury. *J. Neurosci.* **2017**, *37*, 11731–11743. [CrossRef]

78. Dalli, J.; Serhan, C.N. Specific lipid mediator signatures of human phagocytes: Microparticles stimulate macrophage efferocytosis and pro-resolving mediators. *Blood* **2012**, *120*, e60–e72. [CrossRef]

79. Ishida, T.; Yoshida, M.; Arita, M.; Nishitani, Y.; Nishiumi, S.; Masuda, A.; Mizuno, S.; Takagawa, T.; Morita, Y.; Kutsumi, H.; et al. Resolvin E1, an endogenous lipid mediator derived from eicosapentaenoic acid, prevents dextran sulfate sodium-induced colitis. *Inflamm. Bowel Dis.* **2010**, *16*, 87–95. [CrossRef]

80. Chiang, N.; Riley, I.R.; Dalli, J.; Rodriguez, A.R.; Spur, B.W.; Serhan, C.N. New maresin conjugates in tissue regeneration pathway counters leukotriene D4-stimulated vascular responses. *FASEB J.* **2018**, *32*, 4043–4052. [CrossRef]

81. Serhan, C.N.; Levy, B.D. Resolvins in inflammation: Emergence of the pro-resolving superfamily of mediators. *J. Clin. Invest.* **2018**, *128*, 2657–2669. [CrossRef] [PubMed]

82. Wei, J.; Besner, G.E. M1 to M2 macrophage polarization in heparin-binding epidermal growth factor-like growth factor therapy for necrotizing enterocolitis. *J. Surg. Res.* **2015**, *197*, 126–138. [CrossRef] [PubMed]

83. De Gaetano, M.; Crean, D.; Barry, M.; Belton, O. M1- and M2-type macrophage responses are predictive of adverse outcomes in human atherosclerosis. *Front. Immunol.* **2016**, *7*, 275. [CrossRef] [PubMed]

84. Luo, Y.; Shao, L.; Chang, J.; Feng, W.; Liu, Y.L.; Cottler-Fox, M.H.; Emanuel, P.D.; Hauer-Jensen, M.; Bernstein, I.D.; Liu, L.; et al. M1 and M2 macrophages differentially regulate hematopoietic stem cell self-renewal and ex vivo expansion. *Blood Adv.* **2018**, *2*, 859–870. [CrossRef]

85. Helft, J.; Bottcher, J.; Chakravarty, P.; Zelenay, S.; Huotari, J.; Schraml, B.U.; Goubau, D.; Reis e Sousa, C. GM-CSF Mouse Bone Marrow Cultures Comprise a Heterogeneous Population of CD11c(+)MHCII(+) Macrophages and Dendritic Cells. *Immunity* **2015**, *42*, 1197–1211. [CrossRef]

86. Frodermann, V.; Nahrendorf, M. Macrophages and Cardiovascular Health. *Physiol. Rev.* **2018**, *98*, 2523–2569. [CrossRef]

87. Chylikova, J.; Dvorackova, J.; Tauber, Z.; Kamarad, V. M1/M2 macrophage polarization in human obese adipose tissue. *Biomed. Pap. Med. Fac. Univ. Palacky Olomouc Czech Repub.* **2018**, *162*, 79–82. [CrossRef]

88. Duffield, J.S.; Forbes, S.J.; Constandinou, C.M.; Clay, S.; Partolina, M.; Vuthoori, S.; Wu, S.; Lang, R.; Iredale, J.P. Selective depletion of macrophages reveals distinct, opposing roles during liver injury and repair. *J. Clin. Invest.* **2005**, *115*, 56–65. [CrossRef]

89. Mantovani, A.; Locati, M. Tumor-Associated macrophages as a paradigm of macrophage plasticity, diversity, and polarization: Lessons and open questions. *Arterioscler. Thromb Vasc. Biol.* **2013**, *33*, 1478–1483. [CrossRef]

90. Wang, Y.; Smith, W.; Hao, D.; He, B.; Kong, L. M1 and M2 macrophage polarization and potentially therapeutic naturally occurring compounds. *Int. Immunopharmacol.* **2019**, *70*, 459–466. [CrossRef]

91. Chiurchiu, V.; Leuti, A.; Dalli, J.; Jacobsson, A.; Battistini, L.; Maccarrone, M.; Serhan, C.N. Proresolving lipid mediators resolvin D1, resolvin D2, and maresin 1 are critical in modulating T cell responses. *Sci. Transl. Med.* **2016**, *8*, 353ra111. [CrossRef] [PubMed]

92. Marcon, R.; Bento, A.F.; Dutra, R.C.; Bicca, M.A.; Leite, D.F.; Calixto, J.B. Maresin 1, a proresolving lipid mediator derived from omega-3 polyunsaturated fatty acids, exerts protective actions in murine models of colitis. *J. Immunol.* **2013**, *191*, 4288–4298. [CrossRef] [PubMed]

93. Chiang, N.; Fredman, G.; Backhed, F.; Oh, S.F.; Vickery, T.; Schmidt, B.A.; Serhan, C.N. Infection regulates pro-resolving mediators that lower antibiotic requirements. *Nature* **2012**, *484*, 524–528. [CrossRef] [PubMed]

94. Hao, Y.; Zheng, H.; Wang, R.H.; Li, H.; Yang, L.L.; Bhandari, S.; Liu, Y.J.; Han, J.; Smith, F.G.; Gao, H.C.; et al. Maresin1 alleviates metabolic dysfunction in septic mice: A (1)H NMR-based metabolomics analysis. *Mediat. Inflamm.* **2019**, *2019*, 2309175. [CrossRef]

95. David, S.; Lopez-Vales, R.; Wee Yong, V. Harmful and beneficial effects of inflammation after spinal cord injury: Potential therapeutic implications. *Handb. Clin. Neurol.* **2012**, *109*, 485–502.

96. Popovich, P.G. Neuroimmunology of traumatic spinal cord injury: A brief history and overview. *Exp. Neurol.* **2014**, *258*, 1–4. [CrossRef]

97. Kawasaki, Y.; Zhang, L.; Cheng, J.K.; Ji, R.R. Cytokine mechanisms of central sensitization: Distinct and overlapping role of interleukin-1beta, interleukin-6, and tumor necrosis factor-alpha in regulating synaptic and neuronal activity in the superficial spinal cord. *J. Neurosci.* **2008**, *28*, 5189–5194. [CrossRef]

98. Jetten, N.; Roumans, N.; Gijbels, M.J.; Romano, A.; Post, M.J.; de Winther, M.P.; van der Hulst, R.R.; Xanthoulea, S. Wound administration of M2-polarized macrophages does not improve murine cutaneous healing responses. *PLoS ONE* **2014**, *9*, e102994. [CrossRef]

99. Hong, S.; Lu, Y.; Tian, H.; Alapure, B.V.; Wang, Q.; Bunnell, B.A.; Laborde, J.M. Maresin-Like lipid mediators are produced by leukocytes and platelets and rescue reparative function of diabetes-impaired macrophages. *Chem. Biol.* **2014**, *21*, 1318–1329. [CrossRef]

100. Yang, T.; Xu, G.; Newton, P.T.; Chagin, A.S.; Mkrtchian, S.; Carlstrom, M.; Zhang, X.M.; Harris, R.A.; Cooter, M.; Berger, M.; et al. Maresin 1 attenuates neuroinflammation in a mouse model of perioperative neurocognitive disorders. *Br. J. Anaesth.* **2019**, *122*, 350–360. [CrossRef]

101. Bunton-Stasyshyn, R.K.; Saccon, R.A.; Fratta, P.; Fisher, E.M. SOD1 function and its implications for amyotrophic lateral sclerosis pathology: New and renascent themes. *Neuroscientist* **2015**, *21*, 519–529. [CrossRef] [PubMed]

102. Ohuchi, K.; Ono, Y.; Joho, M.; Tsuruma, K.; Ogami, S.; Yamane, S.; Funato, M.; Kaneko, H.; Nakamura, S.; Hara, H.; et al. A docosahexaenoic acid-derived pro-resolving agent, maresin 1, protects motor neuron cells death. *Neurochem. Res.* **2018**, *43*, 1413–1423. [CrossRef] [PubMed]

103. Mokarram, N.; Merchant, A.; Mukhatyar, V.; Patel, G.; Bellamkonda, R.V. Effect of modulating macrophage phenotype on peripheral nerve repair. *Biomaterials* **2012**, *33*, 8793–8801. [CrossRef] [PubMed]

104. Zheng, M.; Duan, J.; He, Z.; Wang, Z.; Mu, S.; Zeng, Z.; Qu, J.; Wang, D.; Zhang, J. Transplantation of bone marrow stromal stem cells overexpressing tropomyosin receptor kinase A for peripheral nerve repair. *Cytotherapy* **2017**, *19*, 916–926. [CrossRef]

105. Murray, P.J.; Wynn, T.A. Protective and pathogenic functions of macrophage subsets. *Nat. Rev. Immunol.* **2011**, *11*, 723–737. [CrossRef]

106. Gordon, S. Alternative activation of macrophages. *Nat. Rev. Immunol.* **2003**, *3*, 23–35. [CrossRef]

107. Cattin, A.L.; Burden, J.J.; Van Emmenis, L.; Mackenzie, F.E.; Hoving, J.J.; Garcia Calavia, N.; Guo, Y.; McLaughlin, M.; Rosenberg, L.H.; Quereda, V.; et al. Macrophage-Induced blood vessels guide schwann cell-mediated regeneration of peripheral nerves. *Cell* **2015**, *162*, 1127–1139. [CrossRef]

108. Valdes, A.M.; Ravipati, S.; Menni, C.; Abhishek, A.; Metrustry, S.; Harris, J.; Nessa, A.; Williams, F.M.K.; Spector, T.D.; Doherty, M.; et al. Association of the resolvin precursor 17-HDHA, but not D- or E-series resolvins, with heat pain sensitivity and osteoarthritis pain in humans. *Sci. Rep.* **2017**, *7*, 10748. [CrossRef]

109. Xu, Z.Z.; Zhang, L.; Liu, T.; Park, J.Y.; Berta, T.; Yang, R.; Serhan, C.N.; Ji, R.R. Resolvins RvE1 and RvD1 attenuate inflammatory pain via central and peripheral actions. *Nat. Med.* **2010**, *16*, 592–597. [CrossRef]

110. Fattori, V.; Amaral, F.A.; Verri, W.A., Jr. Neutrophils and arthritis: Role in disease and pharmacological perspectives. *Pharmacol. Res.* **2016**, *112*, 84–98. [CrossRef]

111. Liao, H.Y.; Hsieh, C.L.; Huang, C.P.; Lin, Y.W. Electroacupuncture attenuates CFA-induced inflammatory pain by suppressing Nav1.8 through S100B, TRPV1, opioid, and adenosine pathways in mice. *Sci. Rep.* **2017**, *7*, 42531. [CrossRef] [PubMed]

112. Yu, Y.Q.; Zhao, F.; Guan, S.M.; Chen, J. Antisense-Mediated knockdown of Na(V)1.8, but not Na(V)1.9, generates inhibitory effects on complete Freund's adjuvant-induced inflammatory pain in rat. *PLoS ONE* **2011**, *6*, e19865. [CrossRef] [PubMed]

113. Blake, K.J.; Baral, P.; Voisin, T.; Lubkin, A.; Pinho-Ribeiro, F.A.; Adams, K.L.; Roberson, D.P.; Ma, Y.C.; Otto, M.; Woolf, C.J.; et al. Staphylococcus aureus produces pain through pore-forming toxins and neuronal TRPV1 that is silenced by QX-314. *Nat. Commun.* **2018**, *9*, 37. [CrossRef] [PubMed]

114. Maruyama, K.; Takayama, Y.; Kondo, T.; Ishibashi, K.I.; Sahoo, B.R.; Kanemaru, H.; Kumagai, Y.; Martino, M.M.; Tanaka, H.; Ohno, N.; et al. Nociceptors boost the resolution of fungal osteoinflammation via the TRP channel-CGRP-Jdp2 axis. *Cell Rep.* **2017**, *19*, 2730–2742. [CrossRef] [PubMed]

115. Cao, D.L.; Zhang, Z.J.; Xie, R.G.; Jiang, B.C.; Ji, R.R.; Gao, Y.J. Chemokine CXCL1 enhances inflammatory pain and increases NMDA receptor activity and COX-2 expression in spinal cord neurons via activation of CXCR2. *Exp. Neurol.* **2014**, *261*, 328–336. [CrossRef] [PubMed]

116. Zhu, M.D.; Zhao, L.X.; Wang, X.T.; Gao, Y.J.; Zhang, Z.J. Ligustilide inhibits microglia-mediated proinflammatory cytokines production and inflammatory pain. *Brain Res. Bull.* **2014**, *109*, 54–60. [CrossRef] [PubMed]

117. Scholz, J.; Woolf, C.J. The neuropathic pain triad: Neurons, immune cells and glia. *Nat. Neurosci.* **2007**, *10*, 1361–1368. [CrossRef]

Review

Restoration of Neurological Function Following Peripheral Nerve Trauma

Damien P. Kuffler [1,*] and Christian Foy [2]

1   Institute of Neurobiology, Medical Sciences Campus, University of Puerto Rico, 201 Blvd. del Valle, San Juan, PR 00901, USA
2   Section of Orthopedic Surgery, Medical Sciences Campus, University of Puerto Rico, San Juan, PR 00901, USA; christian.foy@upr.edu
*   Correspondence: dkuffler@hotmail.com

Received: 12 January 2020; Accepted: 3 March 2020; Published: 6 March 2020

Abstract: Following peripheral nerve trauma that damages a length of the nerve, recovery of function is generally limited. This is because no material tested for bridging nerve gaps promotes good axon regeneration across the gap under conditions associated with common nerve traumas. While many materials have been tested, sensory nerve grafts remain the clinical "gold standard" technique. This is despite the significant limitations in the conditions under which they restore function. Thus, they induce reliable and good recovery only for patients < 25 years old, when gaps are <2 cm in length, and when repairs are performed <2–3 months post trauma. Repairs performed when these values are larger result in a precipitous decrease in neurological recovery. Further, when patients have more than one parameter larger than these values, there is normally no functional recovery. Clinically, there has been little progress in developing new techniques that increase the level of functional recovery following peripheral nerve injury. This paper examines the efficacies and limitations of sensory nerve grafts and various other techniques used to induce functional neurological recovery, and how these might be improved to induce more extensive functional recovery. It also discusses preliminary data from the clinical application of a novel technique that restores neurological function across long nerve gaps, when repairs are performed at long times post-trauma, and in older patients, even under all three of these conditions. Thus, it appears that function can be restored under conditions where sensory nerve grafts are not effective.

Keywords: nerve repair; nerve gaps; platelet-rich plasma (PRP); platelet-rich plasma; axon regeneration; allografts; autografts; nerve conduits

---

1. Introduction

Clinically, traumatic peripheral nerve injuries are common, and are caused by violence, recreational activities, motor vehicle accidents, and iatrogenic injuries during surgery. The majority of nerve injuries occur in the upper extremity [1] with about 1–3% of all upper extremity trauma patients presenting with nerve injuries [2]. These injuries can be severely debilitating and have a significantly negative impact on the individual's lifestyle, function, and work [3,4]. The majority of those who suffer traumatic nerve injuries are young, with an average age of 39 [5]. Less than 50% of such individuals undergo nerve repair surgery, and of those who do, only 40–50% recover good function [6]. Thus, the majority of individuals who suffer peripheral nerve traumas suffer permanent neurological deficits, and frequently also chronic neuropathic pain associated with the nerve injury.

Due to the generally limited extent of neurological recovery, it is essential to develop novel techniques that restore more extensive function to a larger number of patients. This review examines the relative efficacies of different techniques that have been tested for their ability to restore function and discusses a novel technique that shows great promise for inducing recovery under conditions where it is presently not possible.

2. Issues Influencing the Extent of Axon Regeneration and Neurological Recovery

2.1. Type of Nerve Trauma

The type of nerve injury has a major influence on the extent of neurological recovery. Following a traumatic nerve injury, sometimes referred to as an "untidy" wound (shrapnel, bullet, blunt object, open fracture, contaminated), there is significantly less recovery than following a "tidy," or clean-cut, injury (glass, knife, scissors) [7]. This is because untidy injuries damage longer lengths of the nerve, which must be removed, resulting in longer nerve gaps, from which recovery is less than for short gaps.

Another type of nerve injury involves the loss of nerve vascularization, such as occurs with untidy injuries. When nerves lose their blood supply, a significantly lower percentage of those repaired nerves recover function than those following the repair of a tidy injury [7]. This is because of the time required for the nerve graft to be re-vascularized, during which axons do not, or are permanently prevented from, regenerating into the non-vascularized portion of the nerve.

2.2. Gender and Age

Although some behavioral differences are seen in neurons and Schwann cells associated with gender and age, their impact on clinical neurological recovery following nerve trauma is not clear. Thus, it has been observed that the density of epidermal nerve fibers decreases with age, and is lower in men compared with women [8]. This suggests age and gender influence innervation.

In hamsters, recovery of function following facial nerve injury is significantly faster in females than males [9]. While the administration of exogenous steroids accelerates axon regeneration in males, it has a lower impact on the rate of regeneration in females [9]. In rats, continuous exercise training increases the extent of axon regeneration in male, but not female, or castrated rats [10,11]. However, interval exercise training enhances axon regeneration in female, but not male rats [10,11].

In the male animal model, the influence on axon regeneration is associated with the expression of androgens [12]. They influence the extent of axon regeneration in peripheral nerves by regulating motor neurons' expression of brain-derived neurotrophic factor (BDNF) and its receptor, trkB [11,13,14]. These molecules, in turn, influence the extent of axon regeneration [10,12]. The effect of training on axon regeneration in females works through a different mechanism than that of males [12]. Further studies are required to determine whether hormone treatment strategies may be effective in enhancing the extent of neurological recovery following nerve injury.

2.3. Promoting Axon Regeneration Through Crushed Nerves

Two to three days after a crush nerve injury, the severed axons begin to regenerate into the distal part of the nerve and continue to regenerate until they reach and reinnervate their original targets. Axon regeneration is promoted by the denervated Schwann cells in the distal portion of the nerve by their release of neurotrophic factors, and their extracellular matrix [15–21]. The greater the number of axons that regenerate through the distal nerve, the greater the extent of neurological recovery [19,22] Generally, the precision of target reinnervation is extremely high [19].

2.4. Restoration of Function without Surgical Intervention

Following a nerve transection, the nerve stumps normally retract, resulting in a gap of ≤3 mm. Despite this small gap, neurological recovery may develop without surgical intervention. This is due to a cascade of events involving the diffusion of fibrinogen from leaky blood vessels into the nerve gap where it combines with thrombin. This leads to fibrinogen polymerization and the formation of a three-dimensional fibrin matrix within the gap [23]. This matrix provides passive support to axons, which allows them to regenerate to the distal nerve stump.

However, fibrin clots are converted into a matrix that actively promotes axon regeneration by the migration of Schwann cells into the fibrin clot from the central and distal nerve stumps. These Schwann cells release a cocktail of neurotrophic and wound healing factors that bind to the pure fibrin converting it from a passive three-dimensional matrix into one that actively promotes axon regeneration [24]. This results in a significant increase in the number of axons that regenerates across the gap [25].

The efficacy of fibrin in promoting axon regeneration is increased by the platelets and mesenchymal stem cells that become entrapped in the fibrin clot in the nerve gap. They act by multiple mechanisms: (1) They release neurotrophic and other factors that act directly on the axons to promote regeneration [26]. (2) They release factors that promote Schwann cells of the distal nerve pathway to proliferate and release neurotrophic factors, which also enhance the extent of axon regeneration [27]. (3) The mesenchymal stem cells differentiate into Schwann cells, which release neurotrophic and other factors, thus enhancing the concentration of these factors and the extent of axon regeneration [28]. (4) Mesenchymal stem cells release factors that induce angiogenesis, which is essential for axon regeneration [29].

Although factors within the fibrin clot promote axon regeneration, factors are also required to direct axons across the nerve graft. Growth cones extend fine processes that sample the environment around them in search of factors to which they can adhere, and that both promote and direct their growth. When Schwann cell-released neurotrophic factors are distributed in a uniform concentration around neurons and their growth cones, neurite outgrowth is promoted, but the outgrowth is random. However, when neurons and their growth cones are exposed to a concentration gradient of those same factors in vitro and in vivo, the growth cones turn and increase the concentration gradient of the Schwann cell-released factors [19,30]. This is because, as the factors diffuse away from the distal nerve stump, they create a concentration gradient of the factor, which is the highest at the distal nerve stump [30–33]. This directs the axons up the gradient and to the distal stump [19,30,33–35]. Once the axons reach the distal nerve stump, their regeneration continues to be promoted and directed through the distal nerve segment by the concentration gradient of Schwann cell-released factors ahead of them.

2.5. Restoration of Function with Surgical Intervention—Anastomosis

When a nerve has a clean transection, or when the nerve defect is small (only a few millimeters), the nerve stumps can be anastomosed, which leads to the restoration of function. However, to develop functional recovery, the repaired nerve must be tension-free [36]. When anastomosis is performed within 14 days of nerve trauma, functional recovery is good in about 80% of patients [37]. However, with increasing time between nerve trauma and anastomosis, the extent of recovery decreases [38–40]. The types of changes that occur over time that lead to this decrease in recovery are discussed below.

2.6. Promoting Axon Regeneration Across Nerve Gaps

When the gap between the nerve stumps is too long, anastomosis is not possible because the nerve cannot be stretched to extend across the gap. Therefore, to restore function to such nerves, the gaps must be bridged with a material that both supports and promotes axon regeneration entirely across the gap.

2.7. Autografts

It was originally hypothesized that the best material for inducing axons to regenerate across nerve gaps would be a length of the autologous peripheral nerve [41]. The most commonly used donor nerves are the cutaneous saphenous, medial antebrachial cutaneous, and sural nerves [42–45].

The following sections discuss the efficacy of sensory nerve grafts and other techniques in promoting axon regeneration and neurological recovery.

3. Sensory Nerve Grafts: Limitations

3.1. Loss of Sensory Nerve Function

The primary drawback to using lengths of nerve as a graft is that their use requires sacrificing the function of that nerve. This creates a permanent neurological deficit [15,46,47].

3.2. Incorrect Schwann Cell Phenotype

Both sensory and motor nerve grafts have been tested for their efficacy in promoting axon regeneration and restoration of function. Motor nerve grafts induce significantly greater axon regeneration than sensory nerve grafts. This is because sensory and motor nerve Schwann cells express distinctly different phenotypes, and each best supports the regeneration of their specific axon phenotype [16,48]. Although motor nerve grafts are more effective than sensory nerve grafts in promoting axon regeneration across a nerve gap, they are not used because it is considered unethical to sacrifice a motor nerve function, when the loss of a pure sensory nerve has minimal impact on the patient.

3.3. Inflammation

The standard technique for securing nerve grafts in place is to use multiple sutures through the epineurium of the graft and the nerve stumps. However, sutures often cause inflammation and scarring, both of which inhibit axon regeneration [49]. This problem can be overcome by placing a degradable collagen [50] or fibrin [51] conduit around the site of nerve stump anastomosis, which stabilizes the juxtaposition of the nerve stumps. An alternative technique is to apply fibrin glue to the anastomosis site of the nerve stumps [52].

3.4. Necrosis

Sensory nerves generally have a smaller diameter than the mixed sensory/motor nerves they are commonly used to repair. Often, multiple small diameter grafts are used so that the final diameter of the grafts approximates that of the nerve to be repaired. However, smaller diameter grafts are correlated with less functional recovery than larger diameter grafts [53–55]. This is ascribed to the lack of vascularization leading to necrosis of the Schwann cells within the graft [54,56]. Necrosis reduces, if not blocks, axon regeneration through the graft. This situation is not improved when multiple small grafts are used. To avoid necrosis, the best approach is to use vascularized nerve grafts (see the following section on vascularized grafts and inducing vascularization).

3.5. Decreasing Recovery with Increasing Gap Length

Sensory nerve grafts promote good to excellent functional recovery only when nerve gaps are <2 cm in length [57–59]. The extent of recovery decreases to only good for gaps ≥ 3 cm in length [60,61], decreases further for gaps up to 4 cm [58,62,63], and there is a precipitous decrease in recovery for gaps > 4–5 cm [58,64,65]. Few axons regenerate across grafts of 8 cm in length [57,60] and there are no reports of axons regenerating across gaps >10 cm in length [7,58,63,65–67]. Thus, neurological recovery decreases with increasing gap length [53]. Therefore, sensory nerve grafts are only considered reliable for "short" nerve gaps (≤3 cm) [55,68]. Furthermore, no material is Food and Drug Administration (FDA)-approved for repairing nerve gaps >3 cm in length [55,69,70].

The reduction in axon regeneration across long nerve grafts appears correlated with the longer time required to vascularize longer grafts [71]. As mentioned above, without vascularization, the graft environment is ischemic, which inhibits axon regeneration [72].

3.6. Decreasing Recovery with Increasing Time between Nerve Injury and Repair

Anastomosing nerve stumps of non-traumatic transected radial nerves of young males (25 years) immediately [73] or within 14 days [7] of the injury generally results in good neurological recovery for 67% of subjects [73]. However, as the delay in performing the repair increases, the recovery of good function decreases to 30%, fair in 28%, and fails for 42% of patients [7,73].

Similarly, when short nerve gaps are repaired using sensory nerve grafts, recovery is very good to excellent following repairs performed ≤ 14 days post-trauma [7] or good to excellent for repairs performed ≤ 2 months post-trauma [74]. However, the extent of recovery decreases significantly for repairs performed > 3 months post-trauma [62,75,76]. Thus, delays of >2 months result in good recovery in only 49% of patients [62], but are poor for repairs performed > 6 months post-trauma [62,77–79]. No recovery is reported for repairs performed > 10 months post-trauma [80,81].

3.7. Schwann Cell Senescence

Axon regeneration across long nerve gaps requires Schwann cells of the proximal nerve stump to proliferate extensively so they can both promote and accompany the axons as they regenerate. The limited regeneration of axons across long nerve gaps, and when nerves are repaired at long times post-trauma, is in part, attributed to Schwann cell senescence [69]. Senescence is associated with increased expression of markers for β-galactosidase, p16^{INK4A}, and interleukin (IL)6 [82]. Thus, over time, without contact with an axon, Schwann cells lose their ability to proliferate, synthesize, and release neurotrophic factors, which are required to promote axon regeneration [82,83].

3.8. Neuron Loss of Ability to Regenerate

Another explanation for the significant decrease in axon regeneration with increasing time of motor neuron axotomy is that many motor neurons lose the ability to extend axons [83]. The decrease in the ability of motor neurons to regenerate with increasing time of axotomy appears to be associated with the downregulation of neuregulin 1, which is required for axon regeneration [38,84,85]. However, it is important to note that while some motor neurons lose this capacity, others can regenerate even after many years of axotomy. In a clinical case, motor neurons that were axotomized for 22 years were able to extend axons to reinnervate newly denervated muscles [86].

It is not known what determines which motor neurons retain or lose the capacity to regenerate. However, understanding this regulation might provide insights into how neurons' gene expression can be modulated to promote enhanced axon outgrowth. Thus, it would be interesting to compare the gene expression between motor neurons with and without the capacity to regenerate after prolonged axotomy to determine the gene expression that underlies the capacity to regenerate normally. As is discussed later, techniques have been developed that induce motor neurons, which appear to have lost the ability to regenerate, to extend axons.

3.9. Decreasing Recovery with Patient Age

The recovery of function following nerve graft repair is best for patients < 20–25 years of age [87], and the extent of recovery decreases significantly with increasing patient age [87,88]. This is, in part, attributed to the decreasing capacity of sensory nerve grafts to promote axon regeneration (i.e., their Schwann cells becoming senescent) [69]. This change is also associated with the downregulation over time post-axotomy of the ability of neurons to synthesize and release neuregulin 1, which is required for axon regeneration [38,84,85].

Endoneurial vasculature is required for the outgrowth of axons from the proximal stump, and angiogenesis is essential for nerve regeneration [89]. However, clinically, with increasing age, there is a reduction in, or lack of, angiogenesis in response to injury [90]. This change is due to the decrease in nerve injury-induced upregulation of the expression and release of vascular endothelial growth factor (VEGF) [91,92]. VEGF is required for inducing vascularization, which, in turn, is required for axon regeneration. This suggests that vascular abnormalities might play a role in the decreasing ability of axons to regenerate with increasing age. This further suggests that promoting vascularization may increase the extent of neurological recovery in older patients.

3.10. Enhancing the Efficacy of Autografts to Promote Axon Regeneration

The extent and distance axons regenerate decreases with increasing graft length, increasing delays between nerve injury and repair, and increasing age. As already stated, these limitations are associated with (1) the inability of neurons to extend axons, (2) development of Schwann cell senescence, and (3) the failure, or slow process of, graft re-vascularization. Despite these challenges, various techniques overcome these limitations and promote axon regeneration.

Axon regeneration can be triggered from neurons that no longer extend axons, and the rate and extent of axon regeneration increases by refreshing central nerve stumps and then stimulating them electrically, or by applying neurotrophic factors [93–95]. These techniques restore the capacity of neurons to regenerate [96–98] while also inducing the senescent Schwann cells of the distal portion of the nerve to proliferate and release neurotrophic factors that promote the extension of axons from long-term axotomized neurons [99,100].

4. Electrical Stimulation

4.1. Promoting Axotomized Neurons to Extend Axons

As mentioned previously, within increasing the time of axotomy, neurons lose their ability to extend axons [83]. However, these neurons can be induced to extend axons by electrical stimulation of the proximal portion of the transected nerves for as little as one hour [94,101,102] This results in a 34–50% increase in the number of neurons that extend axons [98,103,104]. Electrical stimulation also induces a 2.3-fold increase in the extent of axon sprouting from transected axons [105] while increasing the speed of axon regeneration [101,103,106]. At the same time, in animal models, electrical stimulation increases the distance axons regenerate across nerve gaps, the accuracy of sensory vs. motor axon innervation of their appropriate targets, and extent of functional recovery [107–110]. Electrical stimulation of peripheral nerve clinically also induces enhanced axon regeneration [102].

Electrical stimulation acts by inducing neurons to upregulate their level of cyclic-AMP [89,103]. This, in turn, induces motor neurons to upregulate their expression and synthesis of the neurotrophic factor BDNF and its trkB receptor mRNA, as well as the mRNA for other factors that enhance axon regeneration [99,111] These actions make neurons more receptive to regeneration-promoting factors [112].

4.2. Activating Senescent Schwann Cells

The decrease in axon regeneration across long nerve grafts, and with increasing time between nerve injury and repair, is attributed in part to Schwann cells becoming senescent when they lose contact with axons [69,75]. Thus, they stop proliferating and releasing neurotrophic factors that are required to promote axon regeneration. Electrical stimulation enhances axon regeneration by inducing the senescent Schwann cells to proliferate, migrate, and upregulate their synthesis and release of neurotrophic factors, which act to promote axon regeneration [99,113].

Schwann cells can also be induced to exit their senescent state by the application of VEGF [76,112,114] and marrow-derived mesenchymal stem cells. Thus, the Schwann cells reinitiate their ability to proliferate and to express and release neurotrophic factors [80].

4.3. Vascularized Nerve Grafts and Promoting Vascularization

The standard sensory nerve graft is cut from a donor nerve without maintaining its vasculature. As stated earlier, non-vascularized grafts become necrotic, which creates a toxic environment that inhibits axons regeneration until re-vascularization occurs. However, re-vascularized takes days to develop, and takes more time for longer nerve grafts. This is because vascularization normally progresses from one end of the graft to the other.

The limitation of using non-vascularized grafts is avoided by using vascularized nerve grafts. In the rat sciatic nerve model, vascularized grafts induce significantly greater neurological recovery than non-vascularized nerve grafts [115]. Clinically, vascularized nerve grafts are required for axons to regenerate across gaps of longer than 6 cm [116]. Although vascularized nerve grafts are more effective in restoring function than non-vascularized grafts, they are not commonly used because the surgery is more complicated and time-consuming.

An alternative technique to using vascularized autografts is to induce the rapid re-vascularization of non-vascularized grafts. This can be done by pre-treating nerve grafts with VEGF before using them [117]. This treatment stimulates neovascularization of the graft, and Schwann cell invasion into the graft [117] and can reduce the time of graft ischemia by three days [118].

Axon regeneration can also be enhanced by using autografts with cells overexpressing VEGF, which leads to hyper-vascularization [119]. This enhances axon regeneration by reducing endoneurial scarring, by maintaining the viability of Schwann and other cells within the graft, and by decreasing fibroblast infiltration. This results in a good nutritional environment for supporting axonal regeneration.

The decrease in axon regeneration through nerve grafts with increasing age is also attributed to reduced graft vascularization. This is because aging is associated with a decrease in the upregulation of the expression, and release of VEGF following nerve injury [91]. Following nerve injury to aged mice, there is a significant reduction in the upregulation of VEGF synthesis and release, and thus, a failure of axons to regenerate. These findings suggest that, with increasing age, vascular abnormalities might play a role in the decreasing ability of axons to regenerate. They also suggest that clinically, inducing enhanced vascularization might enhance axon regeneration and functional recovery.

4.4. Conclusion about Sensory Nerve Grafts

The use of sensory nerve grafts leads to a permanent neurological deficit of the donor nerve. While such grafts can induce good to excellent functional recovery, such recovery is only for young patients [120,121], short gaps [65,67] (Aszmann et al., 2008b), and 3 when the repairs are performed within a short time post-trauma [77,79,81]. As any one of these values increases, the extent of recovery decreases precipitously. When the values of two or all three of these parameters increase, there is minimal to no functional recovery. However, even when nerve repair surgery is offered to patients who are considered good candidates for recovery function, <50% of them recover function [122]. Thus, most individuals who suffer peripheral nerve traumas suffer permanent neurological deficits and commonly chronic neuropathic pain. Therefore, there is a need for novel techniques that induce recovery under conditions where sensory nerve grafts are not effective.

The following sections examine other techniques that have been tested for their efficacy in enhancing the extent of axon regeneration and neurological recovery across nerve gaps. They also examine methods tested for increasing their efficacy in enhancing the extent of axon regeneration. The final section briefly discusses a novel technique that holds promise for restoring function, even when simultaneously the values of all three nerve injury parameters far exceed those when sensory nerve grafts are effective in promoting axon regeneration.

5. Allografts

Conceptually, a good alternative to autographs is cellular cadaveric allografts. First, they would avoid the need to sacrifice a sensory nerve function; second, they provide both a three-dimensional extracellular matrix for supporting and promoting axon regeneration and Schwann cells, which can release neurotrophic factors for promoting axon regeneration. However, using allografts requires the administration of immunosuppressive drugs to avoid graft rejection and regeneration failure [123], but immunosuppressants are associated with significant clinical morbidity [124]. They also cause unwanted side effects, such as suppressing the regeneration-promoting capacity of host Schwann cells [30]. Thus, the use of cellular allografts for peripheral nerve repair is rare and their uses are limited to the most severe cases of nerve injuries, such as those involving repairing long nerve gaps [125].

An alternative to cellular allografts is to use acellular allografts. These can be used without immunosuppression after eliminating their immunogenicity [126]. Although they lack cells, they typically maintain a highly organized extracellular matrix scaffold, which can induce axon regeneration. Acellular nerve allografts, also called processed nerve allografts, are now increasingly used instead of autografts [124,127–131].

In a comparative study bridging 1.4-cm sciatic nerve gaps in rats, acellular allografts, isografts, and empty collagen conduits were seen to induce similar axon regeneration entirely across the gap [126]. Another recent comparative clinical study looked at the success of sensory recovery when digital nerve gaps of 1.4 and 1.8 cm were bridged by acellular nerve grafts and empty collagen tubes. Allografts vs. collagen tubes induced excellent outcomes in 39% vs. 48%, good in 55% vs. 26%, and poor in 6% vs. 26%, respectively [126]. However, for 2.8-cm gaps, isografts were more effective than allografts, but conduits were not effective [120]. Other studies determined that acellular allografts are excellent for promoting axon regeneration across gaps 1–1.5 cm [31], 2–3 cm [131], and up to 5 cm meaningful recovery across gaps [132]. However, similar to autografts, their efficacy decreases with increasing gap length [53] and they are not recommended for (or FDA-approved) use across "long" nerve gaps, considered to be >3 cm in length [55,68,82,125,133–135].

Enhancing the Regeneration-Promoting Capacity of Allografts

The efficacy of acellular allografts in promoting axon regeneration and functional recovery can be increased by infusing them with neurotrophic factors, such as glial-derived neurotrophic factor (GDNF) [136], nerve growth factor (NGF) [24], BDNF plus ciliary neurotrophic factor (CNTF) [137], VEGF [138], and βNGF and VEGF [139].

Additional techniques for enhancing axons regeneration through long allografts grafts include filling them with platelet-rich plasma (PRP) [140], autologous Schwann cells [141,142], adipose-derived mesenchymal stem cells (ADSCs), or primary Schwann cell-like differentiated bone marrow-derived mesenchymal stem cells (DMSCs) [142–145]. These cells induce enhanced axon regeneration by releasing neurotrophic factors [146,147].

Although acellular allografts and autografts induce similar extents of axon regeneration across short nerve gaps, acellular allografts are less effective when used for long nerve gaps [148]. However, when the efficacy of acellular allografts is enhanced, they induce axon regeneration that is comparable to that induced by autografts. Unfortunately, the techniques required to enhance the efficacy of acellular allografts have only been tested in animal models, and none can presently be applied clinically. Therefore, sensory nerve grafts remain the "gold standard" for bridging long nerve gaps.

6. Nerve Conduits

6.1. Conduit Composition

Regardless of their composition, empty conduits longer than 1 cm in length, generally induce poor, if any, axon regeneration. However, conduit composition is important. Silicon conduits induce axon regeneration [149,150] but can have the complication of rigidity, which can result in significant chronic nerve compression and irritation at the implantation site [151]. In this case, they may have to be removed, which endangers any recovered neurological function. Therefore, it is advisable to use a fully degradable matrix that does not negatively affect axon regeneration [152].

Axon regeneration is extensive through conduits composed of fibrin [145,153], hydrogel tubes [154], alginate/chitosan polyelectrolyte [155–157], poly epsilon-caprolactone [158,159], polyglycolic acid [160], poly(lactic-co-glycolic acid) or silk-based [161–164]. Conduits composed of decellularized human umbilical artery [165] and muscles [166] are also effective in promoting axon regeneration across nerve gaps.

Veins are promising as conduits [167,168]. Clinically, empty vein conduits appear to have a 3-cm-long limit for their ability to induce axon regeneration [169]. A meta-analysis of published papers determined that for nerve gaps up to 4 cm in length, vein conduits did not induce any significant improvement in sensory recovery outcome compared to conduits of other materials [170]. However, the axon regeneration-promoting efficacy of vein conduits is enhanced when they are filled with PRP [171–173], muscle [174], pre-degenerated muscle [175,176], muscle seeded with neural-transdifferentiated human mesenchymal stem cells [177], and minced peripheral nerves [178]. One study in sheep showed that using the median epineural sheath as a conduit can restore median nerve function across 6-cm-long nerve gaps [179].

6.2. Conduit Architecture

Electrospun collagen/poly(lactic-*co*-glycolic acid) (PLGA) conduits with a three-dimensional internal structure induce more extensive axon regeneration than conduits without a three-dimensional structure [180]. Functional recovery through conduits filled with pure fibrin gel is significantly increased when three-dimensional collagen tubes are filled with gelatin containing biodegradable poly-epsilon-caprolactone and collagen/ poly ε-caprolactone (PCL) sub-micron scale fibers [181].

6.3. Conduits Containing Neurotrophic and Other Factors

The efficacy of collagen conduits is increased when they contain, or release, neurotrophic or other factors, such as GDNF [180] or neurotrophin-3 (NT-3) [182]. Alginate/chitosan conduits induce more extensive axon regeneration when they contain or release simvastatin [183], NGF [184–187], GDNF [184], VEGF [188], GDNF and NGF [24,189], or pleiotrophin [15]. Efficacy is also increased when alginate/chitosan conduits are combined with fibronectin, laminin [190], or when hydrogel conduits contain Matrigel, collagen, heparin (sulfate), laminin, or fibronectin [190]. Conduit efficacy is further increased by the release of neurotrophic factors within conduits from biodegradable polymeric with aligned heparin-conjugated nanofibers [191,192].

Although pure fibrin-filled conduits induce axon regeneration [153], this influence is increased by adding neurotrophic and other axon regeneration-promoting factors [59]. This increase in efficacy is due to the fibrin binding the growth factors, such as basic fibroblast growth factor (bFGF) [65], NGF, BDNF, and NT-30 and factors from the PDGF/VEGF, FGF, and tumor growth factor-beta (TGF-β) families [73]. Fibrin also facilitates the promotion of axon regeneration by binding Schwann cell-released extracellular matrix factor laminin [59]. The binding of these factors converts the fibrin from a passive to a potent regeneration-promoting three-dimensional matrix. This influence is supported by data showing that the application of neurotrophic factors within fibrin glue to the sites of nerve stump anastomosis significantly increases axon regeneration compared to applying the factors directly without fibrin [73,193]. Regeneration is also enhanced by infusing conduits with FK506, an immunosuppressive agent [109,194].

6.4. Conduits Containing Cells

The efficacy of fibrin conduits is enhanced when they are filled with autologous undifferentiated adipose-derived stem cells [145] or contain mesenchymal stem cells [195], and when hydrogel conduits contain mesenchymal stem cells [196]. The efficacy of chitosan conduits is enhanced when they contain combinations of fibronectin and laminin with mesenchymal stem cells (MSCs) or Schwann cells [190], chitosan/PLGA scaffolds are combined with mesenchymal stem cells [197], and when three-dimensional alginate/chitosan conduits are filled with muscle fibers [198]. Adding PRP to the inside of silicon tubes bridging nerve gaps increases the extent of axon regeneration compared to that induced by empty silicon conduits [149,198,199]. Axon regeneration through conduits can be enhanced by adding olfactory ensheathing cells [200] or dissociated Schwann cells, which release axon regeneration-promoting neurotrophic factors, such as NGF, BDNF, NT-3, CNTF, GDNF, and cell adhesion molecules (CAMs) [175] and by building up a basement membrane [69].

Clinically, the number of axons and the distance they regenerate, are significantly increased by adding minced pieces of peripheral nerve to empty conduits [184]. Clinically, bridging a 5-cm-long radial nerve gap with two sensory nerve grafts within a pure fibrin-filled collagen tube induces excellent sensory and motor recovery across a 5-cm-long nerve gap [201].

6.5. Conduit Composition and Electrical Stimulation

Neurite outgrowth from neuron-like cells in vitro is enhanced when they are grown on nerve guidance channels composed of an electrically conductive polymer (oxidized polypyrrole) [202]. Electrically conductive biodegradable polymer composite materials enhance the rate of neurite outgrowth from cultured PC12 cells [101]. Similarly, electrical stimulation of stem cells seeded onto electrospun conducting polymer nanofibers induces neurite extension [203]. Thus, electrical stimulation of conduits composed of such material may enhance axon regeneration in vivo.

6.6. Conclusion for Conduits

Axon regeneration through conduits can be increased compared to that through empty collagen conduits by modifying their composition, architectures, and the factors/cells they contain. However, no conduit tested is as effective as allografts in inducing axon regeneration across both short and long gaps [55,68,204] under nerve injury conditions that are common clinically, such as a long gap in older patients that must be repaired at a long time post-trauma. An additional challenge is that the conduits that are most effective in animal models cannot be used clinically. Therefore, collagen conduits are the most commonly used clinically.

7. Novel Technique

A novel technique was tested clinically for bridging a nerve gap. It involved bridging a 12-cm-long ulnar nerve gap with a PRP-filled collagen tube [205]. The subject was a 58-year-old male, and the repair was performed post-nerve trauma (Figure 1). The subject recovered good motor and sensory function [205]. Thus, both sensory and motor function can be restored, even when simultaneously, all three nerve trauma values far exceeded those where sensory nerve grafts alone are effective. This result shows that functional recovery can be restored under conditions where sensory nerve grafts, allografts, and conduits are not effective. The technique is presently being further tested.

Support for the clinically observed efficacy of a PRP-filled collagen tube enhancing axon regeneration comes from both a clinical study and a number of animal studies. Clinically, the application of PRP eye drops to the cornea enhances the regeneration of sensory innervation [206]. PRP applied to the site of anastomosed rat nerve stumps enhances the extent of axon regeneration in rats [207–209] and guinea pigs, In rabbits, PRP applied to an autograft increases Schwann cell proliferation and the extent of axon regeneration [210]. Bridging a rat sciatic nerve gap with a PRP-filled silicon tube [198,211] or surrounding the sciatic nerve anastomosis site with a PRP-saturated membrane [212] enhances axon regeneration. In rabbits, filling vein grafts with PRP induces significant axon regeneration compared to empty vein grafts [198,206,213–215].

The influence of PRP in enhancing axon regeneration has been proposed to result from platelet-released neurotrophic and other factors [214–217]. An additional platelet potential contributor to enhanced axon regeneration is VEGF, which, as discussed earlier, induces enhanced axon regeneration by inducing rapid vascularization of the entire nerve gap [218,219]. This result suggests that platelet-released neurotrophic and other factors create an environment within the collagen tube that promotes axon regeneration despite a long nerve gap, a long delay between nerve trauma and repair, and an old patient. These results suggest that the platelet-released factors play a number of roles to induce axon regeneration and functional recovery: (1) They induce neurons to extend axons long after they normally do not; (2) induce the Schwann cells of the proximal nerve stump to proliferate, and release axon regeneration-promoting factors; (3) induce the Schwann cells of the proximal stump to migrate with the elongating axons; (4) induce the Schwann cells of the distal nerve to proliferate and release neurotrophic factors and support axon regeneration into and through the distal nerve to the denervated targets; (5) a platelet-released factor, potentially VEGF, promotes vascularization of the gap region.

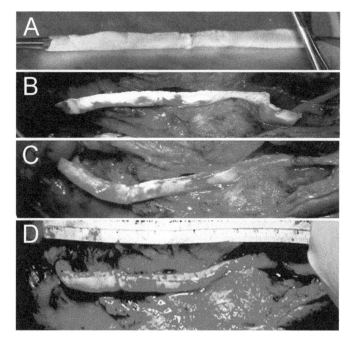

Figure 1. Repairing an ulnar nerve with a 12-cm-long gap. (**A**) Sewing two 4 × 8 cm collagen sheets together end to end, and then into a 16-cm-long tube around the handle of a surgical tool. (**B**) The collagen tube cut to a 12.6 cm length and placed in the nerve gap. (**C**) The proximal and distal nerve stumps secured about 3 mm into the collagen tube. (**D**) Completed nerve gap repair with the collagen tube filled with autologous platelet-rich plasma (PRP).

Confirmation of this result will mean that, without sacrificing a sensory nerve function, neurological recovery can be restored under conditions of long nerve gaps, when repairs are performed years post-trauma and to older patients.

8. Conclusions

Sensory nerve grafts, allografts, and conduits all induce axons to regenerate across nerve gaps. Acellular allografts and conduits are considered to induce neurological outcomes only for nerve gaps <6 cm, although they are routinely used with reliability for "short" nerve gaps considered to be <3 cm, and allografts are FDA-approved only for repairing nerve gaps > 3 cm in length. All three techniques suffer the same imitations of decreasing efficacy with increasing gap length, increasing time between nerve trauma and repair, and increasing patient age. Although the distance across which allografts and conduits induce axon regeneration can be increased by modifying them in various ways, none of those techniques can be used clinically. Therefore, despite their limitations, sensory nerve grafts remain the clinical "gold standard" for repairing peripheral nerves [69,70,166,220–223]. The recovery of function across a 12-cm-long nerve gap of a 58-year-old patient, repaired 3.25 years post-trauma, suggests that functional recovery can be established, even when the values of all three injury parameters far exceed those where autografts are effective. Further testing and development of the technique are required to determine its reliability and the limits of its efficacy.

Author Contributions: Both authors contributed to the design, writing, and final editing of the paper. All authors have read and agreed to the published version of the manuscript.

Funding: This research received no external funding.

Conflicts of Interest: The authors declare no conflicts of interest.

Abbreviations

ADSC	adipose-derived mesenchymal stem cells
bFGF	basic fibroblast growth factor
BDNF	brain-derived neurotrophic factor
CNTF	ciliary neurotrophic factor
DMSC	bone marrow-derived mesenchymal stem cells
FDA	Food and Drug Administration
FGF	fibroblast growth factor
NT-3	neurotrophin-3
NGF	nerve growth factor
GDNF	glial-derived neurotrophic factor
PDGF	platelet-derived neurotrophic factor
PRP	platelet-rich plasma
TGF-β	tumor growth factor-beta
VEGF	vascular endothelial growth factor

References

1. Wenzinger, E.; Rivera-Barrios, A.; Gonzalez, G.; Herrera, F. Trends in Upper Extremity Injuries Presenting to US Emergency Departments. *Hand* **2019**, *14*, 408–412. [CrossRef] [PubMed]
2. Huckhagel, T.; Nuchtern, J.; Regelsberger, J.; Lefering, R.; TraumaRegister, D.G.U. Nerve injury in severe trauma with upper extremity involvement: Evaluation of 49,382 patients from the TraumaRegister DGU(R) between 2002 and 2015. *Scand. J. Trauma Resusc. Emerg. Med.* **2018**, *26*, 76. [CrossRef] [PubMed]
3. Domeshek, L.F.; Krauss, E.M.; Snyder-Warwick, A.K.; Laurido-Soto, O.; Hasak, J.M.; Skolnick, G.B.; Novak, C.B.; Moore, A.M.; Mackinnon, S.E. Surgical Treatment of Neuromas Improves Patient-Reported Pain, Depression, and Quality of Life. *Plast. Reconstr. Surg.* **2017**, *139*, 407–418. [CrossRef] [PubMed]
4. Holmes, S.A.; Barakat, N.; Bhasin, M.; Lopez, N.I.; Lebel, A.; Zurakowski, D.; Thomas, B.; Bhasin, S.; Silva, K.E.; Borra, R.; et al. Biological and behavioral markers of pain following nerve injury in humans. *Neurobiol. Pain* **2020**, *7*, 100038. [CrossRef]
5. Bekelis, K.; Missios, S.; Spinner, R.J. Falls and peripheral nerve injuries: An age-dependent relationship. *J. Neurosurg.* **2015**, *123*, 1223–1229. [CrossRef]
6. Bozkurt, A.; Lassner, F.; O'Dey, D.; Deumens, R.; Bocker, A.; Schwendt, T.; Janzen, C.; Suschek, C.V.; Tolba, R.; Kobayashi, E.; et al. The role of microstructured and interconnected pore channels in a collagen-based nerve guide on axonal regeneration in peripheral nerves. *Biomaterials* **2012**, *33*, 1363–1375. [CrossRef]
7. Shergill, G.; Bonney, G.; Munshi, P.; Birch, R. The radial and posterior interosseous nerves. Results fo 260 repairs. *J. Bone Joint Surg. Br.* **2001**, *83*, 646–649. [CrossRef]
8. Goransson, L.G.; Mellgren, S.I.; Lindal, S.; Omdal, R. The effect of age and gender on epidermal nerve fiber density. *Neurology* **2004**, *62*, 774–777. [CrossRef]
9. Jones, K.J. Recovery from facial paralysis following crush injury of the facial nerve in hamsters: Differential effects of gender and androgen exposure. *Exp. Neurol.* **1993**, *121*, 133–138. [CrossRef]
10. English, A.W.; Wilhelm, J.C.; Ward, P.J. Exercise, neurotrophins, and axon regeneration in the PNS. *Physiology (Bethesda)* **2014**, *29*, 437–445. [CrossRef]
11. Sharma, N.; Marzo, S.J.; Jones, K.J.; Foecking, E.M. Electrical stimulation and testosterone differentially enhance expression of regeneration-associated genes. *Exp. Neurol.* **2010**, *223*, 183–191. [CrossRef] [PubMed]
12. Wood, K.; Wilhelm, J.C.; Sabatier, M.J.; Liu, K.; Gu, J.; English, A.W. Sex differences in the effectiveness of treadmill training in enhancing axon regeneration in injured peripheral nerves. *Dev. Neurobiol.* **2012**, *72*, 688–698. [CrossRef] [PubMed]

13. Osborne, M.C.; Verhovshek, T.; Sengelaub, D.R. Androgen regulates trkB immunolabeling in spinal motoneurons. *J. Neurosci. Res.* **2007**, *85*, 303–309. [CrossRef] [PubMed]
14. Verhovshek, T.; Cai, Y.; Osborne, M.C.; Sengelaub, D.R. Androgen regulates brain-derived neurotrophic factor in spinal motoneurons and their target musculature. *Endocrinology* **2010**, *151*, 253–261. [CrossRef]
15. Alsmadi, N.Z.; Bendale, G.S.; Kanneganti, A.; Shihabeddin, T.; Nguyen, A.H.; Hor, E.; Dash, S.; Johnston, B.; Granja-Vazquez, R.; Romero-Ortega, M.I. Glial-derived growth factor and pleiotrophin synergistically promote axonal regeneration in critical nerve injuries. *Acta Biomater.* **2018**, *78*, 165–177. [CrossRef]
16. Brushart, T.M.; Gerber, J.; Kessens, P.; Chen, Y.G.; Royall, R.M. Contributions of pathway and neuron to preferential motor reinnervation. *J. Neurosci.* **1998**, *18*, 8674–8681. [CrossRef]
17. Chen, Y.G.; Brushart, T.M. The effect of denervated muscle and Schwann cells on axon collateral sprouting. *J. Hand Surg.* **1998**, *23*, 1025–1033. [CrossRef]
18. Evans, G.R.; Brandt, K.; Ang, K.K.; Cromeens, D.; Peden, E.; Gherardini, G.; Gurlek, A.; Tinkey, P.; Williams, J. Peripheral nerve regeneration: The effects of postoperative irradiation. *Plast. Reconstr. Surg.* **1997**, *100*, 375–380. [CrossRef]
19. Kuffler, D.P. Accurate reinnervation of motor end plates after disruption of sheath cells and muscle fibers. *J. Comp. Neurol.* **1986**, *250*, 228–235. [CrossRef]
20. Kuffler, D.P. Isolated satellite cells of a peripheral nerve direct the growth of regenerating frog axons. *J. Comp. Neurol.* **1986**, *249*, 57–64. [CrossRef]
21. Madison, R.D.; Archibald, S.J.; Lacin, R.; Krarup, C. Factors contributing to preferential motor reinnervation in the primate peripheral nervous system. *J. Neurosci.* **1999**, *19*, 11007–11016. [CrossRef] [PubMed]
22. Dagum, A.B. Peripheral nerve regeneration, repair, and grafting. *J. Hand Ther.* **1998**, *11*, 111–117. [CrossRef]
23. Wolberg, A.S. Thrombin generation and fibrin clot structure. *Blood Rev.* **2007**, *21*, 131–142. [CrossRef] [PubMed]
24. Wood, M.D.; MacEwan, M.R.; French, A.R.; Moore, A.M.; Hunter, D.A.; Mackinnon, S.E.; Moran, D.W.; Borschel, G.H.; Sakiyama-Elbert, S.E. Fibrin matrices with affinity-based delivery systems and neurotrophic factors promote functional nerve regeneration. *Biotechnol. Bioeng.* **2010**, *106*, 970–979. [CrossRef] [PubMed]
25. Wood, M.D.; Moore, A.M.; Hunter, D.A.; Tuffaha, S.; Borschel, G.H.; Mackinnon, S.E.; Sakiyama-Elbert, S.E. Affinity-based release of glial-derived neurotrophic factor from fibrin matrices enhances sciatic nerve regeneration. *Acta Biomater.* **2009**, *5*, 959–968. [CrossRef] [PubMed]
26. Schira, J.; Heinen, A.; Poschmann, G.; Ziegler, B.; Hartung, H.P.; Stuhler, K.; Kury, P. Secretome analysis of nerve repair mediating Schwann cells reveals Smad-dependent trophism. *FASEB J.* **2019**, *33*, 4703–4715. [CrossRef]
27. Qin, J.; Wang, L.; Sun, Y.; Sun, X.; Wen, C.; Shahmoradi, M.; Zhou, Y. Concentrated growth factor increases Schwann cell proliferation and neurotrophic factor secretion and promotes functional nerve recovery in vivo. *Int. J. Mol. Med.* **2016**, *37*, 493–500. [CrossRef]
28. Sun, X.; Zhu, Y.; Yin, H.Y.; Guo, Z.Y.; Xu, F.; Xiao, B.; Jiang, W.L.; Guo, W.M.; Meng, H.Y.; Lu, S.B.; et al. Differentiation of adipose-derived stem cells into Schwann cell-like cells through intermittent induction: Potential advantage of cellular transient memory function. *Stem Cell Res. Ther.* **2018**, *9*, 133. [CrossRef]
29. Kot, M.; Musial-Wysocka, A.; Lasota, M.; Ulman, A.; Majka, M. Secretion, migration and adhesion as key processes in the therapeutic activity of mesenchymal stem cells. *Acta Biochim. Pol.* **2019**, *66*, 499–507. [CrossRef]
30. Mai, J.; Fok, L.; Gao, H.; Zhang, X.; Poo, M.M. Axon initiation and growth cone turning on bound protein gradients. *J. Neurosci.* **2009**, *29*, 7450–7458. [CrossRef]
31. Goodhill, G.J. Diffusion in axon guidance. *Eur. J. Neurosci.* **1997**, *9*, 1414–1421. [CrossRef] [PubMed]
32. Perez, N.L.; Sosa, M.A.; Kuffler, D.P. Growth cones turn up concentration gradients of diffusible peripheral target-derived factors. *Exp. Neurol.* **1997**, *145*, 196–202. [CrossRef] [PubMed]
33. Xiang, Y.; Li, Y.; Zhang, Z.; Cui, K.; Wang, S.; Yuan, X.B.; Wu, C.P.; Poo, M.M.; Duan, S. Nerve growth cone guidance mediated by G protein-coupled receptors. *Nat. Neurosci.* **2002**, *5*, 843–848. [CrossRef] [PubMed]
34. De La Torre, J.R.; Hopker, V.H.; Ming, G.L.; Poo, M.M.; Tessier-Lavigne, M.; Hemmati-Brivanlou, A.; Holt, C.E. Turning of retinal growth cones in a netrin-1 gradient mediated by the netrin receptor DCC. *Neuron* **1997**, *19*, 1211–1224. [CrossRef]
35. Zheng, J.Q.; Wan, J.J.; Poo, M.M. Essential role of filopodia in chemotropic turning of nerve growth cone induced by a glutamate gradient. *J. Neurosci.* **1996**, *16*, 1140–1149. [CrossRef] [PubMed]

36. Houschyar, K.S.; Momeni, A.; Pyles, M.N.; Cha, J.Y.; Maan, Z.N.; Duscher, D.; Jew, O.S.; Siemers, F.; Van Schoonhoven, J. The Role of Current Techniques and Concepts in Peripheral Nerve Repair. *Plast. Surg. Int.* **2016**, *2016*, 4175293. [CrossRef]

37. Horteur, C.; Forli, A.; Corcella, D.; Pailhe, R.; Lateur, G.; Saragaglia, D. Short- and long-term results of common peroneal nerve injuries treated by neurolysis, direct suture or nerve graft. *Eur. J. Orthop. Surg. Traumatol.* **2019**, *29*, 893–898. [CrossRef]

38. Ronchi, G.; Cillino, M.; Gambarotta, G.; Fornasari, B.E.; Raimondo, S.; Pugliese, P.; Tos, P.; Cordova, A.; Moschella, F.; Geuna, S. Irreversible changes occurring in long-term denervated Schwann cells affect delayed nerve repair. *J. Neurosurg.* **2017**, *127*, 843–856. [CrossRef]

39. Salomon, D.; Miloro, M.; Kolokythas, A. Outcomes of Immediate Allograft Reconstruction of Long-Span Defects of the Inferior Alveolar Nerve. *J. Oral Maxillofac. Surg.* **2016**, *74*, 2507–2514. [CrossRef]

40. Smith, B.W.; Sakamuri, S.; Spain, D.A.; Joseph, J.R.; Yang, L.J.; Wilson, T.J. An update on the management of adult traumatic nerve injuries-replacing old paradigms: A review. *J. Trauma Acute Care Surg.* **2019**, *86*, 299–306. [CrossRef]

41. Millesi, H. Techniques for nerve grafting. *Hand Clin.* **2000**, *16*, 73–91. [PubMed]

42. Berger, A.; Millesi, H. Nerve grafting. *Clin. Orthop.* **1978**, *133*, 49–55. [CrossRef]

43. Jenq, C.B.; Coggeshall, R.E. The effects of an autologous transplant on patterns of regeneration in rat sciatic nerve. *Brain Res.* **1986**, *364*, 45–56. [CrossRef]

44. Mackinnon, S.E.; Dellon, A.L. A comparison of nerve regeneration across a sural nerve graft and a vascularized pseudosheath. *J. Hand Surg.* **1988**, *13*, 935–942. [CrossRef]

45. Millesi, H. Peripheral nerve injuries. Nerve sutures and nerve grafting. *Scand. J. Plast Reconstr. Surg. Suppl.* **1982**, *19*, 25–37.

46. Pereira Lopes, F.R.; Martin, P.K.; Frattini, F.; Biancalana, A.; Almeida, F.M.; Tomaz, M.A.; Melo, P.A.; Borojevic, R.; Han, S.W.; Martinez, A.M. Double gene therapy with granulocyte colony-stimulating factor and vascular endothelial growth factor acts synergistically to improve nerve regeneration and functional outcome after sciatic nerve injury in mice. *Neuroscience* **2013**, *230*, 184–197. [CrossRef]

47. Reid, A.J.; De Luca, A.C.; Faroni, A.; Downes, S.; Sun, M.; Terenghi, G.; Kingham, P.J. Long term peripheral nerve regeneration using a novel PCL nerve conduit. *Neurosci. Lett.* **2013**, *544*, 125–130. [CrossRef]

48. Hoke, A.; Redett, R.; Hameed, H.; Jari, R.; Zhou, C.; Li, Z.B.; Griffin, J.W.; Brushart, T.M. Schwann cells express motor and sensory phenotypes that regulate axon regeneration. *J. Neurosci.* **2006**, *26*, 9646–9655. [CrossRef]

49. Forman, D.S.; Wood, D.K.; DeSilva, S. Rate of regeneration of sensory axons in transected rat sciatic nerve repaired with epineurial sutures. *J. Neurol. Sci.* **1979**, *44*, 55–59. [CrossRef]

50. Bamba, R.; Riley, D.C.; Kelm, N.D.; Cardwell, N.; Pollins, A.C.; Afshari, A.; Nguyen, L.; Dortch, R.D.; Thayer, W.P. A novel conduit-based coaptation device for primary nerve repair. *Int. J. Neurosci.* **2018**, *128*, 563–569. [CrossRef]

51. Pettersson, J.; Kalbermatten, D.; McGrath, A.; Novikova, L.N. Biodegradable fibrin conduit promotes long-term regeneration after peripheral nerve injury in adult rats. *J. Plast. Reconstr. Aesthet. Surg.* **2010**, *63*, 1893–1899. [CrossRef] [PubMed]

52. Felix, S.P.; Pereira Lopes, F.R.; Marques, S.A.; Martinez, A.M. Comparison between suture and fibrin glue on repair by direct coaptation or tubulization of injured mouse sciatic nerve. *Microsurgery* **2013**, *33*, 468–477. [CrossRef]

53. Penkert, G.; Bini, W.; Samii, M. Revascularization of nerve grafts: An experimental study. *J. Reconstr. Microsurg.* **1988**, *4*, 319–325. [CrossRef] [PubMed]

54. Taylor, G.I. Nerve grafting with simultaneous microvascular reconstruction. *Clin. Orthop. Relat. Res.* **1978**, *133*, 56–70. [CrossRef]

55. Leckenby, J.I.; Furrer, C.; Haug, L.; Juon Personeni, B.; Vogelin, E. A retrospective case series reporting the outcomes of Avance nerve allografts in the treatment of peripheral nerve injuries. *Plast. Reconstr. Surg.* **2019**, *45*, 368e–381e. [CrossRef] [PubMed]

56. Rbia, N.; Shin, A.Y. The Role of Nerve Graft Substitutes in Motor and Mixed Motor/Sensory Peripheral Nerve Injuries. *J. Hand Surg. Am.* **2017**, *42*, 367–377. [CrossRef] [PubMed]

57. Belkas, J.S.; Munro, C.A.; Shoichet, M.S.; Midha, R. Peripheral nerve regeneration through a synthetic hydrogel nerve tube. *Restor. Neurol. Neurosci.* **2005**, *23*, 19–29.

58. Karabeg, R.; Jakirlic, M.; Dujso, V. Sensory recovery after forearm median and ulnar nerve grafting. *Med. Arh.* **2009**, *63*, 97–99.

59. Liu, Q.; Bhat, M.; Bowen, W.D.; Cheng, J. Signaling pathways from cannabinoid receptor-1 activation to inhibition of N-methyl-D-aspartic acid mediated calcium influx and neurotoxicity in dorsal root ganglion neurons. *J. Pharmacol. Exp. Ther.* **2009**, *331*, 1062–1070. [CrossRef]

60. Nichols, C.M.; Brenner, M.J.; Fox, I.K.; Tung, T.H.; Hunter, D.A.; Rickman, S.R.; Mackinnon, S.E. Effects of motor versus sensory nerve grafts on peripheral nerve regeneration. *Exp. Neurol.* **2004**, *190*, 347–355. [CrossRef]

61. Strauch, R.J.; Strauch, B. Nerve conduits: An update on tubular nerve repair and reconstruction. *J. Hand Surg. Am.* **2013**, *38*, 1252–1255. [CrossRef] [PubMed]

62. Matejcik, V. [Reconstructive surgery of the peripheral nerves in the upper extremities with autografts]. *Acta Chir. Orthop. Traumatol. Cech.* **2002**, *69*, 85–87. [PubMed]

63. Terzis, J.K.; Kokkalis, Z.T. Outcomes of secondary reconstruction of ulnar nerve lesions: Our experience. *Plast. Reconstr. Surg.* **2008**, *122*, 1100–1110. [CrossRef]

64. Aszmann, O.C.; Korak, K.J.; Luegmair, M.; Frey, M. Bridging critical nerve defects through an acellular homograft seeded with autologous schwann cells obtained from a regeneration neuroma of the proximal stump. *J. Reconstr. Microsurg.* **2008**, *24*, 151–158. [CrossRef] [PubMed]

65. Matsumoto, K.; Ohnishi, K.; Kiyotani, T.; Sekine, T.; Ueda, H.; Nakamura, T.; Endo, K.; Shimizu, Y. Peripheral nerve regeneration across an 80-mm gap bridged by a polyglycolic acid (PGA)-collagen tube filled with laminin-coated collagen fibers: A histological and electrophysiological evaluation of regenerated nerves. *Brain Res.* **2000**, *868*, 315–328. [CrossRef]

66. Kandenwein, J.A.; Kretschmer, T.; Engelhardt, M.; Richter, H.P.; Antoniadis, G. Surgical interventions for traumatic lesions of the brachial plexus: A retrospective study of 134 cases. *J. Neurosurg.* **2005**, *103*, 614–621. [CrossRef] [PubMed]

67. Nichterwitz, S.; Hoffmann, N.; Hajosch, R.; Oberhoffner, S.; Schlosshauer, B. Bioengineered glial strands for nerve regeneration. *Neurosci. Lett.* **2010**, *484*, 118–122. [CrossRef] [PubMed]

68. Safa, B.; Buncke, G. Autograft Substitutes: Conduits and Processed Nerve Allografts. *Hand Clin.* **2016**, *32*, 127–140. [CrossRef]

69. Hoben, G.M.; Ee, X.; Schellhardt, L.; Yan, Y.; Hunter, D.A.; Moore, A.M.; Snyder-Warwick, A.K.; Stewart, S.; Mackinnon, S.E.; Wood, M.D. Increasing Nerve Autograft Length Increases Senescence and Reduces Regeneration. *Plast. Reconstr. Surg.* **2018**, *142*, 952–961. [CrossRef]

70. Kornfeld, T.; Vogt, P.M.; Radtke, C. Nerve grafting for peripheral nerve injuries with extended defect sizes. *Wien. Med. Wochenschr.* **2019**, *169*, 240–251. [CrossRef]

71. Mani, G.V.; Shurey, C.; Green, C.J. Is early vascularization of nerve grafts necessary? *J. Hand Surg. Br.* **1992**, *17*, 536–543. [CrossRef]

72. Koshima, I.; Harii, K. Experimental study of vascularized nerve grafts: Multifactorial analyses of axonal regeneration of nerves transplanted into an acute burn wound. *J. Hand Surg. Am.* **1985**, *10*, 64–72. [CrossRef]

73. Roganovic, Z.; Pavlicevic, G. Difference in recovery potential of peripheral nerves after graft repairs. *Neurosurgery* **2006**, *59*, 621–633, discussion 621–633. [CrossRef] [PubMed]

74. Kim, D.H.; Kam, A.C.; Chandika, P.; Tiel, R.L.; Kline, D.G. Surgical management and outcome in patients with radial nerve lesions. *J. Neurosurg.* **2001**, *95*, 573–583. [CrossRef]

75. Fu, S.Y.; Gordon, T. Contributing factors to poor functional recovery after delayed nerve repair: Prolonged denervation. *J. Neurosci.* **1995**, *15*, 3886–3895. [CrossRef]

76. Matejcik, V. Peripheral nerve reconstruction by autograft. *Injury* **2002**, *33*, 627–631. [CrossRef]

77. Brenner, M.J.; Hess, J.R.; Myckatyn, T.M.; Hayashi, A.; Hunter, D.A.; Mackinnon, S.E. Repair of motor nerve gaps with sensory nerve inhibits regeneration in rats. *Laryngoscope* **2006**, *116*, 1685–1692. [CrossRef]

78. Jones, R.H. Repair of the trigeminal nerve: A review. *Aust. Dent. J.* **2010**, *55*, 112–119. [CrossRef]

79. Tung, T.H.; Mackinnon, S.E. Nerve transfers: Indications, techniques, and outcomes. *J. Hand Surg. Am.* **2010**, *35*, 332–341. [CrossRef]

80. Gordon, T.; Tyreman, N.; Raji, M.A. The basis for diminished functional recovery after delayed peripheral nerve repair. *J. Neurosci.* **2011**, *31*, 5325–5334. [CrossRef]

81. Saheb-Al-Zamani, M.; Yan, Y.; Farber, S.J.; Hunter, D.A.; Newton, P.; Wood, M.D.; Stewart, S.A.; Johnson, P.J.; Mackinnon, S.E. Limited regeneration in long acellular nerve allografts is associated with increased Schwann cell senescence. *Exp. Neurol.* **2013**, *247*, 165–177. [CrossRef] [PubMed]

82. Furey, M.J.; Midha, R.; Xu, Q.G.; Belkas, J.; Gordon, T. Prolonged target deprivation reduces the capacity of injured motoneurons to regenerate. *Neurosurgery* **2007**, *60*, 723–732. [CrossRef] [PubMed]

83. Fricker, F.R.; Lago, N.; Balarajah, S.; Tsantoulas, C.; Tanna, S.; Zhu, N.; Fageiry, S.K.; Jenkins, M.; Garratt, A.N.; Birchmeier, C.; et al. Axonally derived neuregulin-1 is required for remyelination and regeneration after nerve injury in adulthood. *J. Neurosci.* **2011**, *31*, 3225–3233. [CrossRef] [PubMed]

84. Taveggia, C.; Zanazzi, G.; Petrylak, A.; Yano, H.; Rosenbluth, J.; Einheber, S.; Xu, X.; Esper, R.M.; Loeb, J.A.; Shrager, P.; et al. Neuregulin-1 type III determines the ensheathment fate of axons. *Neuron* **2005**, *47*, 681–694. [CrossRef]

85. Lanzetta, M.; Pozzo, M.; Bottin, A.; Merletti, R.; Farina, D. Reinnervation of motor units in intrinsic muscles of a transplanted hand. *Neurosci. Lett.* **2005**, *373*, 138–143. [CrossRef] [PubMed]

86. Vikstrom, P.; Rosen, B.; Carlsson, I.K.; Bjorkman, A. The effect of early relearning on sensory recovery 4 to 9 years after nerve repair: A report of a randomized controlled study. *J. Hand Surg. Eur. Vol.* **2018**, *43*, 626–630. [CrossRef]

87. Andelkovic, S.Z.; Lesic, A.R.; Bumbasirevic, M.Z.; Rasulic, L.G. The Outcomes of 150 Consecutive Patients with Digital Nerve Injuries Treated in a Single Center. *Turk. Neurosurg.* **2017**, *27*, 289–293. [CrossRef]

88. Sondell, M.; Lundborg, G.; Kanje, M. Vascular endothelial growth factor has neurotrophic activity and stimulates axonal outgrowth, enhancing cell survival and Schwann cell proliferation in the peripheral nervous system. *J. Neurosci.* **1999**, *19*, 5731–5740. [CrossRef]

89. Gunin, A.G.; Petrov, V.V.; Golubtzova, N.N.; Vasilieva, O.V.; Kornilova, N.K. Age-related changes in angiogenesis in human dermis. *Exp. Gerontol.* **2014**, *55*, 143–151. [CrossRef]

90. Rivard, A.; Fabre, J.E.; Silver, M.; Chen, D.; Murohara, T.; Kearney, M.; Magner, M.; Asahara, T.; Isner, J.M. Age-dependent impairment of angiogenesis. *Circulation* **1999**, *99*, 111–120. [CrossRef]

91. Swift, M.E.; Kleinman, H.K.; DiPietro, L.A. Impaired wound repair and delayed angiogenesis in aged mice. *Lab. Investig.* **1999**, *79*, 1479–1487. [PubMed]

92. Iijima, Y.; Ajiki, T.; Murayama, A.; Takeshita, K. Effect of Artificial Nerve Conduit Vascularization on Peripheral Nerve in a Necrotic Bed. *Plast. Reconstr. Surg. Glob. Open.* **2016**, *4*, e665. [CrossRef] [PubMed]

93. Gordon, T.; Brushart, T.M.; Amirjani, N.; Chan, K.M. The potential of electrical stimulation to promote functional recovery after peripheral nerve injury–comparisons between rats and humans. *Acta Neurochir. Suppl.* **2007**, *100*, 3–11. [PubMed]

94. Gordon, T.; Brushart, T.M.; Chan, K.M. Augmenting nerve regeneration with electrical stimulation. *Neurol. Res.* **2008**, *30*, 1012–1022. [CrossRef] [PubMed]

95. Gordon, T.; Chan, K.M.; Sulaiman, O.A.; Udina, E.; Amirjani, N.; Brushart, T.M. Accelerating axon growth to overcome limitations in functional recovery after peripheral nerve injury. *Neurosurgery* **2009**, *65*, A132–A144. [CrossRef]

96. Al-Majed, A.A.; Brushart, T.M.; Gordon, T. Electrical stimulation accelerates and increases expression of BDNF and trkB mRNA in regenerating rat femoral motoneurons. *Eur. J. Neurosci.* **2000**, *12*, 4381–4390. [PubMed]

97. Al-Majed, A.A.; Tam, S.L.; Gordon, T. Electrical stimulation accelerates and enhances expression of regeneration-associated genes in regenerating rat femoral motoneurons. *Cell Mol. Neurobiol.* **2004**, *24*, 379–402. [CrossRef]

98. Geremia, N.M.; Gordon, T.; Brushart, T.M.; Al-Majed, A.A.; Verge, V.M. Electrical stimulation promotes sensory neuron regeneration and growth-associated gene expression. *Exp. Neurol.* **2007**, *205*, 347–359. [CrossRef]

99. Gordon, T. The role of neurotrophic factors in nerve regeneration. *Neurosurg. Focus* **2009**, *26*, E3. [CrossRef]

100. Ahlborn, P.; Schachner, M.; Irintchev, A. One hour electrical stimulation accelerates functional recovery after femoral nerve repair. *Exp. Neurol.* **2007**, *208*, 137–144. [CrossRef]

101. Gordon, T.; Amirjani, N.; Edwards, D.C.; Chan, K.M. Brief post-surgical electrical stimulation accelerates axon regeneration and muscle reinnervation without affecting the functional measures in carpal tunnel syndrome patients. *Exp. Neurol.* **2010**, *223*, 192–202. [CrossRef] [PubMed]

102. Gordon, T.; Udina, E.; Verge, V.M.; De Chaves, E.I. Brief electrical stimulation accelerates axon regeneration in the peripheral nervous system and promotes sensory axon regeneration in the central nervous system. *Mot. Control.* **2009**, *13*, 412–441. [CrossRef] [PubMed]

103. Li, Y.T.; Peng, C.W.; Chen, L.T.; Lin, W.S.; Chu, C.H.; Chen, J.J. Application of implantable wireless biomicrosystem for monitoring nerve impedance of rat after sciatic nerve injury. *IEEE Trans. Neural Syst. Rehabil. Eng.* **2013**, *21*, 121–128. [CrossRef] [PubMed]

104. Koppes, A.N.; Seggio, A.M.; Thompson, D.M. Neurite outgrowth is significantly increased by the simultaneous presentation of Schwann cells and moderate exogenous electric fields. *J. Neural Eng.* **2011**, *8*, 046023. [CrossRef]

105. Singh, B.; Xu, Q.G.; Franz, C.K.; Zhang, R.; Dalton, C.; Gordon, T.; Verge, V.M.; Midha, R.; Zochodne, D.W. Accelerated axon outgrowth, guidance, and target reinnervation across nerve transection gaps following a brief electrical stimulation paradigm. *J. Neurosurg.* **2012**, *116*, 498–512. [CrossRef]

106. Franz, C.K.; Singh, B.; Martinez, J.A.; Zochodne, D.W.; Midha, R. Brief transvertebral electrical stimulation of the spinal cord improves the specificity of femoral nerve reinnervation. *Neurorehabilit. Neural Repair* **2013**, *27*, 260–268. [CrossRef]

107. Huang, J.; Zhang, Y.; Lu, L.; Hu, X.; Luo, Z. Electrical stimulation accelerates nerve regeneration and functional recovery in delayed peripheral nerve injury in rats. *Eur. J. Neurosci.* **2013**, *38*, 3691–3701. [CrossRef]

108. Jo, S.; Pan, D.; Halevi, A.E.; Roh, J.; Schellhardt, L.; Hunter Ra, D.A.; Snyder-Warwick, A.K.; Moore, A.M.; Mackinnon, S.E.; Wood, M.D. Comparing electrical stimulation and tacrolimus (FK506) to enhance treating nerve injuries. *Muscle Nerve* **2019**, *60*, 629–636. [CrossRef]

109. Zuo, K.J.; Shafa, G.; Antonyshyn, K.; Chan, K.; Gordon, T.; Borschel, G.H. A single session of brief electrical stimulation enhances axon regeneration through nerve autografts. *Exp. Neurol.* **2020**, *323*, 113074. [CrossRef]

110. Udina, E.; Furey, M.; Busch, S.; Silver, J.; Gordon, T.; Fouad, K. Electrical stimulation of intact peripheral sensory axons in rats promotes outgrowth of their central projections. *Exp. Neurol.* **2008**, *210*, 238–247. [CrossRef]

111. English, A.W.; Schwartz, G.; Meador, W.; Sabatier, M.J.; Mulligan, A. Electrical stimulation promotes peripheral axon regeneration by enhanced neuronal neurotrophin signaling. *Dev. Neurobiol.* **2007**, *67*, 158–172. [CrossRef] [PubMed]

112. Behan, B.L.; DeWitt, D.G.; Bogdanowicz, D.R.; Koppes, A.N.; Bale, S.S.; Thompson, D.M. Single-walled carbon nanotubes alter Schwann cell behavior differentially within 2D and 3D environments. *J. Biomed. Mater. Res. A* **2011**, *96*, 46–57. [CrossRef]

113. Pola, R.; Aprahamian, T.R.; Bosch-Marce, M.; Curry, C.; Gaetani, E.; Flex, A.; Smith, R.C.; Isner, J.M.; Losordo, D.W. Age-dependent VEGF expression and intraneural neovascularization during regeneration of peripheral nerves. *Neurobiol. Aging* **2004**, *25*, 1361–1368. [CrossRef] [PubMed]

114. Kanaya, F.; Firrell, J.; Tsai, T.M.; Breidenbach, W.C. Functional results of vascularized versus nonvascularized nerve grafting. *Plast. Reconstr. Surg.* **1992**, *89*, 924–930. [CrossRef] [PubMed]

115. Doi, K.; Tamaru, K.; Sakai, K.; Kuwata, N.; Kurafuji, Y.; Kawai, S. A comparison of vascularized and conventional sural nerve grafts. *J. Hand Surg. Am.* **1992**, *17*, 670–676. [CrossRef]

116. Sondell, M.; Lundborg, G.; Kanje, M. Vascular endothelial growth factor stimulates Schwann cell invasion and neovascularization of acellular nerve grafts. *Brain Res.* **1999**, *846*, 219–228. [CrossRef]

117. Wongtrakul, S.; Bishop, A.T.; Friedrich, P.F. Vascular endothelial growth factor promotion of neoangiogenesis in conventional nerve grafts. *J. Hand Surg. Am.* **2002**, *27*, 277–285. [CrossRef]

118. Hoyng, S.A.; De Winter, F.; Gnavi, S.; de Boer, R.; Boon, L.I.; Korvers, L.M.; Tannemaat, M.R.; Malessy, M.J.; Verhaagen, J. A comparative morphological, electrophysiological and functional analysis of axon regeneration through peripheral nerve autografts genetically modified to overexpress BDNF, CNTF, GDNF, NGF, NT3 or VEGF. *Exp. Neurol.* **2014**, *261*, 578–593. [CrossRef]

119. Apel, P.J.; Ma, J.; Callahan, M.; Northam, C.N.; Alton, T.B.; Sonntag, W.E.; Li, Z. Effect of locally delivered IGF-1 on nerve regeneration during aging: An experimental study in rats. *Muscle Nerve* **2010**, *41*, 335–341. [CrossRef]

120. Kawabuchi, M.; Tan, H.; Wang, S. Age affects reciprocal cellular interactions in neuromuscular synapses following peripheral nerve injury. *Ageing Res. Rev.* **2011**, *10*, 43–53. [CrossRef]

121. Grinsell, D.; Keating, C.P. Peripheral nerve reconstruction after injury: A review of clinical and experimental therapies. *Biomed. Res. Int.* **2014**, *2014*, 698256. [CrossRef] [PubMed]

122. Mackinnon, S.E.; Doolabh, V.B.; Novak, C.B.; Trulock, E.P. Clinical outcome following nerve allograft transplantation. *Plast. Reconstr. Surg.* **2001**, *107*, 1419–1429. [CrossRef] [PubMed]

123. Tung, T.H. Tacrolimus (FK506): Safety and Applications in Reconstructive Surgery. *Hand* **2010**, *5*, 1–8. [CrossRef] [PubMed]

124. Whitlock, E.L.; Tuffaha, S.H.; Luciano, J.P.; Yan, Y.; Hunter, D.A.; Magill, C.K.; Moore, A.M.; Tong, A.Y.; Mackinnon, S.E.; Borschel, G.H. Processed allografts and type I collagen conduits for repair of peripheral nerve gaps. *Muscle Nerve* **2009**, *39*, 787–799. [CrossRef] [PubMed]

125. Azouz, S.M.; Lucas, H.D.; Mahabir, R.C.; Noland, S.S. A Survey of the Prevalence and Practice Patterns of Human Acellular Nerve Allograft Use. *Plast. Reconstr. Surg. Glob. Open* **2018**, *6*, e1803. [CrossRef] [PubMed]

126. Johnson, P.J.; Wood, M.D.; Moore, A.M.; Mackinnon, S.E. Tissue engineered constructs for peripheral nerve surgery. *Eur. Surg.* **2013**, *45*. [CrossRef]

127. Szynkaruk, M.; Kemp, S.W.; Wood, M.D.; Gordon, T.; Borschel, G.H. Experimental and clinical evidence for use of decellularized nerve allografts in peripheral nerve gap reconstruction. *Tissue Eng. Part. B Rev.* **2013**, *19*, 83–96. [CrossRef]

128. Wood, M.D.; Kemp, S.W.; Liu, E.H.; Szynkaruk, M.; Gordon, T.; Borschel, G.H. Rat-derived processed nerve allografts support more axon regeneration in rat than human-derived processed nerve xenografts. *J. Biomed. Mater. Res. A* **2014**, *102*, 1085–1091. [CrossRef]

129. Wood, M.D.; Kemp, S.W.; Weber, C.; Borschel, G.H.; Gordon, T. Outcome measures of peripheral nerve regeneration. *Ann. Anat.* **2011**, *193*, 321–333. [CrossRef]

130. Rbia, N.; Bulstra, L.F.; Saffari, T.M.; Hovius, S.E.R.; Shin, A.Y. Collagen Nerve Conduits and Processed Nerve Allografts for the Reconstruction of Digital Nerve Gaps: A Single-Institution Case Series and Review of the Literature. *World Neurosurg.* **2019**, *127*, e1176–e1184. [CrossRef]

131. Kuffler, D.P. Regeneration of muscle axons in the frog is directed by diffusible factors from denervated muscle and nerve tubes. *J. Comp. Neurol.* **1989**, *281*, 416–425. [CrossRef] [PubMed]

132. Brooks, D.N.; Weber, R.V.; Chao, J.D.; Rinker, B.D.; Zoldos, J.; Robichaux, M.R.; Ruggeri, S.B.; Anderson, K.A.; Bonatz, E.E.; Wisotsky, S.M.; et al. Processed nerve allografts for peripheral nerve reconstruction: A multicenter study of utilization and outcomes in sensory, mixed, and motor nerve reconstructions. *Microsurgery* **2012**, *32*, 1–14. [CrossRef] [PubMed]

133. Cho, M.S.; Rinker, B.D.; Weber, R.V.; Chao, J.D.; Ingari, J.V.; Brooks, D.; Buncke, G.M. Functional outcome following nerve repair in the upper extremity using processed nerve allograft. *J. Hand Surg. Am.* **2012**, *37*, 2340–2349. [CrossRef] [PubMed]

134. Karabekmez, F.E.; Duymaz, A.; Moran, S.L. Early clinical outcomes with the use of decellularized nerve allograft for repair of sensory defects within the hand. *Hand* **2009**, *4*, 245–249. [CrossRef] [PubMed]

135. Taras, J.S.; Amin, N.; Patel, N.; McCabe, L.A. Allograft reconstruction for digital nerve loss. *J. Hand Surg. Am.* **2013**, *38*, 1965–1971. [CrossRef] [PubMed]

136. Deiner, M.S.; Kennedy, T.E.; Fazeli, A.; Serafini, T.; Tessier-Lavigne, M.; Sretavan, D.W. Netrin-1 and DCC mediate axon guidance locally at the optic disc: Loss of function leads to optic nerve hypoplasia. *Neuron* **1997**, *19*, 575–589. [CrossRef]

137. Tajdaran, K.; Gordon, T.; Wood, M.D.; Shoichet, M.S.; Borschel, G.H. A glial cell line-derived neurotrophic factor delivery system enhances nerve regeneration across acellular nerve allografts. *Acta Biomater.* **2016**, *29*, 62–70. [CrossRef]

138. Zhang, Y.R.; Ka, K.; Zhang, G.C.; Zhang, H.; Shang, Y.; Zhao, G.Q.; Huang, W.H. Repair of peripheral nerve defects with chemically extracted acellular nerve allografts loaded with neurotrophic factors-transfected bone marrow mesenchymal stem cells. *Neural Regen. Res.* **2015**, *10*, 1498–1506. [CrossRef]

139. Hoben, G.; Yan, Y.; Iyer, N.; Newton, P.; Hunter, D.A.; Moore, A.M.; Sakiyama-Elbert, S.E.; Wood, M.D.; Mackinnon, S.E. Comparison of acellular nerve allograft modification with Schwann cells or VEGF. *Hand* **2015**, *10*, 396–402. [CrossRef]

140. Kim, B.S.; Yoo, J.J.; Atala, A. Peripheral nerve regeneration using acellular nerve grafts. *J. Biomed. Mater. Res. A* **2004**, *68*, 201–209. [CrossRef]

141. Zheng, C.; Zhu, Q.; Liu, X.; Huang, X.; He, C.; Jiang, L.; Quan, D. Improved peripheral nerve regeneration using acellular nerve allografts loaded with platelet-rich plasma. *Tissue Eng. Part. A* **2014**, *20*, 3228–3240. [CrossRef] [PubMed]

142. Frerichs, O.; Fansa, H.; Schicht, C.; Wolf, G.; Schneider, W.; Keilhoff, G. Reconstruction of peripheral nerves using acellular nerve grafts with implanted cultured Schwann cells. *Microsurgery* **2002**, *22*, 311–315. [CrossRef] [PubMed]

143. Hess, J.R.; Brenner, M.J.; Fox, I.K.; Nichols, C.M.; Myckatyn, T.M.; Hunter, D.A.; Rickman, S.R.; Mackinnon, S.E. Use of cold-preserved allografts seeded with autologous Schwann cells in the treatment of a long-gap peripheral nerve injury. *Plast. Reconstr. Surg.* **2007**, *119*, 246–259. [CrossRef] [PubMed]

144. Liu, G.; Cheng, Y.; Guo, S.; Feng, Y.; Li, Q.; Jia, H.; Wang, Y.; Tong, L.; Tong, X. Transplantation of adipose-derived stem cells for peripheral nerve repair. *Int. J. Mol. Med.* **2011**, *28*, 565–572. [CrossRef] [PubMed]

145. Saller, M.M.; Huettl, R.E.; Mayer, J.M.; Feuchtinger, A.; Krug, C.; Holzbach, T.; Volkmer, E. Validation of a novel animal model for sciatic nerve repair with an adipose-derived stem cell loaded fibrin conduit. *Neural Regen. Res.* **2018**, *13*, 854–861. [CrossRef] [PubMed]

146. Rbia, N.; Bulstra, L.F.; Lewallen, E.A.; Hovius, S.E.R.; van Wijnen, A.J.; Shin, A.Y. Seeding decellularized nerve allografts with adipose-derived mesenchymal stromal cells: An in vitro analysis of the gene expression and growth factors produced. *J. Plast. Reconstr. Aesthet. Surg.* **2019**, *72*, 1316–1325. [CrossRef]

147. Zhang, Y.; Luo, H.; Zhang, Z.; Lu, Y.; Huang, X.; Yang, L.; Xu, J.; Yang, W.; Fan, X.; Du, B.; et al. A nerve graft constructed with xenogeneic acellular nerve matrix and autologous adipose-derived mesenchymal stem cells. *Biomaterials* **2010**, *31*, 5312–5324. [CrossRef]

148. Yan, Y.; Hunter, D.A.; Schellhardt, L.; Ee, X.; Snyder-Warwick, A.K.; Moore, A.M.; Mackinnon, S.E.; Wood, M.D. Nerve stepping stone has minimal impact in aiding regeneration across long acellular nerve allografts. *Muscle Nerve* **2018**, *57*, 260–267. [CrossRef]

149. Abbasipour-Dalivand, S.; Mohammadi, R.; Mohammadi, V. Effects of Local Administration of Platelet Rich Plasma on Functional Recovery after Bridging Sciatic Nerve Defect Using Silicone Rubber Chamber; An Experimental Study. *Bull. Emerg. Trauma* **2015**, *3*, 1–7.

150. Boecker, A.H.; van Neerven, S.G.; Scheffel, J.; Tank, J.; Altinova, H.; Seidensticker, K.; Deumens, R.; Tolba, R.; Weis, J.; Brook, G.A.; et al. Pre-differentiation of mesenchymal stromal cells in combination with a microstructured nerve guide supports peripheral nerve regeneration in the rat sciatic nerve model. *Eur. J. Neurosci.* **2016**, *43*, 404–416. [CrossRef]

151. Battiston, B.; Geuna, S.; Ferrero, M.; Tos, P. Nerve repair by means of tubulization: Literature review and personal clinical experience comparing biological and synthetic conduits for sensory nerve repair. *Microsurgery* **2005**, *25*, 258–267. [CrossRef] [PubMed]

152. Schmidt, C.E.; Leach, J.B. Neural tissue engineering: Strategies for repair and regeneration. *Annu. Rev. Biomed. Eng.* **2003**, *5*, 293–347. [CrossRef] [PubMed]

153. Wang, W.; Degrugillier, L.; Tremp, M.; Prautsch, K.; Sottaz, L.; Schaefer, D.J.; Madduri, S.; Kalbermatten, D. Nerve Repair With Fibrin Nerve Conduit and Modified Suture Placement. *Anat. Rec.* **2018**, *301*, 1690–1696. [CrossRef] [PubMed]

154. Stocco, E.; Barbon, S.; Lora, L.; Grandi, F.; Sartore, L.; Tiengo, C.; Petrelli, L.; Dalzoppo, D.; Parnigotto, P.P.; Macchi, V.; et al. Partially oxidized polyvinyl alcohol conduitfor peripheral nerve regeneration. *Sci. Rep.* **2018**, *8*, 604. [CrossRef] [PubMed]

155. Boecker, A.; Daeschler, S.C.; Kneser, U.; Harhaus, L. Relevance and Recent Developments of Chitosan in Peripheral Nerve Surgery. *Front. Cell Neurosci.* **2019**, *13*, 104. [CrossRef] [PubMed]

156. Jiang, Z.; Song, Y.; Qiao, J.; Yang, Y.; Zhang, W.; Liu, W.; Han, B. Rat sciatic nerve regeneration across a 10-mm defect bridged by a chitin/CM-chitosan artificial nerve graft. *Int. J. Biol. Macromol.* **2019**, *129*, 997–1005. [CrossRef]

157. Neubrech, F.; Sauerbier, M.; Moll, W.; Seegmuller, J.; Heider, S.; Harhaus, L.; Bickert, B.; Kneser, U.; Kremer, T. Enhancing the Outcome of Traumatic Sensory Nerve Lesions of the Hand by Additional Use of a Chitosan Nerve Tube in Primary Nerve Repair: A Randomized Controlled Bicentric Trial. *Plast. Reconstr. Surg.* **2018**, *142*, 415–424. [CrossRef]

158. Lopez, J.; Xin, K.; Quan, A.; Xiang, S.; Leto Barone, A.A.; Budihardjo, J.; Musavi, L.; Mulla, S.; Redett, R.; Martin, R.; et al. Poly(epsilon-Caprolactone) Nanofiber Wrap Improves Nerve Regeneration and Functional Outcomes after Delayed Nerve Repair. *Plast. Reconstr. Surg.* **2019**, *144*, 48e–57e. [CrossRef]

159. Yen, C.M.; Shen, C.C.; Yang, Y.C.; Liu, B.S.; Lee, H.T.; Sheu, M.L.; Tsai, M.H.; Cheng, W.Y. Novel electrospun poly(epsilon-caprolactone)/type I collagen nanofiber conduits for repair of peripheral nerve injury. *Neural Regen. Res.* **2019**, *14*, 1617–1625. [CrossRef]

160. Hou, Y.; Wang, X.; Zhang, Z.; Luo, J.; Cai, Z.; Wang, Y.; Li, Y. Repairing Transected Peripheral Nerve Using a Biomimetic Nerve Guidance Conduit Containing Intraluminal Sponge Fillers. *Adv. Healthc. Mater.* **2019**, *8*, e1900913. [CrossRef]

161. Kim, S.M.; Lee, M.S.; Jeon, J.; Lee, D.H.; Yang, K.; Cho, S.W.; Han, I.; Yang, H.S. Biodegradable Nerve Guidance Conduit with Microporous and Micropatterned Poly(lactic-co-glycolic acid)-Accelerated Sciatic Nerve Regeneration. *Macromol. Biosci.* **2018**, *18*, e1800290. [CrossRef] [PubMed]

162. Magaz, A.; Faroni, A.; Gough, J.E.; Reid, A.J.; Li, X.; Blaker, J.J. Bioactive Silk-Based Nerve Guidance Conduits for Augmenting Peripheral Nerve Repair. *Adv. Healthc. Mater.* **2018**, *7*, e1800308. [CrossRef] [PubMed]

163. Rao, J.; Cheng, Y.; Liu, Y.; Ye, Z.; Zhan, B.; Quan, D.; Xu, Y. A multi-walled silk fibroin/silk sericin nerve conduit coated with poly(lactic-co-glycolic acid) sheath for peripheral nerve regeneration. *Mater. Sci. Eng. C Mater. Biol. Appl.* **2017**, *73*, 319–332. [CrossRef] [PubMed]

164. Wang, C.; Jia, Y.; Yang, W.; Zhang, C.; Zhang, K.; Chai, Y. Silk fibroin enhances peripheral nerve regeneration by improving vascularization within nerve conduits. *J. Biomed. Mater. Res. A* **2018**, *106*, 2070–2077. [CrossRef] [PubMed]

165. Gontika, I.; Katsimpoulas, M.; Antoniou, E.; Kostakis, A.; Stavropoulos-Giokas, C.; Michalopoulos, E. Decellularized Human Umbilical Artery Used as Nerve Conduit. *Bioengineering* **2018**, *5*, 100. [CrossRef] [PubMed]

166. Pan, D.; Mackinnon, S.E.; Wood, M.D. Advances in the repair of segmental nerve injuries and trends in reconstruction. *Muscle Nerve* **2019**. [CrossRef]

167. Patel, N.P.; Lyon, K.A.; Huang, J.H. An update-tissue engineered nerve grafts for the repair of peripheral nerve injuries. *Neural Regen. Res.* **2018**, *13*, 764–774. [CrossRef]

168. Pinet, R.; Raimbeau, G.; Saint-Cast, Y.; Fouque, P.A.; Rabarin, F. Vein conduit with microsurgical suture repair of superficial branch of the radial nerve injuries at the wrist. *Hand Surg. Rehabil.* **2018**. [CrossRef]

169. Griffin, J.W.; Hogan, M.V.; Chhabra, A.B.; Deal, D.N. Peripheral nerve repair and reconstruction. *J. Bone Joint Surg. Am.* **2013**, *95*, 2144–2151. [CrossRef]

170. Paprottka, F.J.; Wolf, P.; Harder, Y.; Kern, Y.; Paprottka, P.M.; Machens, H.G.; Lohmeyer, J.A. Sensory recovery outcome after digital nerve repair in relation to different reconstructive techniques: Meta-analysis and systematic review. *Plast. Surg. Int.* **2013**, *2013*, 704589. [CrossRef]

171. Kim, J.Y.; Jeon, W.J.; Kim, D.H.; Rhyu, I.J.; Kim, Y.H.; Youn, I.; Park, J.W. An inside-out vein graft filled with platelet-rich plasma for repair of a short sciatic nerve defect in rats. *Neural Regen. Res.* **2014**, *9*, 1351–1357. [CrossRef] [PubMed]

172. Roque, J.S.; Pomini, K.T.; Buchaim, R.L.; Buchaim, D.V.; Andreo, J.C.; Roque, D.D.; Rodrigues, A.C.; Rosa, G.M.J.; Moraes, L.H.R.; Viterbo, F. Inside-out and standard vein grafts associated with platelet-rich plasma (PRP) in sciatic nerve repair. A histomorphometric study. *Acta Cir. Bras.* **2017**, *32*, 617–625. [CrossRef] [PubMed]

173. Sabongi, R.G.; Fernandes, M.; Dos Santos, J.B. Peripheral nerve regeneration with conduits: Use of vein tubes. *Neural Regen. Res.* **2015**, *10*, 529–533. [CrossRef] [PubMed]

174. Ronchi, G.; Fornasari, B.E.; Crosio, A.; Budau, C.A.; Tos, P.; Perroteau, I.; Battiston, B.; Geuna, S.; Raimondo, S.; Gambarotta, G. Chitosan Tubes Enriched with Fresh Skeletal Muscle Fibers for Primary Nerve Repair. *Biomed. Res. Int.* **2018**, *2018*, 9175248. [CrossRef] [PubMed]

175. Chen, Z.X.; Lu, H.B.; Jin, X.L.; Feng, W.F.; Yang, X.N.; Qi, Z.L. Skeletal muscle-derived cells repair peripheral nerve defects in mice. *Neural Regen. Res.* **2020**, *15*, 152–161. [CrossRef] [PubMed]

176. Mohammadi, J.; Delaviz, H.; Mohammadi, B.; Delaviz, H.; Rad, P. Comparison of repair of peripheral nerve transection in predegenerated muscle with and without a vein graft. *BMC Neurol.* **2016**, *16*, 237. [CrossRef]

177. Ramli, K.; Gasim, A.I.; Ahmad, A.A.; Htwe, O.; Mohamed Haflah, N.H.; Law, Z.K.; Hasan, S.; Naicker, A.S.; Mokhtar, S.A.; Muhamad Ariffin, M.H.; et al. Efficacy of Human Cell-Seeded Muscle-Stuffed Vein Conduit in Rat Sciatic Nerve Repair. *Tissue Eng. Part. A* **2019**, *25*, 1438–1455. [CrossRef]

178. Sahin, C.; Karagoz, H.; Kulahci, Y.; Sever, C.; Akakin, D.; Kolbasi, B.; Ulkur, E.; Peker, F. Minced nerve tissue in vein grafts used as conduits in rat tibial nerves. *Ann. Plast. Surg.* **2014**, *73*, 540–546. [CrossRef]

179. Siemionow, M.; Cwykiel, J.; Uygur, S.; Kwiecien, G.; Ozturk, C.; Szopinski, J.; Madajka, M. Application of epineural sheath conduit for restoration of 6-cm long nerve defects in a sheep median nerve model. *Microsurgery* **2019**, *39*, 332–339. [CrossRef]

180. Ouyang, Y.; Huang, C.; Zhu, Y.; Fan, C.; Ke, Q. Fabrication of seamless electrospun collagen/PLGA conduits whose walls comprise highly longitudinal aligned nanofibers for nerve regeneration. *J. Biomed. Nanotechnol.* **2013**, *9*, 931–943. [CrossRef]

181. Kriebel, A.; Hodde, D.; Kuenzel, T.; Engels, J.; Brook, G.; Mey, J. Cell-free artificial implants of electrospun fibres in a three-dimensional gelatin matrix support sciatic nerve regeneration in vivo. *J. Tissue Eng. Regen. Med.* **2017**, *11*, 3289–3304. [CrossRef]

182. Ma, F.; Xu, F.; Li, R.; Zheng, Y.; Wang, F.; Wei, N.; Zhong, J.; Tang, Q.; Zhu, T.; Wang, Z.; et al. Sustained delivery of glial cell-derived neurotrophic factors in collagen conduits for facial nerve regeneration. *Acta Biomater.* **2018**, *69*, 146–155. [CrossRef] [PubMed]

183. Chen, X.; Zhao, Y.; Li, X.; Xiao, Z.; Yao, Y.; Chu, Y.; Farkas, B.; Romano, I.; Brandi, F.; Dai, J. Functional Multichannel Poly(Propylene Fumarate)-Collagen Scaffold with Collagen-Binding Neurotrophic Factor 3 Promotes Neural Regeneration After Transected Spinal Cord Injury. *Adv. Healthc. Mater.* **2018**, *7*, e1800315. [CrossRef] [PubMed]

184. Guo, Q.; Liu, C.; Hai, B.; Ma, T.; Zhang, W.; Tan, J.; Fu, X.; Wang, H.; Xu, Y.; Song, C. Chitosan conduits filled with simvastatin/Pluronic F-127 hydrogel promote peripheral nerve regeneration in rats. *J. Biomed. Mater. Res. B Appl. Biomater.* **2018**, *106*, 787–799. [CrossRef] [PubMed]

185. Liu, Y.; Yu, S.; Gu, X.; Cao, R.; Cui, S. Tissue-engineered nerve grafts using a scaffold-independent and injectable drug delivery system: A novel design with translational advantages. *J. Neural Eng.* **2019**, *16*, 036030. [CrossRef] [PubMed]

186. Pfister, L.A.; Alther, E.; Papaloizos, M.; Merkle, H.P.; Gander, B. Controlled nerve growth factor release from multi-ply alginate/chitosan-based nerve conduits. *Eur. J. Pharm. Biopharm.* **2008**, *69*, 563–572. [CrossRef]

187. Wu, H.; Fang, Q.; Liu, J.; Yu, X.; Xu, Y.; Wan, Y.; Xiao, B. Multi-tubule conduit-filler constructs loaded with gradient-distributed growth factors for neural tissue engineering applications. *J. Mech. Behav. Biomed. Mater.* **2018**, *77*, 671–682. [CrossRef]

188. Madduri, S.; Feldman, K.; Tervoort, T.; Papaloizos, M.; Gander, B. Collagen nerve conduits releasing the neurotrophic factors GDNF and NGF. *J. Control. Release* **2010**, *143*, 168–174. [CrossRef]

189. Gonzalez-Perez, F.; Hernandez, J.; Heimann, C.; Phillips, J.B.; Udina, E.; Navarro, X. Schwann cells and mesenchymal stem cells in laminin- or fibronectin-aligned matrices and regeneration across a critical size defect of 15 mm in the rat sciatic nerve. *J. Neurosurg. Spine* **2018**, *28*, 109–118. [CrossRef]

190. Farzamfar, S.; Salehi, M.; Tavangar, S.M.; Verdi, J.; Mansouri, K.; Ai, A.; Malekshahi, Z.V.; Ai, J. A novel polycaprolactone/carbon nanofiber composite as a conductive neural guidance channel: An in vitro and in vivo study. *Prog. Biomater.* **2019**, *8*, 239–248. [CrossRef]

191. Ikegami, Y.; Ijima, H. Development of heparin-conjugated nanofibers and a novel biological signal by immobilized growth factors for peripheral nerve regeneration. *J. Biosci. Bioeng.* **2019**. [CrossRef]

192. Beaumont, E.; Cloutier, F.C.; Atlan, M.; Rouleau, D.M.; Beaumont, P.H. Chondroitinase ABC and acute electrical stimulation are beneficial for muscle reinnervation after sciatic nerve transection in rats. *Restor. Neurol. Neurosci.* **2009**, *27*, 297–305. [CrossRef] [PubMed]

193. Chaiyasate, K.; Schaffner, A.; Jackson, I.T.; Mittal, V. Comparing FK-506 with basic fibroblast growth factor (b-FGF) on the repair of a peripheral nerve defect using an autogenous vein bridge model. *J. Investig. Surg.* **2009**, *22*, 401–405. [CrossRef] [PubMed]

194. Chato-Astrain, J.; Campos, F.; Roda, O.; Miralles, E.; Durand-Herrera, D.; Saez-Moreno, J.A.; Garcia-Garcia, S.; Alaminos, M.; Campos, A.; Carriel, V. In vivo Evaluation of Nanostructured Fibrin-Agarose Hydrogels With Mesenchymal Stem Cells for Peripheral Nerve Repair. *Front. Cell. Neurosci.* **2018**, *12*, 501. [CrossRef] [PubMed]

195. Wang, F.; Su, X.X.; Guo, Y.C.; Li, A.; Zhang, Y.C.; Zhou, H.; Qiao, H.; Guan, L.M.; Zou, M.; Si, X.Q. Bone regeneration by nanohydroxyapatite/chitosan/poly(lactide-co-glycolide) scaffolds seeded with human umbilical cord mesenchymal stem cells in the calvarial defects of the nude mice. *Biomed. Res. Int.* **2015**, *2015*, 261938. [CrossRef] [PubMed]

196. Crosio, A.; Fornasari, B.E.; Gambarotta, G.; Geuna, S.; Raimondo, S.; Battiston, B.; Tos, P.; Ronchi, G. Chitosan tubes enriched with fresh skeletal muscle fibers for delayed repair of peripheral nerve defects. *Neural Regen. Res.* **2019**, *14*, 1079–1084. [CrossRef]

197. Lichtenfels, M.; Colome, L.; Sebben, A.D.; Braga-Silva, J. Effect of Platelet Rich Plasma and Platelet Rich Fibrin on sciatic nerve regeneration in a rat model. *Microsurgery* **2013**, *33*, 383–390. [CrossRef]

198. Sariguney, Y.; Yavuzer, R.; Elmas, C.; Yenicesu, I.; Bolay, H.; Atabay, K. Effect of platelet-rich plasma on peripheral nerve regeneration. *J. Reconstr. Microsurg.* **2008**, *24*, 159–167. [CrossRef]

199. Boecker, A.H.; Bozkurt, A.; Kim, B.S.; Altinova, H.; Tank, J.; Deumens, R.; Tolba, R.; Weis, J.; Brook, G.A.; Pallua, N.; et al. Cell-enrichment with olfactory ensheathing cells has limited local extra beneficial effects on nerve regeneration supported by the nerve guide Perimaix. *J. Tissue Eng. Regen. Med.* **2018**, *12*, 2125–2137. [CrossRef]

200. Santiago-Figueroa, J.; Sosa, I.; Reyes, O.; Guzman, H.; Hernandez, R.; Kuffler, D. A novel technique for reducing and eliminating peripheral neuropathic pain: A clinical study. *J. Pain Manag.* **2011**, *4*, 387–394.

201. Schmidt, C.E.; Shastri, V.R.; Vacanti, J.P.; Langer, R. Stimulation of neurite outgrowth using an electrically conducting polymer. *Proc. Natl. Acad. Sci. USA* **1997**, *94*, 8948–8953. [CrossRef] [PubMed]

202. Prabhakaran, M.P.; Ghasemi-Mobarakeh, L.; Jin, G.; Ramakrishna, S. Electrospun conducting polymer nanofibers and electrical stimulation of nerve stem cells. *J. Biosci. Bioeng.* **2011**, *112*, 501–507. [CrossRef] [PubMed]

203. Braga Silva, J.; Marchese, G.M.; Cauduro, C.G.; Debiasi, M. Nerve conduits for treating peripheral nerve injuries: A systematic literature review. *Hand Surg. Rehabil.* **2017**, *36*, 71–85. [CrossRef] [PubMed]

204. Senses, F.; Onder, M.E.; Kocyigit, I.D.; Kul, O.; Aydin, G.; Inal, E.; Atil, F.; Tekin, U. Effect of Platelet-Rich Fibrin on Peripheral Nerve Regeneration. *J. Craniofac. Surg.* **2016**, *27*, 1759–1764. [CrossRef] [PubMed]

205. Kuffler, D.P.; Reyes, O.; Sosa, I.J.; Santiago-Figueroa, J. Neurological Recovery across a 12-cm Long Ulnar Nerve Gap Repaired 3.25 Years Post: A Case Report. *Neurosurgery* **2011**. [CrossRef] [PubMed]

206. Javaloy, J.; Alio, J.L.; Rodriguez, A.E.; Vega, A.; Munoz, G. Effect of platelet-rich plasma in nerve regeneration after LASIK. *J. Refract. Surg.* **2013**, *29*, 213–219. [CrossRef] [PubMed]

207. Ding, X.G.; Li, S.W.; Zheng, X.M.; Hu, L.Q.; Hu, W.L.; Luo, Y. The effect of platelet-rich plasma on cavernous nerve regeneration in a rat model. *Asian J. Androl.* **2009**, *11*, 215–221. [CrossRef]

208. Farrag, T.Y.; Lehar, M.; Verhaegen, P.; Carson, K.A.; Byrne, P.J. Effect of platelet rich plasma and fibrin sealant on facial nerve regeneration in a rat model. *Laryngoscope* **2007**, *117*, 157–165. [CrossRef]

209. Cho, H.H.; Jang, S.; Lee, S.C.; Jeong, H.S.; Park, J.S.; Han, J.Y.; Lee, K.H.; Cho, Y.B. Effect of neural-induced mesenchymal stem cells and platelet-rich plasma on facial nerve regeneration in an acute nerve injury model. *Laryngoscope* **2010**, *120*, 907–913. [CrossRef]

210. Ikumi, A.; Hara, Y.; Yoshioka, T.; Kanamori, A.; Yamazaki, M. Effect of local administration of platelet-rich plasma (PRP) on peripheral nerve regeneration: An experimental study in the rabbit model. *Microsurgery* **2018**, *38*, 300–309. [CrossRef]

211. Golzadeh, A.; Mohammadi, R. Effect of local administration of platelet-derived growth factor B on functional recovery of peripheral nerve regeneration: A sciatic nerve transection model. *Dent. Res. J.* **2016**, *13*, 225–232. [CrossRef]

212. Giannessi, E.; Coli, A.; Stornelli, M.R.; Miragliotta, V.; Pirone, A.; Lenzi, C.; Burchielli, S.; Vozzi, G.; De Maria, C.; Giorgetti, M. An autologously generated platelet-rich plasma suturable membrane may enhance peripheral nerve regeneration after neurorraphy in an acute injury model of sciatic nerve neurotmesis. *J. Reconstr. Microsurg.* **2014**, *30*, 617–626. [CrossRef] [PubMed]

213. Choi, B.H.; Han, S.G.; Kim, S.H.; Zhu, S.J.; Huh, J.Y.; Jung, J.H.; Lee, S.H.; Kim, B.Y. Autologous fibrin glue in peripheral nerve regeneration in vivo. *Microsurgery* **2005**, *25*, 495–499. [CrossRef] [PubMed]

214. Sebben, A.D.; Lichtenfels, M.; Da Silva, J.L. Peripheral Nerve Regeneration: Cell Therapy and Neurotrophic Factors. *Rev. Bras. Ortop.* **2011**, *46*, 643–649. [CrossRef] [PubMed]

215. Yamamoto, H.; Gurney, M.E. Human platelets contain brain-derived neurotrophic factor. *J. Neurosci.* **1990**, *10*, 3469–3478. [CrossRef]

216. Kuffler, D.P. An assessment of current techniques for inducing axon regeneration and neurological recovery following peripheral nerve trauma. *Prog. Neurobiol.* **2014**, *116*, 1–12. [CrossRef]

217. Kuffler, D.P. Platelet-Rich Plasma Promotes Axon Regeneration, Wound Healing, and Pain Reduction: Fact or Fiction. *Mol. Neurobiol.* **2015**, *52*, 990–1014. [CrossRef]

218. Wartiovaara, U.; Salven, P.; Mikkola, H.; Lassila, R.; Kaukonen, J.; Joukov, V.; Orpana, A.; Ristimaki, A.; Heikinheimo, M.; Joensuu, H.; et al. Peripheral blood platelets express VEGF-C and VEGF which are released during platelet activation. *Thromb. Haemost.* **1998**, *80*, 171–175. [CrossRef]

219. Webb, N.J.; Bottomley, M.J.; Watson, C.J.; Brenchley, P.E. Vascular endothelial growth factor (VEGF) is released from platelets during blood clotting: Implications for measurement of circulating VEGF levels in clinical disease. *Clin. Sci.* **1998**, *94*, 395–404. [CrossRef]

220. Geissler, J.; Stevanovic, M. Management of large peripheral nerve defects with autografting. *Injury* **2019**, *50* (Suppl. 5), S64–S67. [CrossRef]

221. Giusti, G.; Willems, W.F.; Kremer, T.; Friedrich, P.F.; Bishop, A.T.; Shin, A.Y. Return of motor function after segmental nerve loss in a rat model: Comparison of autogenous nerve graft, collagen conduit, and processed allograft (AxoGen). *J. Bone Joint Surg. Am.* **2012**, *94*, 410–417. [CrossRef] [PubMed]

222. Labroo, P.; Hilgart, D.; Davis, B.; Lambert, C.; Sant, H.; Gale, B.; Shea, J.E.; Agarwal, J. Drug-delivering nerve conduit improves regeneration in a critical-sized gap. *Biotechnol. Bioeng.* **2019**, *116*, 143–154. [CrossRef] [PubMed]

223. Saltzman, E.B.; Villa, J.C.; Doty, S.B.; Feinberg, J.H.; Lee, S.K.; Wolfe, S.W. A Comparison Between Two Collagen Nerve Conduits and Nerve Autograft: A Rat Model of Motor Nerve Regeneration. *J. Hand Surg.* **2019**, *44*, 700.e1–700.e9. [CrossRef] [PubMed]

Review

The Role of Immune Cells and Cytokines in Intestinal Wound Healing

Xiang Xue * and Daniel M. Falcon

Department of Biochemistry and Molecular Biology, University of New Mexico, Albuquerque, NM 87131, USA;
DmFalcon@salud.unm.edu
* Correspondence: xxue@salud.unm.edu

Received: 8 October 2019; Accepted: 29 November 2019; Published: 3 December 2019

Abstract: Intestinal wound healing is a complicated process that not only involves epithelial cells but also immune cells. In this brief review, we will focus on discussing the contribution and regulation of four major immune cell types (neutrophils, macrophages, regulatory T cells, and innate lymphoid cells) and four cytokines (interleukin-10, tumor necrosis factor alpha, interleukin-6, and interleukin-22) to the wound repair process in the gut. Better understanding of these immune factors will be important for developing novel targeted therapy.

Keywords: immune cells; cytokines; wound healing; intestine; inflammatory bowel disease

1. Introduction

Wound healing in the intestine is a critical process affecting the prognosis of inflammatory bowel disease (IBD) [1]. Failure of healing could result in prolonged hospitalization, critical illness, and even death. Intestinal wound healing is consisted of three cellular events: restitution, proliferation, and differentiation of epithelial cells adjacent to the wounded area [2]. After intestinal tissue damage, the initial response is dominated by a proinflammatory type 1 immune response, whereas during the wound repair process, a more anti-inflammatory type 2 immune response will dominate to promote tissue regeneration and maintain tissue homeostasis [3]. A diverse array of evolutionarily ancient hematopoietic immune cell types, including lymphocytes, dendritic cells (DCs), monocytes, macrophages, and granulocytes, participate in this process. These immune cells secrete large amounts of cytokines and growth factors to signal to local tissue progenitors and stromal cells and promote wound repair. Here, we will discuss the contribution of four major immune cell types (neutrophils, macrophages, and regulatory T cells (Treg) and innate lymphoid cells (ILCs)) and four cytokines (interleukin-10 (IL-10), tumor necrosis factor alpha (TNF-α), IL-6, and IL-22) to the wound healing process in the intestine (Figure 1).

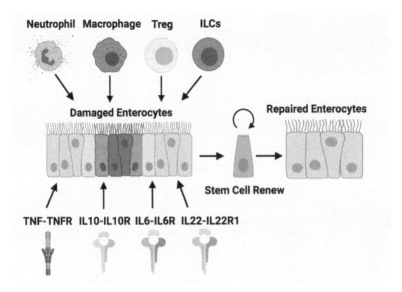

Figure 1. Immune cells and cytokines are contributing to intestinal wound repair. Four major immune cell types (neutrophils, macrophages, Treg) and ILCs), four cytokines (IL-10, TNF-α, IL-6, and IL-22) and their corresponding receptors are involved in stem cell renew and wound healing process in the intestine.

2. Immune Cells

The innate immunity is our first line of nonspecific and rapid defense against pathogens, whereas adaptive immunity confers specific long-lasting memory. Innate immune cells include neutrophils, macrophages, and DCs. The roles of neutrophils and macrophages in wound repair are discussed in detail below. DCs are antigen presenting cells mediating T cell activation and adaptive immunity, thus playing key roles in the crosstalk between innate and adaptive immunity [4].

2.1. Neutrophils

Neutrophils are the first responding leukocytes to sites of inflammation when the intestinal epithelial barrier is breached and the gut microbiota invade [5]. Mouse neutrophils migrate to wounded tissues begins 4 h and reach peak numbers 18 to 24 h after injury [6]. Neutrophils are short-lived cells with a half-life in the circulation of approximately 1.5 h and 19 h in mice and humans, respectively [7,8]. However, proinflammatory cytokines such as TNF-α, IL-1β, and IL-6 increase the lifespan of neutrophils [9], which may contribute to the resolution of inflammation [7].

2.1.1. The Function of Neutrophils

The neutrophils can exert both destructive and protective effects in wound healing (Figure 2) [10]. Excess neutrophils in injured tissues impair healing and correlate with the crypt destruction and ulceration [11,12]. During intestinal inflammation, neutrophils undergo transepithelial migration and secrete a large amount of matrix metalloproteinase-9 (MMP-9) to disrupt epithelial intercellular adhesions, which leads to enhanced epithelial injury [13]. Neutrophil-derived miR-23a–and miR-155-containing microparticles also promote accumulation of double-strand breaks, which leads to impaired colonic healing [14].

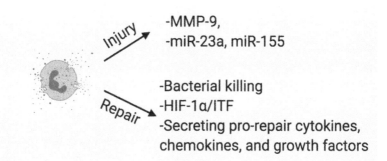

Figure 2. Neutrophils are a double edge sword in intestinal wound repair. Neutrophils damage intestinal mucosal through secreting MMP-9 and miRNA containing microparticles at acute phase of injury, but they can also promote wound repair through killing bacteria, modulating HIF-1α/ITF signaling and secreting pro-repair cytokines, chemokines, and growth factors.

As neutrophils have a key role in controlling microbial contamination and attracting monocytes and/or macrophages [15], individuals with too few neutrophils display not only higher risk for developing wound infections, but also delayed wound healing [16]. However, blocking neutrophil invasion or neutrophil depletion led to aggravated experimental colitis in animals, indicating a protective role of neutrophils in mucosal repair process [17].

Neutrophils kill bacteria through phagocytosis, neutrophils extracellular traps [18], antimicrobial peptides (including cathelicidins and β-defensins), microbicidal reactive oxygen species, and cytotoxic enzymes such as elastases, myeloperoxidase, and MMPs [19]. Infiltrating neutrophils deplete local oxygen to stabilize the transcription factor hypoxia inducible factor (HIF)-1α in wounded human and murine intestinal mucosa and promote resolution of inflammation. HIF-1α stabilization also protects barrier function through induction of intestinal trefoil factor (ITF) [20,21]. It has been shown that the probiotic *Lactobacillus rhamnosus* GG restored alcohol-reduced ITF in a HIF dependent manner [22].

In addition to eliminating bacteria and adjusting the wound microenvironment through oxygen metabolism, neutrophils promote wound repair by secreting pro-repair cytokines, chemokines, and growth factors. After dextran sodium sulfate (DSS)-induced mucosal injury, neutrophil-derived transforming growth factor-beta (TGF-β) activates MEK1/2 signaling and induces the production of the EGF-like molecule amphiregulin (AREG) in intestinal epithelial cells, which protects intestinal epithelial barrier function and ameliorates DSS-induced colitis [23].

2.1.2. The Regulation of Neutrophils

Antibiotic treatment of dams reduced circulating and bone marrow neutrophils via reducing IL-17-producing cells in the intestine and their production of granulocyte colony-stimulating factor (G-CSF) [24]. In contrast to the mucosal protective effects of acute HIF-1α activation described above, we have previously showed that chronic activation of epithelial HIF-2α increased the proinflammatory response [25] and cancer development [26,27]. Among various mechanisms, HIF-2α can directly regulate the expression of neutrophil chemokine CXCL1, which facilitates the recruitment of neutrophils in colitis associated colon tumor [28]. Similarly, during intestinal inflammation, the intestinal epithelial production of neutrophil chemotactic cytokine IL-8 (chemokine C-X-C motif ligand 8, CXCL8) is increased by proinflammatory cytokines IL-1β, TNF-α, or interferon-γ (IFN-γ) [29]. A recent report also showed that IFN-γ induced expression of a neutrophil ligand intercellular adhesion molecule-1 (ICAM-1) on the intestinal epithelium apical membrane, which led to enhanced epithelial permeability and facilitated neutrophil transepithelial migration [30]. Interestingly, the enhanced ICAM-1 and neutrophil binding results in decreased neutrophil apoptosis, activation of Akt and β-catenin signaling, increased epithelial cell proliferation, and wound repair [31]. Il-23 signaling is also required for maximal neutrophil recruitment after DSS treatment [32].

2.2. Macrophages

Intestine contains the largest pool of macrophages in the body [33]. It was long considered that, different from other tissues, embryonic-derived macrophages only populate the colon during neonatal stage. Ly6C (hi) circulating monocytes that recruited and differentiated locally into anti-inflammatory macrophages gradually replace embryonic macrophages at the time of weaning. However, a recent study found that there are three subpopulations of macrophage in the mouse gut: Tim-4+CD4+ macrophages are locally maintained, whereas Tim4-CD4+ and Tim4-CD4− macrophages are replenished from blood monocytes [34]. Another study showed that a population of self-maintaining macrophages aroused from embryonic precursors and bone marrow derived monocytes persists in the intestine throughout adulthood. Deficiency of this population leads to vascular leakage, reduced intestinal secretion and motility [35]. In mice, colonic macrophages are identified by the following marker expression profile: CX3CR1int/hi CD64+ CD11b+ CD11clo/int F4/80+ Ly6C-/lo MHCII+ CD172α+ CD103− SiglecF− CCR7− [36,37]. The lifespan of macrophages is at least 1–2 week [36,38].

2.2.1. The Function of Macrophages

Defects in macrophage differentiation may contribute to increased susceptibility to IBD [39]. Compared with blood monocytes, human intestinal macrophages display downregulated cytokine production upon bacterial products stimulation but preserve phagocytic and bactericidal activity [40]. Thus, intestinal macrophages (CX3CR1 hi) normally possess an anti-inflammatory phenotype during homeostasis via constitutive production of IL-10 [41], whereas Toll-like receptor-responsive proinflammatory macrophages accumulate in the colon and may contribute to disease severity and progression in IBD [37]. However, colonic anti-inflammatory macrophages are still present and promote tissue repair after injury [42]. Studies in mice lacking macrophages suggested that macrophages are necessary for proper epithelial regeneration after DSS injury [43]. Furthermore, Trem2 expressing macrophages are required for efficient mucosal regeneration after colonic biopsy injury [44]. In addition, macrophage-secreted WNT ligands enhance intestinal regeneration response against radiation [45]. Transfer of anti-inflammatory macrophages accelerate mucosal repair in 2, 4, 6-trinitrobenzenesulfonic acid (TNBS)-treated mice through the activation of the Wnt signaling pathway [46].

2.2.2. The Regulation of Macrophages

Macrophage-dependent wound repair in response to DSS-induced colonic injury is markedly diminished in germ-free mice, indicating an essential role of microbiota in macrophage-mediated wound healing [43]. Commensal microbiota-derived local signals in the intestine are essential for recruiting macrophages from circulating monocytes [33]. Breeding of mice in germ-free conditions had a detrimental effect on the number of mature macrophages populating the adult colon compared to mice house in conventional conditions.

However, the small intestine macrophages are regulated by dietary amino acids but not microbiota [47]. Mice fed a protein-free diet had significantly lower levels of IL-10-producing macrophages but not IL-10-producing CD4+ T cells in their small intestine, compared with control-diet fed mice [47]. Depletion of commensal bacteria did not affect numbers of mature macrophages in the small intestine, spleen, or bone marrow, indicating that the recruitment of macrophages to the small intestine is regulated independently of the microbiota [47]. Depletion of microbiota also has no effect on the repair of small intestinal injury [48].

2.3. Regulatory T Cells (Treg)

Treg cells are a subset of CD4+ T cells that can inhibit T helper (Th) cells through the release of anti-inflammatory cytokines, such as IL-10 and TGF-β, or by direct contact with Th cells [49]. Th1 cells are induced by IL-12 and secrets IFN-γ, whereas Th2 cells are induced by IL-4 and releases IL-5 and IL-13 [50]. Crohn's disease (CD) has been long considered to be driven by a Th1 response, whereas the notion that UC is mediated by Th2 response is still controversial [50]. There are two best-characterized subsets of Treg cells that suppress the immune response: forkhead box P3+ (Foxp3+)-positive Treg cells and Foxp3-negative type 1 Treg (Tr1) cells [51]. Foxp3+ Tregs are mainly derived from the thymus, and some travel to the intestine where they inhibit inappropriate immune reactions. Tregs are significantly reduced in peripheral blood and colonic mucosa of IBD patients [52].

2.3.1. The Function of Treg

Foxp3+Tregs promotes the healing of UC through endogenous vascular endothelial growth factor receptor 1 tyrosine kinase (VEGFR1-TK) signaling as mucosal repair of DSS-induced colitis is delayed in VEGFR1-TK knockout mice [53]. For Tr1 cells, in addition to secreting immunosuppressive cytokines IL-10 and TGF-β [54], they secrete IL-22 to regulate repair of the epithelium and protect barrier function of human intestinal epithelial cells [55]. It has been shown recently that patients with refractory in CD were well tolerated with ovalbumin-specific Tr1-based therapy and had a dose-related efficacy [56].

2.3.2. The Regulation of Treg

The microbiota affects the frequency and function of mucosal Tregs. The frequency of Tregs increased in the colon and lamina propria of the small intestine after weaning suggesting a role of the microbiota [57]. Post-weaning accumulation of Tregs was impaired in germ-free or antibiotic-treated mice compared with conventionally housed mice. In addition, germ-free mice fed fecal suspensions from conventionally housed mice saw a substantial increase in Treg levels. Indigenous Clostridium species were reported to play a central role in the induction of IL-10 producing Foxp3+ Tregs in the colon and small intestine in mice [57]. Additionally, it appears as though Clostridia bacteria have a direct role in modulating immune cell populations in the gut as many Clostridium-colonized mice were observed to have Tregs negative for Helios—a transcription factor reported to be expressed in thymus-derived "natural" Tregs. Therefore, the absence of Helios suggests that increasing levels of Tregs in the colon may be induced Treg (iTregs). Indeed, the culture of splenic CD4+ cells in the presence of supernatant of intestinal epithelial cells from Clostridium-colonized mice induced the differentiation of FoxP3-expressing cells. Furthermore, this effect was diminished by neutralizing antibody against TGF-β. Interestingly, it appears that iTregs also play a role in maintaining gut homeostasis as demonstrated in a DSS treatment model of colitis. Symptoms of colitis, such as weight loss, rectal bleeding, colon shortening, edema, mucosal erosion, crypt loss, and cellular infiltration, were all reduced in Clostridium-colonized mice treated with DSS compared to controls.

Different from microbiota-induced Treg cells, dietary antigens from solid food induce the main part of the short-lived small intestinal periphery Treg cells [58].

2.4. Innate Lymphoid Cells (ILCs)

ILCs are mainly tissue-resident lymphocytes that lack adaptive antigen receptors expressed on T cells and B cells (Figure 3) [59]. They are generally classified into three subgroups according to their cytokine and transcription factor expression, which parallel with adaptive CD4+ Th cell subsets: group 1 (ILC1), group 2 (ILC2), and group 3 (ILC3) [59–61]. ILC1s are dependent on the T-box transcription factor (T-bet) for their development and function, and they produce IFN-γ and TNF-α [62]. ILC2s are dependent on GATA binding protein 3 (GATA3) and RAR-related orphan receptor alpha (RORα) [63], and produce type 2 cytokines, including IL-4, IL-5, IL-9, and IL-13 [64]. ILC3s are dependent on the transcription factor RAR-related orphan receptor gamma (RORγt) and can produce IL-17 and/or IL-22 [59,65]. ILC1s react to intracellular pathogens, such as viruses and tumors; ILC2s respond to large extracellular parasites and allergens; and ILC3s combat extracellular microbes, such as bacteria and fungi [59]. In addition, a recent report identified a regulatory subpopulation of ILCs (called ILCregs) that exists in the mouse and human gut and Id3 is a fate decision marker for their development [66].

Compared with these ILC subsets, conventional natural killer (NK) cells has a similar developmental process and quick effector functions, thus NK cells are defined as cytotoxic ILCs, which parallel with adaptive CD8+ cytotoxic T lymphocytes [61]. Mature NK cells are dependent on the transcription factor eomesodermin (Eomes), and produce perforins, IFNγ, and granzymes [67]. NK cells control certain viruses such as herpesviruses and cytomegalovirus and tumors [68].

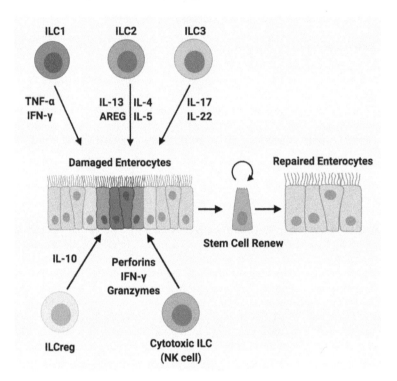

Figure 3. ILCs contribute to the process of intestinal wound repair. During wound healing, ILC1 secretes TNF-α and IFN-γ; ILC2 secretes IL-4, IL-5, IL-13, and AREG; ILC3 secretes IL-17 and IL-22; ILCreg secretes IL-10; and cytotoxic ILC (NK cell) secrete perforins, IFN-γ, and granzymes.

2.4.1. The Function of ILCs

ILCs maintain tissue homeostasis but also contribute to inflammatory diseases including IBD [69]. ILCs promote the resolution of inflammation and tissue repair [70].

ILC1s have a crucial role in promoting innate immunity to intracellular pathogens, such as T. gondii, by secreting TNF-α and IFN-γ to recruit inflammatory myeloid cells [70]. Intraepithelial ILC1s expand in CD patients and depletion of intraepithelial ILC1s reduced proximal colon inflammation in the anti-CD40-induced colitis model in mice [71].

ILC2s rapidly respond to helminth parasite infection [70]. ILC2s are increased in patients with ulcerative colitis (UC) and play an important role in the tissue reparative response [72]. ILC2s secreted IL-13 binds with its receptor IL-13Rα1 and activates transcription factor Foxp1 to promote β-catenin pathway-dependent intestinal stem cell renewal [73]. In addition, IL-33 can stimulate ILC2s to produce AREG in the colon and promote intestinal epithelial cell regeneration in a model of DSS-induced colitis [74].

ILC3s promotes innate immunity to extracellular bacteria and fungi, such as *Citrobacter rodentium* and *Candida albicans* [70]. ILC3s are decreased in inflamed tissue in both CD and UC patients [72] and are required for tissue repair and regeneration in the inflamed intestine [75]. Adherent CD-associated microbiota induces the CX3CR1+ mononuclear phagocyte-derived TNF-like ligand 1A (TL1A) [76], which stimulates the production of ILC3-derived IL-22 and increases mucosal healing in human IBD [77]. ILC3s are the main source of intestinal IL-22 and the symbiotic commensal microbiota represses this IL-22 production via inducing epithelial expression of IL-25 [75]. In graft versus host disease, radioresistant ILC3s-produced IL-22 protects intestinal stem cells from immune-mediated tissue damage [78]. Mechanistically, IL-22 activates signal transducer and activator of transcription 3 (STAT3) signaling to increase antiapoptotic proliferative response in Lgr5+ stem cells, promoting epithelial regeneration and reducing intestinal pathology and mortality from graft-versus-host disease [79]. Moreover, dietary aryl hydrocarbon receptor aryl hydrocarbon receptor (Ahr) ligands such as glucosinolates promote IL-22 production from ILC3s and protect intestinal stem cells against genotoxic stress [80]. In addition, ILC3s produced IL-22 production also protects damage to the intestine induced by infection and chemotherapy [81,82]. Apart from IL-22, ILC3s secreted IL-17 and IFN-γ is dependent on IL-23 stimulation and is required in *Helicobacter hepaticus*-mediated innate colitis [83].

ILCregs suppress the activation of ILC1s and ILC3s via secretion of IL-10 and promote innate intestinal inflammation resolution induced by several inflammatory stimuli including DSS, anti-CD40 antibody, *Salmonella typhimurium*, and *Citrobacter rodentium* in Rag1 −/− mice [59].

NK cells with cytolytic potential are accumulated in colonic lamina propria of individuals with active IBD [84], and thiopurines can normalize NK cell numbers by inhibition of Rac1 activity to induce apoptosis [85]. Activated NK cells produce proinflammatory cytokines such as IFN-γ and TNF-α to augment CD4+ T cell proliferation and Th17 differentiation, which contributes to exacerbated inflammatory response [86].

2.4.2. The Regulation of ILCs

Commensal microbiota regulates the transcriptional gene expression and epigenetic regulation in ILCs [87]. RNA- and ATAC-seq integration identified that c-MAF and BCL6 regulate the plasticity between ILC1 and ILC3 in the intestine [69]. Moreover, the Ahr signaling is critical in regulating intestinal ILC2-ILC3 balance. This was demonstrated by the fact that Ahr knockout mice have altered gut ILC2 transcription with increased expression of anti-helminth cytokines such as IL-5 and IL-13, whereas Ahr activation increases gut ILC3 to better control *Citrobacter rodentium* infection [88]. Furthermore, ILC1 and ILC3 undergo retinoic-acid dependent upregulation of gut homing receptors CCR9 and α4β7, while ILC2 acquire these receptors during development in the bone marrow [89]. These gut homing receptors are also critical for optimal control of *Citrobacter rodentium* infection. For ILCregs, autocrine TGF-β1 is critical for their expansion during inflammation [66]. NK cells are regulated by various cytokines such as type I IFN, IL-12, IL-18, IL-15, IL-2, and TGF-β1 [90].

3. Cytokines

3.1. IL-10

3.1.1. The Source of IL-10

IL-10 production in the colon was mainly from lamina propria macrophage and regulatory T cells [91]. Macrophage-specific knockout of IL-10 had a detrimental effect on intestinal wound healing using a colon biopsy-induced injury model in vivo indicating macrophages are an important source of IL-10 [92]. In addition, intestinal epithelial cells and Th1 cells are also able to produce IL-10 [93,94].

3.1.2. The Function of IL-10

Analysis of biopsy-induced murine colonic wounds revealed an increase in IL-10 as soon as 24 h post-injury suggesting an upregulation during intestinal wound repair [92]. Exposure of intestinal epithelial cells to recombinant IL-10 was demonstrated to enhance wound repair in vitro whereas knockdown of IL-10 receptor ameliorated this effect. IL-10 promotes epithelial activation of cAMP response element-binding protein (CREB) and secretion of pro-repair WNT1-inducible signaling protein 1.

In a mouse model of small intestine epithelial injury induced by Indomethacin, MHC-II$^+$ CD64$^+$ Ly6C$^+$ macrophage-derived IL-10 produced during the acute phase of injury was demonstrated to be critical for wound recovery [48].

3.1.3. The Regulation of IL-10

Macrophage- and regulatory T cell-derived IL-10 production was demonstrated to be microbiota-dependent in the colon, as germ-free mice responded to LPS-stimulation by producing more TNF-α and IL-6 but less IL-10 [91]. In Th1 cells, microbiota-derived short-chain fatty acids promote IL-10 production via G-protein coupled receptors 43/B lymphocyte induced maturation protein 1 signaling [94].

3.2. TNF-α

TNF-α, also known as TNF, was first identified as a tumoricidal protein that mediates endotoxin-induced hemorrhagic necrosis in sarcoma and other transplanted tumors in 1975 [95]. Later in 1984 human TNF was cloned [96].

3.2.1. The Source of TNF-α

TNF is produced predominantly by activated macrophages and T lymphocytes as a plasma membrane bound 26 kDa precursor glycoprotein. TNF-α converting enzyme (TACE; also known as ADAM-17) mediates the cleavage in the extracellular domain of TNF-α precursor and releases a soluble 17 kDA form [97]. In addition to macrophages and T lymphocytes lineage, a wide range of cells can produce TNF-α, including mast cells, B lymphocytes, natural killer (NK) cells, neutrophils, endothelial cells, intestinal epithelial cells (IECs), smooth and cardiac muscle cells, fibroblasts, and osteoclasts [98,99]. TNF-α is not usually detectable in healthy individuals, but elevated serum and tissue levels are found in inflammatory conditions [100], and serum levels correlate with the severity of infections [101,102].

3.2.2. The Function of TNF-α

TNF-α is a key regulator of inflammation and has been involved in many human diseases, including psoriasis, rheumatoid arthritis, and IBD [103]. Anti-TNF-α therapy is the best available therapeutic option to induce mucosal repair and clinical remission in IBD patients [104]. However, a recent report showed that TNF-α blockage may cause dysbiosis and increased Th17 cell population in the colon of healthy mice [104]. Another report demonstrated that TNF-α promotes colonic mucosal repair through induction of the platelet activating factor receptor (PAFR) via NF-B signaling in the intestinal epithelium. Increased PAFR expression leads to activation of epidermal growth factor receptor Src as well as increased Rac1 and FAK signaling to promote cellular migration and wound closure. Consistently, TNF-α neutralization ablates PAFR upregulation and impairs intestinal wound repair [105]. In addition, bone marrow-derived TNF-α binds to epithelial TNF receptors (TNFRs) and activates epithelial beta-catenin signaling, promotes intestinal stem cell proliferation and IEC expansion, and helps mucosal healing in chronic colitis patients [98]. This was shown as enhanced apoptosis, reduced IEC proliferation, and decreased Wnt signaling when stimulated with anti-CD3 mAb in TNF-deficient (Tnf −/−) mice [76]. TNFR2 was increased in the epithelial cells from IBD patients and disruption of TNFR2 in naïve CD8+ T cells increased the severity of colitis in Rag 2 −/− mice [106,107]. TNF-induced intestinal NF-κB activation is also crucial for prevention of local intestinal injury following ischemia–reperfusion [108].

3.2.3. The Regulation of TNF-α

At the transcriptional level, the TNF gene is induced in response to a diversity of specific stimuli including inflammation, infection, and stress [109]. Bacterial endotoxin specially activates TNF-α gene expression [110]. Analysis of human TNF-α promoter indicated that transcription factors such as Ets and c-Jun are involved in the transcriptional regulation of TNF-α [111]. Previously, we have also shown that HIF-2α is a positive regulator of TNF-α production in the intestinal epithelium [25].

3.3. IL-6

The IL-6 family of cytokines include IL-6, IL-11, IL-27, IL-31, oncostatin M, leukaemia inhibitory factor, ciliary neurotrophic factor, cardiotrophin 1, and cardiotrophin- like cytokine factor 1 [112]. They play crucial roles in cell proliferation, survival, migration, invasion, and inflammation [113].

3.3.1. The Source of IL-6

IL-6 is mainly produced by lymphocytes, myeloid cells, fibroblasts and epithelial cells [114]. Enterocyte IL-6 production is increased during inflammatory conditions such as sepsis and endotoxemia [115].

3.3.2. The Function of IL-6

IL-6 and its soluble receptor s-IL6R are highly elevated in the colonic mucosa of IBD [116]. The single nucleotide polymorphism rs2228145 in IL-6R associates with increased levels of s-IL6R, as well as reduced IL-6R signaling and risk of IBD [117]. A randomized clinic trial in 36 patients with active CD showed that 80% of the patients given a human anti-IL-6R monoclonal antibody biweekly at a dose of 8 mg/kg had a clinical response compared with only 31% of placebo injected patients, indicating that targeting IL-6 signaling may serve as a promising strategy for CD [118].

IL-6 promotes IEC proliferation and regeneration, and IL6-deficient mice exhibit elevated IEC apoptosis following exposure with DSS [119]. The proliferative and antiapoptotic effects of IL-6 are mainly mediated by the transcription factor STAT3, whose IEC-specific ablation leads to more severe DSS-induced colitis compared to wild-type mice [98]. In addition, the IL-6 co-receptor gp130 stimulates intestinal epithelial cell proliferation through Yes-associated protein (YAP) and Notch signaling, which leads to aberrant differentiation and promotion of mucosal regeneration [120]. Activation of YAP [121] and Notch [122] are required for mucosal regeneration after DSS challenge.

3.3.3. The Regulation of IL-6

IL-6 is a multifunctional NF-kB-regulated cytokine that acts on epithelial and immune cells [119]. Endotoxin and IL1-β stimulates IL-6 production from IEC [123]. IFN-γ alone did not stimulate but synergistically potentiated the effect of IL-1β stimulated IL-6 production [124]. In contrast, TGF-β and cAMP were found to enhance IL-6 secretion, and they could potentiate IL-1β stimulated IL-6 production [125,126]. All four major transcription factors, i.e., NF-B, activator protein-1, CCAAT/enhancer binding protein, and CREB, are involved in the cAMP activated IL-6 production [126].

3.4. IL-22

IL-22, a cytokine of the IL-10 superfamily, was originally identified as an IL-9-induced gene in mouse T cells, and was named as IL-10-related T cell-derived inducible factor as it shares 22% amino acid identity with IL-10 [127]. IL-22 binds to a functional receptor complex composed of two chains: IL-22 receptor 1 (IL-22R1) and IL-10R2 [128].

3.4.1. The Source of IL-22

IL-22 is produced from many different cell types such as activated T, NK cells and CD11c+ cells [129–131]. As mentioned above, in the intestine ILC3s are the main source of IL-22 [75].

3.4.2. The Function of IL-22

IL-22 is increased in the intestine in patients with IBD as well as murine DSS colitis [132–135]. Although IL-22 increases the gene expression of other proinflammatory cytokines, such as IL-8 and TNF-α in intestinal epithelial cells, IL-22 promotes wound healing of the intestinal epithelium in vitro through stimulation of cell migration via phosphatidylinsitol 3-kinase signaling and beta-defensin-2 expression [135]. In addition, as mentioned above, IL-22 protects intestinal stem cells in graft versus host disease via activating STAT3 signaling and protects against genotoxic stress [78–80]. IL-22 knockout mice showed delayed recovery from biopsy forceps and DSS induced mucosal injury [129,130]. Due to decreased production of antimicrobial proteins, such as RegIIIβ and RegIIIγ, IL-22 knockout mice have increased susceptibility to *Citrobacter rodentium* infection [134]. A recent study showed that IL-22 induces expression of H19 long noncoding RNA in epithelial cells to promote epithelial proliferation and mucosal regeneration [136]. Exogenous IL-22 also mitigates *Citrobacter rodentium* infection mediated colitis in mice with depletion of CX3CR1+ mononuclear phagocytes [77]. Local gene delivery of IL-22 into the colon promotes recovery from acute intestinal injury via STAT3 mediated mucus production [137].

3.4.3. The Regulation of IL-22

Human intestinal ILC3 production of IL-22 is regulated by microbial stimulated IL-23 and IL-1β from CX3CR1+ mononuclear phagocytes [77]. IL-22 can be neutralized by its soluble receptor IL-22 binding protein (IL-22BP; also known as IL-22RA2), which specifically binds IL-22 and prevents its binding with membrane-bound IL-22R1 [138]. IL-22 is most highly expressed at the peak of DSS and biopsy induced intestinal tissue damage, whereas IL-22BP has the lowest expression at this time [139]. AhR also increases IL-22 production to protect against trinitrobenzene sulfonic acid-induced colitis [140]. A recent report showed that the receptor-interacting protein kinase 3 promotes intestinal tissue repair after DSS colitis via induction of IL-22 expression in a IL-23 and IL-1β dependent manner [141].

4. Concluding Remarks and Perspectives

In conclusion, inflammatory cells and cytokines play critical roles in intestinal tissue repair. The introduction of anti-TNF-α antibodies has already been a great advance for IBD targeted therapy. Thus, targeting the above cells and cytokines may represent novel therapies for IBD. A recent phase II clinical trial showed that a human blocking antibody against T cell and NK cell receptor natural killer group 2D induced significant clinical remission in active CD patients after 12 weeks [142].

This review only covered some of the most important immune cell types and cytokines; others may also play an important role in wound healing. For example, IL-36γ was induced during experimental colitis and human IBD in a microbiota-dependent manner [143]. IL-36R-deficient mice showed delayed recovery after DSS-induced intestinal injury with profound IL-22 reduction and impaired neutrophil accumulation. In addition, we did provide much detail about the interaction between different cell types; for example, inflammatory monocytes may inhibit neutrophil activation in a prostaglandin E2 dependent manner [144]. Also, the bidirectional interactions between macrophages and lymphocytes were previously reviewed [145].

As discussed above, microbiota is essential in regulating neutrophil recruitment, colonic macrophage development, Treg function, and gene expression of ILCs (Figure 4). Thus, it is also critical to investigate microbiota and other emerging factors such as nutrients for developing novel targeted therapy to promote intestine repair.

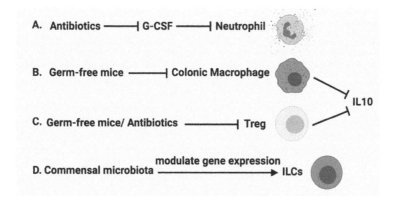

Figure 4. Regulation of immune cells by microbiota. A. Antibiotics can inhibit the recruitment of neutrophils by inhibition of G-CSF production. B. Colonic macrophages and their secretion of IL-10 are significantly reduced in germ-free mice. C. Tregs and their production of IL-10 are reduced in germ-free mice as well as antibiotics treatment. D. The gene expression of ILCs are modulated by commensal microbiota.

Author Contributions: X.X. conceived the topic, wrote the manuscript and generated the figures. D.M.F. performed some literature review and wrote a portion of the draft. All authors approved the final version of this manuscript.

Funding: This research was funded by the National Institutes of Health (K01DK114390), a Research Scholar Grant from the American Cancer Society (RSG-18-050-01-NEC), a Research Pilot Project Grant from University of New Mexico Environmental Health Signature Program and Superfund (P42 ES025589), a Shared Resources Pilot Project Award and a Research Program Support Pilot Project Award from UNM comprehensive cancer center (P30CA118100), and a new investigator award from the Dedicated Health Research Funds at the University of New Mexico School of Medicine. The APC was funded by the National Institutes of Health (K01DK114390). D.M.F. was supported by the Academic Science Education and Research Training program at the University of New Mexico Health Sciences Center (NIGMS Institutional Research and Academic Career Development Award; K12-GM088021).

Conflicts of Interest: The authors declare no conflicts of interest.

References

1. Mukherjee, K.; Kavalukas, S.L.; Barbul, A. Nutritional Aspects of Gastrointestinal Wound Healing. *Adv. Wound Care* **2016**, *5*, 507–515. [CrossRef] [PubMed]

2. Iizuka, M.; Konno, S. Wound healing of intestinal epithelial cells. *World J. Gastroenterol.* **2011**, *17*, 2161–2171. [CrossRef] [PubMed]

3. Rankin, L.C.; Artis, D. Beyond Host Defense: Emerging Functions of the Immune System in Regulating Complex Tissue Physiology. *Cell* **2018**, *173*, 554–567. [CrossRef] [PubMed]

4. Rossi, M.; Young, J.W. Human Dendritic Cells: Potent Antigen-Presenting Cells at the Crossroads of Innate and Adaptive Immunity. *J. Immunol.* **2005**, *175*, 1373–1381. [CrossRef]

5. Brazil, J.C.; Quiros, M.; Nusrat, A.; Parkos, C.A. Innate immune cell–epithelial crosstalk during wound repair. *J. Clin. Investig.* **2019**, *129*, 2983–2993. [CrossRef]

6. Kim, M.-H.; Liu, W.; Borjesson, D.L.; Curry, F.-R.E.; Miller, L.S.; Cheung, A.L.; Liu, F.-T.; Isseroff, R.R.; Simon, S.I. Dynamics of neutrophil infiltration during cutaneous wound healing and infection using fluorescence imaging. *J. Investig. Dermatol.* **2008**, *128*, 1812–1820. [CrossRef]

7. Kolaczkowska, E.; Kubes, P. Neutrophil recruitment and function in health and inflammation. *Nat. Rev. Immunol.* **2013**, *13*, 159–175. [CrossRef]

8. Lahoz-Beneytez, J.; Elemans, M.; Zhang, Y.; Ahmed, R.; Salam, A.; Block, M.; Niederalt, C.; Asquith, B.; Macallan, D. Human neutrophil kinetics: Modeling of stable isotope labeling data supports short blood neutrophil half-lives. *Blood* **2016**, *127*, 3431–3438. [CrossRef]

9. Colotta, F.; Re, F.; Polentarutti, N.; Sozzani, S.; Mantovani, A. Modulation of granulocyte survival and programmed cell death by cytokines and bacterial products. *Blood* **1992**, *80*, 2012–2020. [CrossRef]
10. Williams, I.R.; Parkos, C.A. Colonic Neutrophils in Inflammatory Bowel Disease: Double-Edged Swords of the Innate Immune System with Protective and Destructive Capacity. *Gastroenterology* **2007**, *133*, 2049–2052. [CrossRef]
11. Bressenot, A.; Salleron, J.; Bastien, C.; Danese, S.; Boulagnon-Rombi, C.; Peyrin-Biroulet, L. Comparing histological activity indexes in UC. *Gut* **2015**, *64*, 1412–1418. [CrossRef] [PubMed]
12. Geboes, K.; Riddell, R.; Ost, A.; Jensfelt, B.; Persson, T.; Löfberg, R. A reproducible grading scale for histological assessment of inflammation in ulcerative colitis. *Gut* **2000**, *47*, 404–409. [CrossRef] [PubMed]
13. Butin-Israeli, V.; Houser, M.C.; Feng, M.; Thorp, E.B.; Nusrat, A.; Parkos, C.A.; Sumagin, R. Deposition of microparticles by neutrophils onto inflamed epithelium: A new mechanism to disrupt epithelial intercellular adhesions and promote transepithelial migration. *FASEB J.* **2016**, *30*, 4007–4020. [CrossRef] [PubMed]
14. Butin-Israeli, V.; Bui, T.M.; Wiesolek, H.L.; Mascarenhas, L.; Lee, J.J.; Mehl, L.C.; Knutson, K.R.; Adam, S.A.; Goldman, R.D.; Beyder, A.; et al. Neutrophil-induced genomic instability impedes resolution of inflammation and wound healing. *J. Clin. Investig.* **2019**, *129*, 712–726. [CrossRef] [PubMed]
15. Nathan, C. Neutrophils and immunity: Challenges and opportunities. *Nat. Rev. Immunol.* **2006**, *6*, 173–182. [CrossRef] [PubMed]
16. Anderson, D.C.; Schmalsteig, F.C.; Finegold, M.J.; Hughes, B.J.; Rothlein, R.; Miller, L.J.; Kohl, S.; Tosi, M.F.; Jacobs, R.L.; Waldrop, T.C.; et al. The Severe and Moderate Phenotypes of Heritable Mac-1, LFA-1 Deficiency: Their Quantitative Definition and Relation to Leukocyte Dysfunction and Clinical Features. *J. Infect. Dis.* **1985**, *152*, 668–689. [CrossRef] [PubMed]
17. Kühl, A.A.; Kakirman, H.; Janotta, M.; Dreher, S.; Cremer, P.; Pawlowski, N.N.; Loddenkemper, C.; Heimesaat, M.M.; Grollich, K.; Zeitz, M.; et al. Aggravation of Different Types of Experimental Colitis by Depletion or Adhesion Blockade of Neutrophils. *Gastroenterology* **2007**, *133*, 1882–1892. [CrossRef]
18. Brinkmann, V.; Reichard, U.; Goosmann, C.; Fauler, B.; Uhlemann, Y.; Weiss, D.S.; Weinrauch, Y.; Zychlinsky, A. Neutrophil Extracellular Traps Kill Bacteria. *Science* **2004**, *303*, 1532–1535. [CrossRef]
19. McNamee, E.N. Neutrophil-derived microRNAs put the (DNA) breaks on intestinal mucosal healing. *J. Clin. Investig.* **2019**, *129*, 499–502. [CrossRef]
20. Campbell, E.L.; Bruyninckx, W.J.; Kelly, C.J.; Glover, L.E.; McNamee, E.N.; Bowers, B.E.; Bayless, A.J.; Scully, M.; Saeedi, B.J.; Golden-Mason, L.; et al. Transmigrating neutrophils shape the mucosal microenvironment through localized oxygen depletion to influence resolution of inflammation. *Immunity* **2014**, *40*, 66–77. [CrossRef]
21. Furuta, G.T.; Turner, J.R.; Taylor, C.T.; Hershberg, R.M.; Comerford, K.; Narravula, S.; Podolsky, D.K.; Colgan, S.P. Hypoxia-inducible factor 1-dependent induction of intestinal trefoil factor protects barrier function during hypoxia. *J. Exp. Med.* **2001**, *193*, 1027–1034. [CrossRef] [PubMed]
22. Wang, Y.; Kirpich, I.; Liu, Y.; Ma, Z.; Barve, S.; McClain, C.J.; Feng, W. Lactobacillus rhamnosus GG Treatment Potentiates Intestinal Hypoxia-Inducible Factor, Promotes Intestinal Integrity and Ameliorates Alcohol-Induced Liver Injury. *Am. J. Pathol.* **2011**, *179*, 2866–2875. [CrossRef] [PubMed]
23. Chen, F.; Yang, W.; Huang, X.; Cao, A.T.; Bilotta, A.J.; Xiao, Y.; Sun, M.; Chen, L.; Ma, C.; Liu, X.; et al. Neutrophils Promote Amphiregulin Production in Intestinal Epithelial Cells through TGF-β and Contribute to Intestinal Homeostasis. *J. Immunol.* **2018**, *201*, 2492–2501. [CrossRef] [PubMed]
24. Deshmukh, H.S.; Liu, Y.; Menkiti, O.R.; Mei, J.; Dai, N.; O'Leary, C.E.; Oliver, P.M.; Kolls, J.K.; Weiser, J.N.; Worthen, G.S. The microbiota regulates neutrophil homeostasis and host resistance to Escherichia coli K1 sepsis in neonatal mice. *Nat. Med.* **2014**, *20*, 524–530. [CrossRef]
25. Xue, X.; Ramakrishnan, S.; Anderson, E.; Taylor, M.; Zimmermann, E.M.; Spence, J.R.; Huang, S.; Greenson, J.K.; Shah, Y.M. Endothelial PAS Domain Protein 1 Activates the Inflammatory Response in the Intestinal Epithelium to Promote Colitis in Mice. *Gastroenterology* **2013**, *145*, 831–841. [CrossRef]
26. Xue, X.; Shah, Y.M. Hypoxia-inducible factor-2α is essential in activating the COX2/mPGES-1/PGE 2 signaling axis in colon cancer. *Carcinogenesis* **2013**, *34*, 163–169. [CrossRef]
27. Xue, X.; Taylor, M.; Anderson, E.; Hao, C.; Qu, A.; Greenson, J.K.; Zimmermann, E.M.; Gonzalez, F.J.; Shah, Y.M. Hypoxia-Inducible Factor-2α Activation Promotes Colorectal Cancer Progression by Dysregulating Iron Homeostasis. *Cancer Res.* **2012**, *72*, 2285–2293. [CrossRef]

28. Triner, D.; Xue, X.; Schwartz, A.J.; Jung, I.; Colacino, J.A.; Shah, Y.M. Epithelial Hypoxia-Inducible Factor 2α Facilitates the Progression of Colon Tumors through Recruiting Neutrophils. *Mol. Cell. Biol.* **2017**, *37*, e00481-16. [CrossRef]

29. Schuerer-Maly, C.C.; Eckmann, L.; Kagnoff, M.F.; Falco, M.T.; Maly, F.E. Colonic epithelial cell lines as a source of interleukin-8: Stimulation by inflammatory cytokines and bacterial lipopolysaccharide. *Immunology* **1994**, *81*, 85–91.

30. Sumagin, R.; Robin, A.Z.; Nusrat, A.; Parkos, C.A. Transmigrated neutrophils in the intestinal lumen engage ICAM-1 to regulate the epithelial barrier and neutrophil recruitment. *Mucosal Immunol.* **2014**, *7*, 905–915. [CrossRef]

31. Sumagin, R.; Brazil, J.C.; Nava, P.; Nishio, H.; Alam, A.; Luissint, A.C.; Weber, D.A.; Neish, A.S.; Nusrat, A.; Parkos, C.A. Neutrophil interactions with epithelial-expressed ICAM-1 enhances intestinal mucosal wound healing. *Mucosal Immunol.* **2016**, *9*, 1151–1162. [CrossRef] [PubMed]

32. Cox, J.H.; Kljavin, N.M.; Ota, N.; Leonard, J.; Roose-Girma, M.; Diehl, L.; Ouyang, W.; Ghilardi, N. Opposing consequences of IL-23 signaling mediated by innate and adaptive cells in chemically induced colitis in mice. *Mucosal Immunol.* **2012**, *5*, 99–109. [CrossRef] [PubMed]

33. Bain, C.C.; Bravo-Blas, A.; Scott, C.L.; Perdiguero, E.G.; Geissmann, F.; Henri, S.; Malissen, B.; Osborne, L.C.; Artis, D.; Mowat, A.M. Constant replenishment from circulating monocytes maintains the macrophage pool in the intestine of adult mice. *Nat. Immunol.* **2014**, *15*, 929–937. [CrossRef] [PubMed]

34. Shaw, T.N.; Houston, S.A.; Wemyss, K.; Bridgeman, H.M.; Barbera, T.A.; Zangerle-Murray, T.; Strangward, P.; Ridley, A.J.L.; Wang, P.; Tamoutounour, S.; et al. Tissue-resident macrophages in the intestine are long lived and defined by Tim-4 and CD4 expression. *J. Exp. Med.* **2018**, *215*, 1507–1518. [CrossRef]

35. De Schepper, S.; Verheijden, S.; Aguilera-Lizarraga, J.; Viola, M.F.; Boesmans, W.; Stakenborg, N.; Voytyuk, I.; Schmidt, I.; Boeckx, B.; Dierckx de Casterlé, I.; et al. Self-Maintaining Gut Macrophages Are Essential for Intestinal Homeostasis. *Cell* **2018**, *175*, 400–415. [CrossRef]

36. Bain, C.C.; Scott, C.L.; Uronen-Hansson, H.; Gudjonsson, S.; Jansson, O.; Grip, O.; Guilliams, M.; Malissen, B.; Agace, W.W.; Mowat, A.M. Resident and pro-inflammatory macrophages in the colon represent alternative context-dependent fates of the same Ly6Chi monocyte precursors. *Mucosal Immunol.* **2013**, *6*, 498–510. [CrossRef]

37. Isidro, R.A.; Appleyard, C.B. Colonic macrophage polarization in homeostasis, inflammation, and cancer. *Am. J. Physiol.-Gastrointest. Liver Physiol.* **2016**, *311*, G59–G73. [CrossRef]

38. Rivollier, A.; He, J.; Kole, A.; Valatas, V.; Kelsall, B.L. Inflammation switches the differentiation program of Ly6Chi monocytes from antiinflammatory macrophages to inflammatory dendritic cells in the colon. *J. Exp. Med.* **2012**, *209*, 139–155. [CrossRef]

39. Baillie, J.K.; Arner, E.; Daub, C.; De Hoon, M.; Itoh, M.; Kawaji, H.; Lassmann, T.; Carninci, P.; Forrest, A.R.R.; Hayashizaki, Y.; et al. Analysis of the human monocyte-derived macrophage transcriptome and response to lipopolysaccharide provides new insights into genetic aetiology of inflammatory bowel disease. *PLoS Genet.* **2017**, *13*, e1006641. [CrossRef]

40. Smythies, L.E.; Sellers, M.; Clements, R.H.; Mosteller-Barnum, M.; Meng, G.; Benjamin, W.H.; Orenstein, J.M.; Smith, P.D. Human intestinal macrophages display profound inflammatory anergy despite avid phagocytic and bacteriocidal activity. *J. Clin. Investig.* **2005**, *115*, 66–75. [CrossRef]

41. Bain, C.C.; Mowat, A.M. Macrophages in intestinal homeostasis and inflammation. *Immunol. Rev.* **2014**, *260*, 102–117. [CrossRef] [PubMed]

42. Na, Y.R.; Stakenborg, M.; Seok, S.H.; Matteoli, G. Macrophages in intestinal inflammation and resolution: A potential therapeutic target in IBD. *Nat. Rev. Gastroenterol. Hepatol.* **2019**, *16*, 531–543. [CrossRef]

43. Pull, S.L.; Doherty, J.M.; Mills, J.C.; Gordon, J.I.; Stappenbeck, T.S. Activated macrophages are an adaptive element of the colonic epithelial progenitor niche necessary for regenerative responses to injury. *Proc. Natl. Acad. Sci. USA* **2005**, *102*, 99–104. [CrossRef] [PubMed]

44. Seno, H.; Miyoshi, H.; Brown, S.L.; Geske, M.J.; Colonna, M.; Stappenbeck, T.S. Efficient colonic mucosal wound repair requires Trem2 signaling. *Proc. Natl. Acad. Sci. USA* **2009**, *106*, 256–261. [CrossRef]

45. Saha, S.; Aranda, E.; Hayakawa, Y.; Bhanja, P.; Atay, S.; Brodin, N.P.; Li, J.; Asfaha, S.; Liu, L.; Tailor, Y.; et al. Macrophage-derived extracellular vesicle-packaged WNTs rescue intestinal stem cells and enhance survival after radiation injury. *Nat. Commun.* **2016**, *7*, 13096. [CrossRef]

46. Cosín-Roger, J.; Ortiz-Masiá, D.; Calatayud, S.; Hernández, C.; Esplugues, J.V.; Barrachina, M.D. The activation of Wnt signaling by a STAT6-dependent macrophage phenotype promotes mucosal repair in murine IBD. *Mucosal Immunol.* **2016**, *9*, 986–998. [CrossRef]

47. Ochi, T.; Feng, Y.; Kitamoto, S.; Nagao-Kitamoto, H.; Kuffa, P.; Atarashi, K.; Honda, K.; Teitelbaum, D.H.; Kamada, N. Diet-dependent, microbiota-independent regulation of IL-10-producing lamina propria macrophages in the small intestine. *Sci. Rep.* **2016**, *6*, 27634. [CrossRef]

48. Morhardt, T.L.; Hayashi, A.; Ochi, T.; Quirós, M.; Kitamoto, S.; Nagao-Kitamoto, H.; Kuffa, P.; Atarashi, K.; Honda, K.; Kao, J.Y.; et al. IL-10 produced by macrophages regulates epithelial integrity in the small intestine. *Sci. Rep.* **2019**, *9*, 1223. [CrossRef]

49. Huang, Y.; Chen, Z. Inflammatory bowel disease related innate immunity and adaptive immunity. *Am. J. Transl. Res.* **2016**, *8*, 2490–2497.

50. Geremia, A.; Biancheri, P.; Allan, P.; Corazza, G.R.; Di Sabatino, A. Innate and adaptive immunity in inflammatory bowel disease. *Autoimmun. Rev.* **2014**, *13*, 3–10. [CrossRef]

51. Roncarolo, M.G.; Gregori, S.; Bacchetta, R.; Battaglia, M.; Gagliani, N. The Biology of T Regulatory Type 1 Cells and Their Therapeutic Application in Immune-Mediated Diseases. *Immunity* **2018**, *49*, 1004–1019. [CrossRef] [PubMed]

52. Silva, F.A.R.; Rodrigues, B.L.; Ayrizono, M.D.L.S.; Leal, R.F. The Immunological Basis of Inflammatory Bowel Disease. *Gastroenterol. Res. Pract.* **2016**, *2016*, 2097274. [CrossRef]

53. Betto, T.; Amano, H.; Ito, Y.; Eshima, K.; Yoshida, T.; Matsui, Y.; Yamane, S.; Inoue, T.; Otaka, F.; Kobayashi, K.; et al. Vascular endothelial growth factor receptor 1 tyrosine kinase signaling facilitates healing of DSS-induced colitis by accumulation of Tregs in ulcer area. *Biomed. Pharmacother.* **2019**, *111*, 131–141. [CrossRef] [PubMed]

54. Yao, Y.; Vent-Schmidt, J.; McGeough, M.D.; Wong, M.; Hoffman, H.M.; Steiner, T.S.; Levings, M.K. Tr1 Cells, but Not Foxp3+ Regulatory T Cells, Suppress NLRP3 Inflammasome Activation via an IL-10–Dependent Mechanism. *J. Immunol.* **2015**, *195*, 488–497. [CrossRef]

55. Cook, L.; Stahl, M.; Han, X.; Nazli, A.; MacDonald, K.N.; Wong, M.Q.; Tsai, K.; Dizzell, S.; Jacobson, K.; Bressler, B.; et al. Suppressive and Gut Reparative Functions of Human Type 1 T-regulatory Cells. *Gastroenterology* **2019**. [CrossRef]

56. Desreumaux, P.; Foussat, A.; Allez, M.; Beaugerie, L.; Hébuterne, X.; Bouhnik, Y.; Nachury, M.; Brun, V.; Bastian, H.; Belmonte, N.; et al. Safety and Efficacy of Antigen-Specific Regulatory T-Cell Therapy for Patients with Refractory Crohn's Disease. *Gastroenterology* **2012**, *143*, 1207–1217. [CrossRef]

57. Atarashi, K.; Tanoue, T.; Shima, T.; Imaoka, A.; Kuwahara, T.; Momose, Y.; Cheng, G.; Yamasaki, S.; Saito, T.; Ohba, Y.; et al. Induction of colonic regulatory T cells by indigenous Clostridium species. *Science* **2011**, *331*, 337–341. [CrossRef]

58. Kim, K.S.; Hong, S.-W.; Han, D.; Yi, J.; Jung, J.; Yang, B.-G.; Lee, J.Y.; Lee, M.; Surh, C.D. Dietary antigens limit mucosal immunity by inducing regulatory T cells in the small intestine. *Science* **2016**, *351*, 858–863. [CrossRef]

59. Vivier, E.; Artis, D.; Colonna, M.; Diefenbach, A.; Di Santo, J.P.; Eberl, G.; Koyasu, S.; Locksley, R.M.; McKenzie, A.N.J.; Mebius, R.E.; et al. Innate Lymphoid Cells: 10 Years On. *Cell* **2018**, *174*, 1054–1066. [CrossRef]

60. Spits, H.; Artis, D.; Colonna, M.; Diefenbach, A.; Di Santo, J.P.; Eberl, G.; Koyasu, S.; Locksley, R.M.; McKenzie, A.N.J.; Mebius, R.E.; et al. Innate lymphoid cells—A proposal for uniform nomenclature. *Nat. Rev. Immunol.* **2013**, *13*, 145–149. [CrossRef]

61. Cherrier, D.E.; Serafini, N.; Di Santo, J.P. Innate Lymphoid Cell Development: A T Cell Perspective. *Immunity* **2018**, *48*, 1091–1103. [CrossRef] [PubMed]

62. Artis, D.; Spits, H. The biology of innate lymphoid cells. *Nature* **2015**, *517*, 293–301. [CrossRef] [PubMed]

63. Wong, S.H.; Walker, J.A.; Jolin, H.E.; Drynan, L.F.; Hams, E.; Camelo, A.; Barlow, J.L.; Neill, D.R.; Panova, V.; Koch, U.; et al. Transcription factor RORα is critical for nuocyte development. *Nat. Immunol.* **2012**, *13*, 229–236. [CrossRef] [PubMed]

64. Moro, K.; Yamada, T.; Tanabe, M.; Takeuchi, T.; Ikawa, T.; Kawamoto, H.; Furusawa, J.; Ohtani, M.; Fujii, H.; Koyasu, S. Innate production of TH2 cytokines by adipose tissue-associated c-Kit+Sca-1+ lymphoid cells. *Nature* **2010**, *463*, 540–544. [CrossRef]

65. Cupedo, T.; Crellin, N.K.; Papazian, N.; Rombouts, E.J.; Weijer, K.; Grogan, J.L.; Fibbe, W.E.; Cornelissen, J.J.; Spits, H. Human fetal lymphoid tissue–inducer cells are interleukin 17–producing precursors to RORC+ CD127+ natural killer–like cells. *Nat. Immunol.* **2009**, *10*, 66–74. [CrossRef]

66. Wang, S.; Xia, P.; Chen, Y.; Qu, Y.; Xiong, Z.; Ye, B.; Du, Y.; Tian, Y.; Yin, Z.; Xu, Z.; et al. Regulatory Innate Lymphoid Cells Control Innate Intestinal Inflammation. *Cell* **2017**, *171*, 201–216. [CrossRef]

67. Robinette, M.L.; Fuchs, A.; Cortez, V.S.; Lee, J.S.; Wang, Y.; Durum, S.K.; Gilfillan, S.; Colonna, M.; Shaw, L.; Yu, B.; et al. Transcriptional programs define molecular characteristics of innate lymphoid cell classes and subsets. *Nat. Immunol.* **2015**, *16*, 306–317. [CrossRef]

68. Cerwenka, A.; Lanier, L.L. Natural killer cells, viruses and cancer. *Nat. Rev. Immunol.* **2001**, *1*, 41–49. [CrossRef]

69. Pokrovskii, M.; Hall, J.A.; Ochayon, D.E.; Yi, R.; Chaimowitz, N.S.; Seelamneni, H.; Carriero, N.; Watters, A.; Waggoner, S.N.; Littman, D.R.; et al. Characterization of Transcriptional Regulatory Networks that Promote and Restrict Identities and Functions of Intestinal Innate Lymphoid Cells. *Immunity* **2019**, *51*, 185–197. [CrossRef]

70. Sonnenberg, G.F.; Artis, D. Innate lymphoid cells in the initiation, regulation and resolution of inflammation. *Nat. Med.* **2015**, *21*, 698–708. [CrossRef]

71. Fuchs, A.; Vermi, W.; Lee, J.S.; Lonardi, S.; Gilfillan, S.; Newberry, R.D.; Cella, M.; Colonna, M. Intraepithelial type 1 innate lymphoid cells are a unique subset of IL-12-and IL-15-responsive IFN-γ-producing cells. *Immunity* **2013**, *38*, 769–781. [CrossRef] [PubMed]

72. Forkel, M.; van Tol, S.; Höög, C.; Michaëlsson, J.; Almer, S.; Mjösberg, J. Distinct Alterations in the Composition of Mucosal Innate Lymphoid Cells in Newly Diagnosed and Established Crohn's Disease and Ulcerative Colitis. *J. Crohn's Colitis* **2018**, *13*, 67–78. [CrossRef] [PubMed]

73. Zhu, P.; Zhu, X.; Wu, J.; He, L.; Lu, T.; Wang, Y.; Liu, B.; Ye, B.; Sun, L.; Fan, D.; et al. IL-13 secreted by ILC2s promotes the self-renewal of intestinal stem cells through circular RNA circPan3. *Nat. Immunol.* **2019**, *20*, 183–194. [CrossRef]

74. Monticelli, L.A.; Osborne, L.C.; Noti, M.; Tran, S.V.; Zaiss, D.M.W.; Artis, D. IL-33 promotes an innate immune pathway of intestinal tissue protection dependent on amphiregulin-EGFR interactions. *Proc. Natl. Acad. Sci. USA* **2015**, *112*, 10762–10767. [CrossRef] [PubMed]

75. Sawa, S.; Lochner, M.; Satoh-Takayama, N.; Dulauroy, S.; Bérard, M.; Kleinschek, M.; Cua, D.; Di Santo, J.P.; Eberl, G. RORγt+ innate lymphoid cells regulate intestinal homeostasis by integrating negative signals from the symbiotic microbiota. *Nat. Immunol.* **2011**, *12*, 320–326. [CrossRef] [PubMed]

76. Castellanos, J.G.; Woo, V.; Viladomiu, M.; Putzel, G.; Lima, S.; Diehl, G.E.; Marderstein, A.R.; Gandara, J.; Perez, A.R.; Withers, D.R.; et al. Microbiota-Induced TNF-like Ligand 1A Drives Group 3 Innate Lymphoid Cell-Mediated Barrier Protection and Intestinal T Cell Activation during Colitis. *Immunity* **2018**, *49*, 1077–1089. [CrossRef]

77. Longman, R.S.; Diehl, G.E.; Victorio, D.A.; Huh, J.R.; Galan, C.; Miraldi, E.R.; Swaminath, A.; Bonneau, R.; Scherl, E.J.; Littman, D.R. CX₃CR1+ mononuclear phagocytes support colitis-associated innate lymphoid cell production of IL-22. *J. Exp. Med.* **2014**, *211*, 1571–1583. [CrossRef]

78. Hanash, A.M.; Dudakov, J.A.; Hua, G.; O'Connor, M.H.; Young, L.F.; Singer, N.V.; West, M.L.; Jenq, R.R.; Holland, A.M.; Kappel, L.W.; et al. Interleukin-22 protects intestinal stem cells from immune-mediated tissue damage and regulates sensitivity to graft versus host disease. *Immunity* **2012**, *37*, 339–350. [CrossRef]

79. Lindemans, C.A.; Calafiore, M.; Mertelsmann, A.M.; O'Connor, M.H.; Dudakov, J.A.; Jenq, R.R.; Velardi, E.; Young, L.F.; Smith, O.M.; Lawrence, G.; et al. Interleukin-22 promotes intestinal-stem-cell-mediated epithelial regeneration. *Nature* **2015**, *528*, 560–564. [CrossRef]

80. Gronke, K.; Hernández, P.P.; Zimmermann, J.; Klose, C.S.N.; Kofoed-Branzk, M.; Guendel, F.; Witkowski, M.; Tizian, C.; Amann, L.; Schumacher, F.; et al. Interleukin-22 protects intestinal stem cells against genotoxic stress. *Nature* **2019**, *566*, 249–253. [CrossRef]

81. Sonnenberg, G.F.; Monticelli, L.A.; Elloso, M.M.; Fouser, L.A.; Artis, D. CD4+ lymphoid tissue-inducer cells promote innate immunity in the gut. *Immunity* **2011**, *34*, 122–134. [CrossRef] [PubMed]

82. Aparicio-Domingo, P.; Romera-Hernandez, M.; Karrich, J.J.; Cornelissen, F.; Papazian, N.; Lindenbergh-Kortleve, D.J.; Butler, J.A.; Boon, L.; Coles, M.C.; Samsom, J.N.; et al. Type 3 innate lymphoid cells maintain intestinal epithelial stem cells after tissue damage. *J. Exp. Med.* **2015**, *212*, 1783–1791. [CrossRef] [PubMed]

83. Buonocore, S.; Ahern, P.P.; Uhlig, H.H.; Ivanov, I.I.; Littman, D.R.; Maloy, K.J.; Powrie, F. Innate lymphoid cells drive interleukin-23-dependent innate intestinal pathology. *Nature* **2010**, *464*, 1371–1375. [CrossRef] [PubMed]

84. Steel, A.W.; Mela, C.M.; Lindsay, J.O.; Gazzard, B.G.; Goodier, M.R. Increased proportion of CD16+ NK cells in the colonic lamina propria of inflammatory bowel disease patients, but not after azathioprine treatment. *Aliment. Pharmacol. Ther.* **2011**, *33*, 115–126. [CrossRef]

85. Yusung, S.; McGovern, D.; Lin, L.; Hommes, D.; Lagishetty, V.; Braun, J. NK cells are biologic and biochemical targets of 6-mercaptopurine in Crohn's disease patients. *Clin. Immunol.* **2017**, *175*, 82–90. [CrossRef]

86. Lin, L.; Ma, C.; Wei, B.; Aziz, N.; Rajalingam, R.; Yusung, S.; Erlich, H.A.; Trachtenberg, E.A.; Targan, S.R.; McGovern, D.P.B.; et al. Human NK Cells Licensed by Killer Ig Receptor Genes Have an Altered Cytokine Program That Modifies CD4+ T Cell Function. *J. Immunol.* **2014**, *193*, 940–949. [CrossRef]

87. Gury-BenAri, M.; Thaiss, C.A.; Serafini, N.; Winter, D.R.; Giladi, A.; Lara-Astiaso, D.; Levy, M.; Salame, T.M.; Weiner, A.; David, E.; et al. The Spectrum and Regulatory Landscape of Intestinal Innate Lymphoid Cells Are Shaped by the Microbiome. *Cell* **2016**, *166*, 1231–1246. [CrossRef]

88. Li, S.; Bostick, J.W.; Ye, J.; Qiu, J.; Zhang, B.; Urban, J.F.; Avram, D.; Zhou, L. Aryl Hydrocarbon Receptor Signaling Cell Intrinsically Inhibits Intestinal Group 2 Innate Lymphoid Cell Function. *Immunity* **2018**, *49*, 915–928. [CrossRef]

89. Kim, M.H.; Taparowsky, E.J.; Kim, C.H. Retinoic Acid Differentially Regulates the Migration of Innate Lymphoid Cell Subsets to the Gut. *Immunity* **2015**, *43*, 107–119. [CrossRef]

90. Vivier, E.; Tomasello, E.; Baratin, M.; Walzer, T.; Ugolini, S. Functions of natural killer cells. *Nat. Immunol.* **2008**, *9*, 503–510. [CrossRef]

91. Ueda, Y.; Kayama, H.; Jeon, S.G.; Kusu, T.; Isaka, Y.; Rakugi, H.; Yamamoto, M.; Takeda, K. Commensal microbiota induce LPS hyporesponsiveness in colonic macrophages via the production of IL-10. *Int. Immunol.* **2010**, *22*, 953–962. [CrossRef] [PubMed]

92. Quiros, M.; Nishio, H.; Neumann, P.A.; Siuda, D.; Brazil, J.C.; Azcutia, V.; Hilgarth, R.; O'Leary, M.N.; Garcia-Hernandez, V.; Leoni, G.; et al. Macrophage-derived IL-10 mediates mucosal repair by epithelial WISP-1 signaling. *J. Clin. Investig.* **2017**, *127*, 3510–3520. [CrossRef] [PubMed]

93. Latorre, E.; Layunta, E.; Grasa, L.; Pardo, J.; García, S.; Alcalde, A.I.; Mesonero, J.E. Toll-like receptors 2 and 4 modulate intestinal IL-10 differently in ileum and colon. *United Eur. Gastroenterol. J.* **2018**, *6*, 446–453. [CrossRef]

94. Sun, M.; Wu, W.; Chen, L.; Yang, W.; Huang, X.; Ma, C.; Chen, F.; Xiao, Y.; Zhao, Y.; Ma, C.; et al. Microbiota-derived short-chain fatty acids promote Th1 cell IL-10 production to maintain intestinal homeostasis. *Nat. Commun.* **2018**, *9*, 3555. [CrossRef] [PubMed]

95. Carswell, E.A.; Old, L.J.; Kassel, R.L.; Green, S.; Fiore, N.; Williamson, B. An endotoxin-induced serum factor that causes necrosis of tumors. *Proc. Natl. Acad. Sci. USA* **1975**, *72*, 3666–3670. [CrossRef]

96. Pennica, D.; Nedwin, G.E.; Hayflick, J.S.; Seeburg, P.H.; Derynck, R.; Palladino, M.A.; Kohr, W.J.; Aggarwal, B.B.; Goeddel, D. V Human tumour necrosis factor: Precursor structure, expression and homology to lymphotoxin. *Nature* **1984**, *312*, 724–729. [CrossRef]

97. Black, R.A.; Rauch, C.T.; Kozlosky, C.J.; Peschon, J.J.; Slack, J.L.; Wolfson, M.F.; Castner, B.J.; Stocking, K.L.; Reddy, P.; Srinivasan, S.; et al. A metalloproteinase disintegrin that releases tumour-necrosis factor-α from cells. *Nature* **1997**, *385*, 729–733. [CrossRef]

98. Bradford, E.M.; Ryu, S.H.; Singh, A.P.; Lee, G.; Goretsky, T.; Sinh, P.; Williams, D.B.; Cloud, A.L.; Gounaris, E.; Patel, V.; et al. Epithelial TNF Receptor Signaling Promotes Mucosal Repair in Inflammatory Bowel Disease. *J. Immunol.* **2017**, *199*, 1886–1897. [CrossRef]

99. Roulis, M.; Armaka, M.; Manoloukos, M.; Apostolaki, M.; Kollias, G. Intestinal epithelial cells as producers but not targets of chronic TNF suffice to cause murine Crohn-like pathology. *Proc. Natl. Acad. Sci. USA* **2011**, *108*, 5396–5401. [CrossRef]

100. Robak, T.; Gladalska, A.; Stępień, H. The tumour necrosis factor family of receptors/ligands in the serum of patients with rheumatoid arthritis. *Eur. Cytokine Netw.* **1998**, *9*, 145–154.

101. Waage, A.; Halstensen, A.; Espevik, T. Association between tumour necrosis factor in serum and fatal outcome in patients with meningococcal disease. *Lancet* **1987**, *329*, 355–357. [CrossRef]

102. Kwiatkowski, D.; Sambou, I.; Twumasi, P.; Greenwood, B.M.; Hill, A.V.S.; Manogue, K.R.; Cerami, A.; Castracane, J.; Brewster, D.R. TNF concentration in fatal cerebral, non-fatal cerebral, and uncomplicated Plasmodium falciparum malaria. *Lancet* **1990**, *336*, 1201–1204. [CrossRef]

103. Bradley, J.R. TNF-mediated inflammatory disease. *J. Pathol.* **2008**, *214*, 149–160. [CrossRef] [PubMed]

104. Petito, V.; Graziani, C.; Lopetuso, L.R.; Fossati, M.; Battaglia, A.; Arena, V.; Scannone, D.; Quaranta, G.; Quagliariello, A.; Del Chierico, F.; et al. Anti-tumor necrosis factor α therapy associates to type 17 helper T lymphocytes immunological shift and significant microbial changes in dextran sodium sulphate colitis. *World J. Gastroenterol.* **2019**, *25*, 1465–1477. [CrossRef]

105. Pogrel, M.A. Compression osteosynthesis in mandibular fractures. *Int. J. Oral Maxillofac. Surg.* **1986**, *15*, 521–524. [CrossRef]

106. Mizoguchi, E.; Mizoguchi, A.; Takedatsu, H.; Cario, E.; De Jong, Y.P.; Ooi, C.J.; Xavier, R.J.; Terhorst, C.; Podolsky, D.K.; Bhan, A.K. Role of tumor necrosis factor receptor 2 (TNFR2) in colonic epithelial hyperplasia and chronic intestinal inflammation in mice. *Gastroenterology* **2002**, *122*, 134–144. [CrossRef]

107. Punit, S.; Dubé, P.E.; Liu, C.Y.; Girish, N.; Washington, M.K.; Polk, D.B. Tumor Necrosis Factor Receptor 2 Restricts the Pathogenicity of CD8(+) T Cells in Mice with Colitis. *Gastroenterology* **2015**, *149*, 993–1005. [CrossRef]

108. Chen, L.-W.; Egan, L.; Li, Z.-W.; Greten, F.R.; Kagnoff, M.F.; Karin, M. The two faces of IKK and NF-κB inhibition: Prevention of systemic inflammation but increased local injury following intestinal ischemia-reperfusion. *Nat. Med.* **2003**, *9*, 575–581. [CrossRef]

109. Falvo, J.V.; Tsytsykova, A.V.; Goldfeld, A.E. Transcriptional control of the TNF gene. *TNF Pathophysiol.* **2010**, *11*, 27–60.

110. Drouet, C.; Shakhov, A.N.; Jongeneel, C. V Enhancers and transcription factors controlling the inducibility of the tumor necrosis factor-alpha promoter in primary macrophages. *J. Immunol.* **1991**, *147*, 1694–1700.

111. Krämer, B.; Wiegmann, K.; Krönke, M. Regulation of the Human TNF Promoter by the Transcription Factor Ets. *J. Biol. Chem.* **1995**, *270*, 6577–6583. [CrossRef] [PubMed]

112. Jones, S.A.; Jenkins, B.J. Recent insights into targeting the IL-6 cytokine family in inflammatory diseases and cancer. *Nat. Rev. Immunol.* **2018**, *18*, 773–789. [CrossRef] [PubMed]

113. Garbers, C.; Hermanns, H.M.; Schaper, F.; Müller-Newen, G.; Grötzinger, J.; Rose-John, S.; Scheller, J. Plasticity and cross-talk of Interleukin 6-type cytokines. *Cytokine Growth Factor Rev.* **2012**, *23*, 85–97. [CrossRef] [PubMed]

114. Karin, M.; Clevers, H. Reparative inflammation takes charge of tissue regeneration. *Nature* **2016**, *529*, 307–315. [CrossRef]

115. Meyer, T.A.; Wang, J.; Tiao, G.M.; Ogle, C.K.; Fischer, J.E.; Hasselgren, P.-O. Sepsis and endotoxemia stimulate intestinal interleukin-6 production. *Surgery* **1995**, *118*, 336–342. [CrossRef]

116. Hosokawa, T.; Kusugami, K.; Ina, K.; Ando, T.; Shinoda, M.; Imada, A.; Ohsuga, M.; Sakai, T.; Matsuura, T.; Ito, K.; et al. Interleukin-6 and soluble interleukin-6 receptor in the colonic mucosa of inflammatory bowel disease. *J. Gastroenterol. Hepatol.* **1999**, *14*, 987–996. [CrossRef]

117. Parisinos, C.A.; Serghiou, S.; Katsoulis, M.; George, M.J.; Patel, R.S.; Hemingway, H.; Hingorani, A.D. Variation in Interleukin 6 Receptor Gene Associates with Risk of Crohn's Disease and Ulcerative Colitis. *Gastroenterology* **2018**, *155*, 303–306. [CrossRef]

118. Ito, H.; Takazoe, M.; Fukuda, Y.; Hibi, T.; Kusugami, K.; Andoh, A.; Matsumoto, T.; Yamamura, T.; Azuma, J.; Nishimoto, N.; et al. A pilot randomized trial of a human anti-interleukin-6 receptor monoclonal antibody in active Crohn's disease. *Gastroenterology* **2004**, *126*, 989–996. [CrossRef]

119. Grivennikov, S.; Karin, E.; Terzic, J.; Mucida, D.; Yu, G.-Y.; Vallabhapurapu, S.; Scheller, J.; Rose-John, S.; Cheroutre, H.; Eckmann, L.; et al. IL-6 and Stat3 are required for survival of intestinal epithelial cells and development of colitis-associated cancer. *Cancer Cell* **2009**, *15*, 103–113. [CrossRef]

120. Taniguchi, K.; Wu, L.-W.; Grivennikov, S.I.; de Jong, P.R.; Lian, I.; Yu, F.-X.; Wang, K.; Ho, S.B.; Boland, B.S.; Chang, J.T.; et al. A gp130-Src-YAP module links inflammation to epithelial regeneration. *Nature* **2015**, *519*, 57–62. [CrossRef]

121. Cai, J.; Zhang, N.; Zheng, Y.; de Wilde, R.F.; Maitra, A.; Pan, D. The Hippo signaling pathway restricts the oncogenic potential of an intestinal regeneration program. *Genes Dev.* **2010**, *24*, 2383–2388. [CrossRef] [PubMed]

122. Okamoto, R.; Tsuchiya, K.; Nemoto, Y.; Akiyama, J.; Nakamura, T.; Kanai, T.; Watanabe, M. Requirement of Notch activation during regeneration of the intestinal epithelia. *Am. J. Physiol. Liver Physiol.* **2009**, *296*, G23–G35.

123. Wang, Q.; Wang, J.J.; Boyce, S.; Fischer, J.E.; Hasselgren, P.-O. Endotoxemia and IL-1β Stimulate Mucosal IL-6 Production in Different Parts of the Gastrointestinal Tract. *J. Surg. Res.* **1998**, *76*, 27–31. [PubMed]

124. Parikh, A.A.; Salzman, A.L.; Fischer, J.E.; Szabo, C.; Hasselgren, P.-O. Interleukin-1β and interferon-γ regulate interleukin-6 production in cultured human intestinal epithelial cells. *Shock* **1997**, *29*, 531–537. [CrossRef]

125. McGee, D.W.; Beagley, K.W.; Aicher, W.K.; McGhee, J.R. Transforming growth factor-beta and IL-1 beta act in synergy to enhance IL-6 secretion by the intestinal epithelial cell line, IEC-6. *J. Immunol.* **1993**, *151*, 970–978.

126. Hershko, D.D.; Robb, B.W.; Luo, G.; Hasselgren, P.-O. Multiple transcription factors regulating the IL-6 gene are activated by cAMP in cultured Caco-2 cells. *Am. J. Physiol.* **2002**, *283*, R1140–R1148.

127. Dumoutier, L.; Louahed, J.; Renauld, J.-C. Cloning and Characterization of IL-10-Related T Cell-Derived Inducible Factor (IL-TIF), a Novel Cytokine Structurally Related to IL-10 and Inducible by IL-9. *J. Immunol.* **2000**, *164*, 1814–1819. [CrossRef]

128. Kotenko, S.V.; Izotova, L.S.; Mirochnitchenko, O.V.; Esterova, E.; Dickensheets, H.; Donnelly, R.P.; Pestka, S. Identification of the Functional Interleukin-22 (IL-22) Receptor Complex: The il-10r2 chain (il-10rβ) is a common chain of both the il-10 and il-22 (il-10-related t cell-derived inducible factor, il-tif) receptor complexes. *J. Biol. Chem.* **2001**, *276*, 2725–2732. [CrossRef]

129. Pickert, G.; Neufert, C.; Leppkes, M.; Zheng, Y.; Wittkopf, N.; Warntjen, M.; Lehr, H.-A.; Hirth, S.; Weigmann, B.; Wirtz, S.; et al. STAT3 links IL-22 signaling in intestinal epithelial cells to mucosal wound healing. *J. Exp. Med.* **2009**, *206*, 1465–1472. [CrossRef]

130. Zenewicz, L.A.; Yancopoulos, G.D.; Valenzuela, D.M.; Murphy, A.J.; Stevens, S.; Flavell, R.A. Innate and adaptive interleukin-22 protects mice from inflammatory bowel disease. *Immunity* **2008**, *29*, 947–957. [CrossRef]

131. Wolk, K.; Kunz, S.; Asadullah, K.; Sabat, R. Cutting Edge: Immune Cells as Sources and Targets of the IL-10 Family Members? *J. Immunol.* **2002**, *168*, 5397–5402. [CrossRef] [PubMed]

132. Wolk, K.; Witte, E.; Hoffmann, U.; Doecke, W.-D.; Endesfelder, S.; Asadullah, K.; Sterry, W.; Volk, H.-D.; Wittig, B.M.; Sabat, R. IL-22 Induces Lipopolysaccharide-Binding Protein in Hepatocytes: A Potential Systemic Role of IL-22 in Crohn's Disease. *J. Immunol.* **2007**, *178*, 5973–5981. [CrossRef] [PubMed]

133. Schmechel, S.; Konrad, A.; Diegelmann, J.; Glas, J.; Wetzke, M.; Paschos, E.; Lohse, P.; Göke, B.; Brand, S. Linking genetic susceptibility to Crohn's disease with Th17 cell function: IL-22 serum levels are increased in Crohn's disease and correlate with disease activity and IL23R genotype status. *Inflamm. Bowel Dis.* **2007**, *14*, 204–212. [CrossRef] [PubMed]

134. Zheng, Y.; Valdez, P.A.; Danilenko, D.M.; Hu, Y.; Sa, S.M.; Gong, Q.; Abbas, A.R.; Modrusan, Z.; Ghilardi, N.; de Sauvage, F.J.; et al. Interleukin-22 mediates early host defense against attaching and effacing bacterial pathogens. *Nat. Med.* **2008**, *14*, 282–289. [CrossRef] [PubMed]

135. Brand, S.; Beigel, F.; Olszak, T.; Zitzmann, K.; Eichhorst, S.T.; Otte, J.-M.; Diepolder, H.; Marquardt, A.; Jagla, W.; Popp, A.; et al. IL-22 is increased in active Crohn's disease and promotes proinflammatory gene expression and intestinal epithelial cell migration. *Am. J. Physiol. Liver Physiol.* **2006**, *290*, G827–G838. [CrossRef]

136. Geng, H.; Bu, H.-F.; Liu, F.; Wu, L.; Pfeifer, K.; Chou, P.M.; Wang, X.; Sun, J.; Lu, L.; Pandey, A.; et al. In Inflamed Intestinal Tissues and Epithelial Cells, Interleukin 22 Signaling Increases Expression of H19 Long Noncoding RNA, Which Promotes Mucosal Regeneration. *Gastroenterology* **2018**, *155*, 144–155. [CrossRef]

137. Sugimoto, K.; Ogawa, A.; Mizoguchi, E.; Shimomura, Y.; Andoh, A.; Bhan, A.K.; Blumberg, R.S.; Xavier, R.J.; Mizoguchi, A. IL-22 ameliorates intestinal inflammation in a mouse model of ulcerative colitis. *J. Clin. Investig.* **2008**, *118*, 534–544. [CrossRef]

138. Pelczar, P.; Witkowski, M.; Perez, L.G.; Kempski, J.; Hammel, A.G.; Brockmann, L.; Kleinschmidt, D.; Wende, S.; Haueis, C.; Bedke, T.; et al. A pathogenic role for T cell–derived IL-22BP in inflammatory bowel disease. *Science* **2016**, *354*, 358–362. [CrossRef]

139. Huber, S.; Gagliani, N.; Zenewicz, L.A.; Huber, F.J.; Bosurgi, L.; Hu, B.; Hedl, M.; Zhang, W.; O'Connor Jr, W.; Murphy, A.J.; et al. IL-22BP is regulated by the inflammasome and modulates tumorigenesis in the intestine. *Nature* **2012**, *491*, 259–263. [CrossRef]

140. Monteleone, I.; Rizzo, A.; Sarra, M.; Sica, G.; Sileri, P.; Biancone, L.; MacDonald, T.T.; Pallone, F.; Monteleone, G. Aryl Hydrocarbon Receptor-Induced Signals Up-regulate IL-22 Production and Inhibit Inflammation in the Gastrointestinal Tract. *Gastroenterology* **2011**, *141*, 237–248. [CrossRef]

141. Moriwaki, K.; Balaji, S.; McQuade, T.; Malhotra, N.; Kang, J.; Chan, F.K.-M. The Necroptosis Adaptor RIPK3 Promotes Injury-Induced Cytokine Expression and Tissue Repair. *Immunity* **2014**, *41*, 567–578. [CrossRef] [PubMed]

142. Allez, M.; Skolnick, B.E.; Wisniewska-Jarosinska, M.; Petryka, R.; Overgaard, R.V. Anti-NKG2D monoclonal antibody (NNC0142-0002) in active Crohn's disease: A randomised controlled trial. *Gut* **2017**, *66*, 1918–1925. [CrossRef] [PubMed]

143. Medina-Contreras, O.; Harusato, A.; Nishio, H.; Flannigan, K.L.; Ngo, V.; Leoni, G.; Neumann, P.-A.; Geem, D.; Lili, L.N.; Ramadas, R.A.; et al. Cutting Edge: IL-36 Receptor Promotes Resolution of Intestinal Damage. *J. Immunol.* **2016**, *196*, 34–38. [CrossRef] [PubMed]

144. Grainger, J.R.; Wohlfert, E.A.; Fuss, I.J.; Bouladoux, N.; Askenase, M.H.; Legrand, F.; Koo, L.Y.; Brenchley, J.M.; Fraser, I.D.C.; Belkaid, Y. Inflammatory monocytes regulate pathologic responses to commensals during acute gastrointestinal infection. *Nat. Med.* **2013**, *19*, 713–721. [CrossRef] [PubMed]

145. Biswas, S.K.; Mantovani, A. Macrophage plasticity and interaction with lymphocyte subsets: Cancer as a paradigm. *Nat. Immunol.* **2010**, *11*, 889–896. [CrossRef] [PubMed]

MDPI

St. Alban-Anlage 66

4052 Basel

Switzerland

Tel. +41 61 683 77 34

Fax +41 61 302 89 18

www.mdpi.com

International Journal of Molecular Sciences Editorial Office

E-mail: ijms@mdpi.com

www.mdpi.com/journal/ijms